introduction :::
to biological :::
chemistry :::

introduction
to biological
chemistry

J. AWAPARA : *Professor of Biochemistry, Rice University*

prentice-hall, inc.

englewood cliffs, new jersey

J. AWAPARA, *Introduction to Biological Chemistry*

**prentice-hall
biological science
series ::**
WILLIAM D. McELROY
AND CARL P. SWANSON,
editors

Printed in the United States of America
Library of Congress Catalog Card Number 68-16361
Current printing   10   9   8   7   6   5   4

prentice-hall international, inc., london
prentice-hall of australia, pty. ltd., sydney
prentice-hall of canada, ltd., toronto
prentice-hall of india private ltd., new delhi
prentice-hall of japan, inc., tokyo

preface :::

THE STUDY OF MODERN BIOLOGY IS BECOMING MORE DIFFICULT FOR students without a background in biochemistry. For this reason, at Rice University biochemistry is taught in the first semester of the junior year. In this way our students are prepared to grasp the foundations of modern biology or the foundations of other disciplines in which the language is largely biochemical in nature.

The choice of material for this book was based on my experience gained by teaching an introductory one-semester course in general biochemistry. Our junior students come into biochemistry with a sound background in general and organic chemistry. Nevertheless one-third of the book treats substances of biological importance.

One reason for emphasizing chemistry is that in most organic chemistry courses reaction mechanisms are stressed, leaving little time for substances of interest to the biologist.

Another reason is that quite often students who have learned a chemical concept in the context of a general chemistry course fail to see its immediate application to biochemical problems. Perhaps the reason is that junior students forget temporarily what they have learned in their freshman and sophomore years. Whatever the reason, the student of biochemistry needs either to review or to learn principles in acid-base equilibria, optical isomerism, chemical equilibria and free energy, oxidation-reduction, and other chemical concepts. Some of these principles have been incorporated in the main body of the text in places where I thought they would be most useful. Others, because of their more general nature, have been presented parenthetically (that is, in smaller type and preceded and followed by a small square) to avoid discontinuity in the main theme of the book—*metabolism*.

Metabolism covers a rather large territory, of which only a minor portion can be covered in a one-semester course. Selection was difficult, but in my experience the students profit greatly from the discussion of a few basic principles in some detail.

The few basic topics discussed include enzymes and enzyme reactions, energy production, and biosynthesis. The two chapters on enzymes familiarize the student with the nature of enzyme catalysis and with common cellular chemical reactions.

In dealing with energy production an attempt was made to treat fatty acid oxidation and the citrate cycle as the terminus in the overall flow of carbon in the cell. Glycolysis and the conversion of amino acids to carbohydrate and fatty acid intermediates are treated as part of the carbon flow. Thus intermediary metabolism becomes part of the process leading to the production of suitable substrates for mitochondrial oxidations.

Metabolic interrelations are brought to light by emphasizing common intermediates shared by reactions leading to oxidations and reactions leading to the biosynthesis of cell substances. I have tried not to leave the impression that metabolism is a collection of enzymatic reactions without cellular control.

The inclusion of chromatography in the Appendix was dictated by the general applicability and wide scope of the technique in biochemistry. Chromatography is referred to several times in the text, but its full discussion is reserved for the Appendix.

I wish to express my thanks to my colleague Dr. Charles W. Philpott for contributing his thoughts to Chapter 1 and for the electron micrographs illustrating that chapter.

I should also like to express my thanks to Miss Beth Buvens for diligently translating my scribbles into readable typewritten copy and to the editors of Prentice-Hall for advice and suggestions.

J. AWAPARA

contents   :::

THE AIM OF BIOCHEMISTRY IS TO EXPLAIN BIOLOGICAL PHENOMENA
by chemical and physicochemical laws. In this sense it deals with
the behavior of living matter at the molecular level.

The substances that make up living matter are not different from
any other substance, but they are extremely complex. The proteins
and nucleic acids, for example, are macromolecular substances
with predictable chemical and physical properties. Their biological
properties, however, are not so predictable. Some proteins—the
enzymes—are among the most efficient catalysts, but their catalytic
activity depends upon structural features that we are unable to
recognize at the moment. On the other hand, nucleic acids possess
a biological property that has been traced to their unique structure.
This biological property is self-replication, and nucleic acids are
the only molecules known to display this property.

The study of biological macromolecules is hindered by the distor-
tions introduced when they are liberated from the cell. Because
they are organized into the structural elements of the cell, they can
be isolated only after complete destruction of cell organization.

Despite this barrier, which prevents research into the molecular architecture of the cell, great advances have been made by experi-mentation with isolated cell fragments and by successive approxima-tions to the final state of molecular organization in the living cell.

Much of the progress made in elucidating cell ultrastructure has been due to the introduction of the electron microscope and an array of ingenious techniques for its use. Added to the electron microscope the method of fractional centrifugation has permitted the investigator to isolate intact cell substructures and relate those structures with specific cell functions.

For example, it can be shown that the oxidation of suitable organic molecules in the cell occurs mostly in granular or rod-shaped particles, the *mitochondria*. These can be obtained from cells after disruption and fractional centrifugation. In their isolated state mitochondria have all the necessary components to catalyze complex oxidations that have been predicted to occur in the intact cell. The evidence on hand strongly favors the idea that mitochond-rial function in the experimental situation differs little from its function within the cell.

Another example of cell function in isolated cell fragments is the synthesis of proteins in ribosomal complexes. Ribosomes can be isolated by high-speed centrifugation without losing their property of directing protein synthesis when supplied with the necessary ingredients.

The progress made in understanding the chemical activities within the cell has been impressive, but this is just the beginning. The ultimate goal is to find explanations for cell functions in chemical laws.

Up to now the term "living cell" has been used without qualifica-tion. There are a multitude of types of cells, most of which differ from one another not only in size and shape but also in their organization and function. In the discussion that follows, we shall not refer to any particular cell; the parts of the cell discussed are those parts common to the majority of living cells.

cell membrane and organelles :: 1.1

In Figure 1.1 is shown a composite picture of the cell, its organelles, and its membrane systems in their approximate location and interrelations. The parts distinguished are the cell membrane, the nucleus, the endoplasmic reticulum, the mitochondria, lyso-somes, and the Golgi apparatus. Each will be discussed briefly.

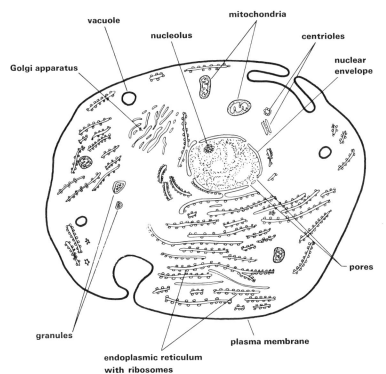

figure 1.1 ::
Composite picture of a
living cell.

CELL MEMBRANE : Cells are limited by a membrane that separates
the cell's interior from its surroundings. Plant cells, in addition to
the membrane, are enveloped by a wall made up mainly of cellulose,
but unlike the membrane, the wall is inert.

The *cell membrane* is not inert; its functions are well defined and
of supreme importance in the regulation of the cell's interaction
with its surroundings. For example, small molecules and ions,
which ordinarily would cross an inert membrane, are "selected" by
the cell membrane. Only particular molecules and ions can cross.
This active process of selection tends to maintain the constant
environment observed within the cell.

The basic structure of the cell membrane is complex. E. Gortner
and F. Grendel extracted lipid from a known number of erythrocytes and measured the area occupied by the lipid monomolecular
layer when it was spread over a surface of water. This experiment
revealed that the extracted lipid covered about twice the total
surface area of the original cells. From other studies of the surface
tension and elastic properties of the cell membrane H. Davson and
J. F. Danielli suggested that a layer of protein was attached to each

of the outer surfaces of the bimolecular lipid leaflet. Danielli's model of the cell membrane received independent support by J. D. Robertson, who described the "unit membrane" from electron micrographs. Three distinct layers could be recognized in images that showed membranes sectioned at a right angle to their flat surfaces. The total thickness of the linear profile was about 80 to 100 angstroms (Å). This trilaminar structure consists of two dark lines (protein) separated by an intermediate light line (lipid); each line was about 30 Å thick. Although the trilaminar-structured unit membrane occurs almost universally in cells, one must not mistakenly infer that all the cell membranes have a common origin and similar physiological activities. An electron micrograph of the cell membrane is shown in Figure 1.2.

The cell surface, which is delimited by the cell membrane, or plasmalemma, may be amplified or extended for a particular purpose. Such is the case in certain intestinal cells and cells that form the proximal convoluted tubule of the kidney. The apical surface of these cells bear many fingerlike projections, the *microvilli*, which increase the effective area for absorption. In other instances, cytoplasmic processes from adjacent cells may interdigitate with one another to form a secure attachment.

NUCLEUS : All cells have either a nucleus or chromosomelike bodies endowed with properties similar to those of the nucleus. Blue-green algae and bacteria, for example, do not have an organized nucleus and are generally called *prokaryotic cells*, in distinction to organisms of *eukaryotic cells*, which possess clearly defined nuclei.

figure 1.2 :: This micrograph shows a small portion of the cell surface and the cell membrane. The cell membrane, or plasmalemma, appears at high magnification as a trilaminar structure. The dense–light–dense appearance of the plasmalemma is believed to represent the protein–bimolecular lipid–protein layers of the Danielli and Davson cell-membrane model. Most cells have a surface coating that is rich in polysaccharides; in this image the surface coat is represented by a prominent layer of more or less radially oriented filaments. Magnification about 134,000. (*Courtesy of Dr. Charles W. Philpott.*)

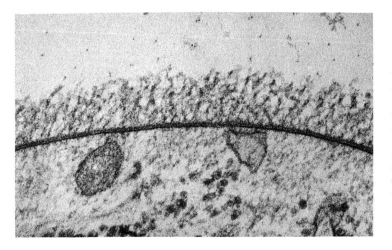

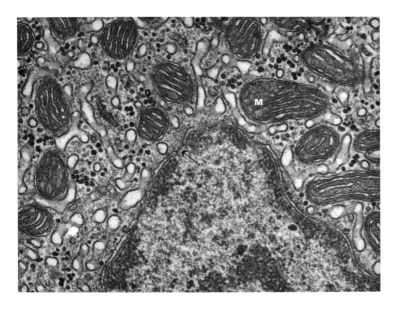

figure 1.3 :: This micrograph shows portions of the nucleus and cytoplasm of a cell. The arrow points to a nuclear pore, the site which represents an area of continuity between the nuclear and cytoplasmic ground substances. Mitochondria (M) are scattered throughout the cytoplasmic ground substance. The dense granules (G) of the cytoplasm represent glycogen particles. Magnification about 27,000. (*Courtesy of Dr. Charles W. Philpott.*)

The *nucleus* in most cells is a sphere-shaped body surrounded by a membranous envelope interrupted by pores, which have an average diameter of 1,000 Å. The nuclear envelope consists of two lamellae, which enclose the perinuclear space. There is communication between this space and the cisternae, which are sacs formed by the membranes of the endoplasmic reticulum. It should also be emphasized that the nuclear and cytoplasmic ground substances are continuous, owing to the nuclear pores (Figure 1.3).

Depending on the stage of the life cycle of the cell, one may recognize in the interphase cell a small spherical body, the nucleolus, and, in dividing cells, rod-shaped chromosomes that contain most of the deoxyribonucleic acid (DNA) of the cell. Chromosomes, which are unusually large in some insects, are easily observed under the light microscope. They stain with characteristic crossbands. DNA combined with protein is present in the darkly stained crossbands.

Genetic information is stored in the chromosomes as DNA molecules of specified structure. But in addition to the genetic control, there seem to be other controls of cell activity within the nucleus and nucleolus.

ENDOPLASMIC RETICULUM : The nuclear membrane or envelope in many cells extends into the cytoplasm as a complex membrane system, the *endoplasmic reticulum.* In tissue-thin sections the endoplasmic reticulum usually appears either vesicular or as a flattened sac. The sacs, called *cisternae*, effectively separate the ground substance into two phases, the ground substance proper and the intracisternal substance.

The membranes of the endoplasmic reticulum may be subdivided into two forms. One type has a smooth outer surface and the other is studded with granules having a diameter of about 150 Å. Biochemical analysis reveals that the granules are largely composed of nucleoprotein. The name *ribosome* has been applied to these particles, which occur also unassociated with membranes in the cytoplasmic ground substance.

The ribosomes are parts of aggregates known as *polysomes*, which are the site of protein synthesis. When polysomes dissociate into free ribosomes they lose their capacity to synthesize protein. The electron micrograph of Figure 1.4 reveals the endoplasmic reticulum with its attached ribosomes.

MITOCHONDRION : The images shown in Figure 1.5 are of mitochondria. These are either granular- or rod-shaped bodies distributed throughout the cell. The average cell may have several hundred mitochondria; their size is about 1.5 to 3.0 microns (μ) in length and 0.5 to 1.0 μ in thickness. Of course, there are variations in the size and the number of the mitochondria that are present in a cell.

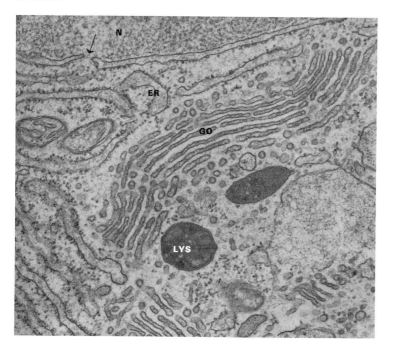

figure 1.4 :: This micrograph demonstrates several of the common features of cells which are specialized for protein synthesis. In cells that are known to produce protein for export, the ribosomes are associated with the outer surfaces of cisternae of the endoplasmic reticulum (ER). Newly synthesized peptides and protein are then transferred to the Golgi region (GO), where they are packaged into membrane-bound droplets or granules. Also seen in this image are lysosomes (LYS) and a small field of the nucleus (N). The arrow at the top points to a nuclear pore. Magnification about 27,000. (*Courtesy of Dr. Charles W. Philpott.*)

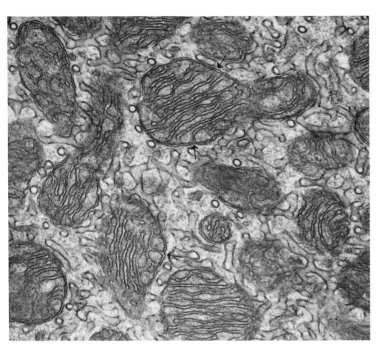

figure 1.5 ::
Mitochondria are numerous in this limited field of cytoplasm. As can be seen at the arrows, cristae represent shelflike infoldings of the inner mitochondrial membrane. Oxidative enzymes are believed to be associated with the cristae membranes. A situation such as this, where mitochondria are numerous and cristae are closely packed, reflects a high metabolic potential for this cell. Magnification about 40,000. (*Courtesy of Dr. Charles W. Philpott.*)

A mitochondrion has an outer membrane that serves as a sac in which is enclosed a second sac. The inner sac has many foldings extending into the inner portion of the mitochondrion. The infoldings or *cristae* are the sites of numerous enzymes involved in oxidations. The innermost part of the mitochondrion contains a semifluid material consisting of protein and lipid—the *matrix.*

The chemical composition of the mitochondrion has been correlated with structured elements observed with the electron microscope. It is quite rich in lipid into which seem to be embedded proteins, many of which are enzymes. The picture of the mitochondrial architecture is now being drawn in its molecular details.

The lipid, a phospholipid, seems to be responsible for much of the organization of the proteins. For example, it has been shown that random aggregates of mitochondrial enzymes organize spontaneously into vesicles only when mitochondrial phospholipid is present.

The recent discovery that the mitochondrion contains DNA supports the idea that these organelles are endowed with the capacity for self-replication, as opposed to the earlier view that they arise from the ground substance *de novo.*

Other details of mitochondrial properties and mitochondrial function will be discussed in Chapter 8.

GOLGI APPARATUS : The presence of a network of membranes and sacs collectively known as the *Golgi complex* is revealed by special stains (see Figure 1.4). The membranes are only of the smooth type. The Golgi complex or apparatus has been and still is the subject of much speculation and controversy. Its function has not been clearly defined, but the prevailing view is that the Golgi is the place where secretory products made in another part of the cell are stored before they are secreted. For example, in the pancreatic acinar cells, zymogens, a group of proteins, are synthesized by the granular endoplasmic reticulum. The newly synthesized proteins move from the cisternae of the endoplasmic reticulum to the Golgi region, where the mixture is formed into a clearly defined secretory droplet surrounded by membrane derived from the Golgi. Before the zymogens are secreted or extruded from the cell, the membrane enclosing the mature droplet must fuse with the cell membrane at its apical surface.

LYSOSOME : The *lysosome* is a particle that contains a number of enzymes, mainly *acid hydrolases*. This organelle displays considerable morphological heterogeneity, and it is therefore difficult to present a definitive morphological description that would aid recognition with an electron micrograph. Usually verification resides either in a biochemical analysis for *acid hydrolases* in centrifugally isolated particles or in cytochemical staining reactions for the localization of acid phosphatase.

As the name lysosome implies, the particles are rich in lytic enzymes. For this reason, they are believed to play an important role in intracellular digestion. It has been suggested, for example, that following *pinocytosis*,† a lysosome may fuse with the phagosome, which contains material to be digested, to form a digestive vacuole. Digestion then proceeds within the digestive vacuole and breakdown products presumably diffuse into the ground substance. There is also evidence that lysosomes sometimes fuse with "worn-out" organelles within the cell to form an autophagic vacuole. This theory holds that old or damaged organelles are digested and that the products may be reutilized by the cell to form new organelles.

CHLOROPLAST : *Chloroplasts* are organelles of plant cells and cells with the capacity for photosynthesis. They, like the mitochondria, are rich in lipid material. Internally they consist of stacks of

† Pinocytosis is a mechanism for the introduction of large molecules or particles from the outside into the interior of the cell.

membranes, to which are attached the *grana*, small bodies containing chlorophyll.

Both the chloroplast and the mitochondrion have been aptly called "biochemical machines." Both convert one form of energy into another, and both do work in the process. A chloroplast converts light energy into chemical-bond energy, which supplies the energy needs of the living world. The mitochondrion, on the other hand, transforms chemical-bond energy into a more suitable form of chemical bond—one readily utilized for the performance of chemical and physical activities of the cell. We are referring to some of the chemical bonds of adenosine triphosphate, which is the compound used by all living cells. The chloroplast, like the mitochondrion, is believed to be a self-replicating organelle.

methods of investigation :: 1.2

With the possible exception of recently developed methods for high-resolution cytochemistry and autoradiography, the assignment of specific biochemical functions to discrete cellular components has been possible only after disruption of the cell and separation of its parts.

The most widely used procedure is that of fractional centrifugation. Cells are broken by mechanical means without destroying the subcellular structural components. Because most cell organelles are different in size and density, they sediment at different rates in the ultracentrifuge.

Modern ultracentrifuges attain speeds of up to 65,000 revolutions per minute (rpm). At this speed a sufficient force is developed to cause the sedimentation of even the smallest particles. The cells, broken up and suspended in a suitable medium (usually a solution of sucrose with known density), are centrifuged at a relatively low speed. The material that sediments can be separated from that which remains suspended. The suspended material is centrifuged at a higher speed and some other material sediments. Repeated centrifugations at increasingly higher speeds will cause the sedimentation of most particles, as shown in Figure 1.6.

The flow diagram in Figure 1.6 is an idealized situation that rarely occurs. As a general rule, the fractions are contaminated with particles from other fractions, although better resolution may be achieved by centrifuging the particles through a gradient of sucrose concentration. Despite this difficulty, an analysis of each fraction is possible. Moreover, when the separation of particles is carefully

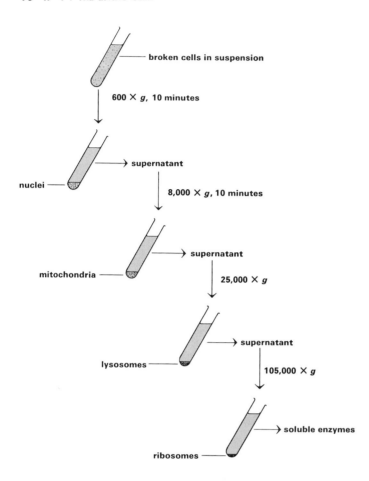

figure 1.6 :: Flow diagram showing the fractionation of cell components by means of centrifugation.

done at low temperature, the particles can still perform the same functions they did when present in the intact cell.

The method is crude if one considers the complexity of the living cell. Unfortunately methods for studying a cell and its functions without disrupting its organization are extremely limited.

references ::

BRACHET, E., and H. E. MIRSKY, *The Cell*. New York: Academic Press, Inc., 1961.
BRACHET, J., "The Living Cell," *Scientific American*, September, 1961.
HURRY, W., *The Microstructure of Cells*. Boston: Houghton Mifflin Company, 1964.

proteins :::

2

THE IMPORTANCE OF PROTEINS IN THE LIVING CELL WAS FIRST
recognized by the German chemist G. T. Mulder in 1835. He
discovered in plants and animals a complex and unstable substance
which he believed to be the most important of the known components of living matter. Mulder used the term *protein* (Gr.
proteios, first) at the suggestion of J. J. Berzelius to describe this
important substance.

Proteins are macromolecules ranging in molecular weight from
6,000 to several million. When boiled with mineral acids they
yield amino acids in varying molar ratios. To date 20 amino
acids have been isolated from proteins, but occasionally a protein
will contain an amino acid not commonly found in most other
proteins.

The amino acids in a protein molecule are connected by amide
linkages (called *peptide bonds* in this case) made from the carboxyl
group of one amino acid and the amino group of the next.

$$H_2NCHCONHCHCO-$$
$$\quad\; \overset{|}{R_1} \qquad \overset{|}{R_2}$$

In this way hundreds of amino acid molecules can be linked together and arranged in an extraordinarily large number of possible combinations of the 20 known amino acids.

Any one combination of amino acids is represented by the *primary structure* of the protein; that is, the primary structure describes the number and order in which amino acids are arranged in the protein molecule. It deals with the covalent bonding between amino acids in a chain (called a *polypeptide chain*).

The polypeptide has a backbone

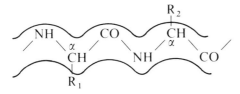

and side chains represented by R groups linked to the α carbons.

The backbone is not rigid; it is free to rotate around the α carbons, and by so doing, the polypeptide can assume any one of many possible shapes, some more stable than others. A spiral shape (α helix), for example, is stabilized by forming hydrogen bonds; or if several polypeptides arrange themselves in parallel, held together by hydrogen bonds, they gain stability. The shape resulting from hydrogen bonding of this type is known as the *secondary structure*.

Tertiary structure describes the shape of the folding that the polypeptide assumes as it becomes packed into a three-dimensional structure. The foldings are made possibly by mutual interactions of the side chains and interactions of the side chains with the solvent.

Quaternary structure describes polymeric aggregates resulting when several protein subunits interact and form a larger unit.

classification :: **2.1**

A systematic classification of proteins based on their structure is clearly not possible. It is customary to classify proteins on the basis of their approximate shape, solubility, and composition. In terms of shape, most proteins fall under one of two categories: *fibrous* or *globular*. Most fibrous proteins tend to be insoluble in water and most ordinary solvents; they possess mechanical strength and are normally found as supporting structures. They are components of hair, nails, skin, and other parts of the organism that have mechanical strength.

By contrast, globular proteins are soluble in water and solutions of salts in water. For the most part they are not very stable in solution. Examples of globular proteins are egg white, milk proteins, blood serum proteins, and most enzymes.

In terms of solubility, proteins are classified into *albumins*, *globulins*, *prolamines*, *glutelins*, and *scleroproteins*. This method of classification has been in use for many years but it has lost much of its usefulness.

In terms of composition proteins are either *simple* or *conjugated*. A simple protein yields only amino acids on hydrolysis. A conjugated protein yields amino acids and another organic substance, such as a sugar, a pigment, or a lipid. The second organic substance is generally a breakdown product of a more complex molecule. For example, a sugar results from the hydrolysis of a polysaccharide attached to the protein; it can also be the undegraded compound originally present in the protein molecule. In conjugated proteins, the organic substance is known as the *prosthetic group*. In hemoglobin, for example, the prosthetic group is the heme molecule, a red pigment containing iron.

Other names used to describe proteins are based on their source or some unique characteristic. For example, proteins rich in phosphorus are called *phosphoproteins*. Those associated with nucleic acids in the nucleus of the cell are called *protamines* and *histones*.

amino acids as components :: 2.2

The symbols, structures, and molecular weights of all 20 amino acids are listed in Table 2.1. In nature, proteins are not necessarily built from all 20 amino acids; some proteins lack one or more amino acids, and there are other proteins in which one amino acid predominates, as in the protein from silk, where glycine makes up 40 percent of the molecule. There are proteins containing amino acids not found in any other protein, but these are extremely rare.

All the amino acids in Table 2.1, with the exception of glycine, have an asymmetric carbon atom, which means that all but glycine are optically active. It should be noted also that, with the exception of proline and hydroxypoline, all amino acids listed are α-amino carboxylic acids of the general type

$$
\begin{array}{c}
CO_2H \\
| \\
H_2N-C-H \\
| \\
R
\end{array}
$$

FORMULA

$$\left(\begin{array}{c} CO_2H \\ H_2N-C-H \\ R \end{array} \right)$$

NAME AND SYMBOL

M.W.

Name and Symbol	Formula	M.W.
Glycine, Gly	$R = H$	75
Alanine, Ala	$R = CH_3$	89
Serine, Ser	$R = CH_2OH$	105
Cysteine, CySH	$R = CH_2SH$	121
Cystine, CySSCy	$R = CH_2-S-S-CH_2$	240
Threonine, Thr	$R = HOCHCH_3$	119
Valine, Val	$R = CH_3CHCH_3$	117
Leucine, Leu	$R = CH_2$ CH_3CHCH_3	131
Isoleucine, Ileu	$R = CH_3CHCH_2CH_3$	131
Methionine, Met	$R = CH_2CH_2SCH_3$	149
Aspartic acid, Asp	$R = CH_2CO_2H$	133
Glutamic acid, Glu	$R = CH_2CH_2CO_2H$	147
Lysine, Lys	$R = CH_2CH_2CH_2CH_2NH_2$	146
Arginine, Arg	$R = CH_2CH_2CH_2NHCNH_2$, $\overset{\|}{NH}$	174
Phenylalanine, Phe	$R = $ 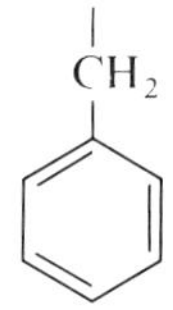 (benzyl group, CH_2)	165
Tyrosine, Tyr	$R = $ 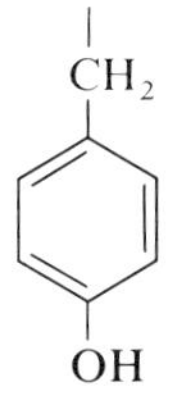 (4-hydroxybenzyl group, CH_2, OH)	181

table 2.1 :: Structures and molecular weights of amino acids

Tryptophan, Try	$R =$ (indole structure with CH_2)	204
Histidine, His	$R =$ (imidazole structure with CH_2, N, NH)	154
Proline, Pro	H_2C——CH_2 / H_2C $CHCO_2H$ / N / H	115
Hydroxyproline, Hypro	$HOHC$——CH_2 / H_2C $CHCO_2H$ / N / H	131

in which the arrangement of the four groups $-NH_2$, $-CO_2H$, $-H$, and $-R$ around the α carbon is the same for all of them. Proline and hydroxyproline do not conform to the general structure of α-amino carboxylic acids; they have a secondary nitrogen and should be—more correctly—named *imino acids*.

GENERAL PROPERTIES OF AMINO ACIDS : All 20 amino acids share some physical and chemical properties that depend on the arrangement of the four substituents on the α carbon atom. Other distinguishing properties of amino acids depend on the chemical nature of the R group. Here we shall deal first with the properties common to all amino acids.

Configuration. Two structures can be written for any amino acid (except glycine):

$$CO_2H \qquad CO_2H$$
$$H_2N \diamondsuit H \qquad H \diamondsuit NH_2$$
$$R \qquad R$$

The two structures are mirror images of each other; they are not superimposable and they represent two different compounds. The two amino acids are optical isomers or *enantiomers*; they are indistinguishable but for one property. They rotate the plane of polarized light in opposite directions. The two amino acids are said to be optically active.

■ †Plane-polarized light is light that vibrates in a single plane and is obtained by allowing light to pass through a properly oriented crystal. Optically active substances have the capacity to rotate that plane. The direction and degree of rotation of the plane of polarized light by a substance is determined with a polarimeter. The solution of the substance is in a tube through which plane-polarized light enters and emerges; the plane of the light emerging is different from the plane of the incident light if the substance is optically active. The angle between the two is measured; if the rotation of the plane is clockwise (with respect to the observer), the substance is dextrorotatory and indicated by a + sign. If the rotation is counterclockwise, the substance is levorotatory and indicated by a − sign.

It is customary to express rotation as *specific optical rotation*, [α], defined by the equation

$$[\alpha] = \frac{\text{observed reading}}{(\text{length of sample})(\text{concentration})}$$

where the reading is in degrees, the length of sample is given by the length of the tube in decimeters, and the concentration is in grams per milliliter.

Enantiomers have equal and opposite specific rotations. A mixture of the two forms in equal molar proportions is a racemic mixture and the rotation is zero. A racemate has the sign ±. ■

The assignment of one or the other structure to amino acids obtained from proteins is based on reference compounds of known configurations. Glyceraldehyde has been used extensively:

$$
\begin{array}{cc}
\text{CHO} & \text{CHO} \\
| & | \\
\text{HO}\!-\!\text{C}\!-\!\text{H} & \text{H}\!-\!\text{C}\!-\!\text{OH} \\
| & | \\
\text{CH}_2\text{OH} & \text{CH}_2\text{OH} \\
\text{L-glyceraldehyde} & \text{D-glyceraldehyde}
\end{array}
$$

The dashed lines represent bonds extending behind the plane of this page, the wedges represent bonds extending in front of the plane, and the solid lines represent bonds on the plane. To the structure with the —OH group on the left side and front is assigned the letter L, and to the structure with the —OH on the right side and front is assigned the letter D. The two compounds are readily distinguished by their optical rotation.

† Material in smaller type and so set off treats general principles pertinent to, but not part of, the main discussion line

An amino acid can be converted to or derived from glyceraldehyde by well-understood chemical reactions. If the product of the conversion is L-glyceraldehyde, the configuration assigned to the amino acid is L.

All 20 amino acids from proteins are of the L configuration, and most are weakly dextrorotatory.

Inner salt structure. Many properties of amino acids are best represented when the general structure is written as an inner salt as originally proposed by N. Bjerrum:

$$H_3N^+ - \overset{\displaystyle CO_2^-}{\underset{\displaystyle R}{\overset{|}{\underset{|}{C}}}} - H$$

The preference of this structure over one in which the molecule is not charged becomes apparent by examining some properties of amino acids. Let us consider the simplest amino acid, glycine.

1. Glycine dissolved in water gives solutions with a pH of about 6, which seems contrary to expectation. Most carboxylic acids would give a more acidic solution.

2. Glycine melts with decomposition at about 260° C, which is an unusually high melting point. Such a high melting point is more like that of a salt than that of a simple carboxylic acid or a simple uncharged amine.

3. Glycine is soluble in water and insoluble in ether. This is also contrary to expectation, because simple carboxylic acids of similar molecular weight normally are soluble in ether.

The properties of glycine (and this applies to all amino acids) are readily understood in terms of the inner salt structure, long referred to as the *zwitterion* (hybrid ion). A high melting point and insolubility in ether are characteristics of highly polar compounds, compounds in which the charges are well separated.

Acid-base equilibria. Before discussing ionic equilibria in amino acids, it would be profitable to review first some general principles.

▪ Acids, by the Brönsted and Bjerrum definition, are substances that yield protons, and bases are substances that accept protons. All the substances listed below are acids according to the definition:

$$HCl \rightleftarrows H^+ + Cl^-$$
$$H_2SO_4 \rightleftarrows H^+ + HSO_4^-$$
$$HSO_4^- \rightleftarrows H^+ + SO_4^{2-}$$
$$H_2O \rightleftarrows H^+ + OH^-$$
$$NH_4^+ \rightleftarrows H^+ + NH_3$$

The strength of an acid depends on its tendency to release protons into the solution. When the solution is in water, the proton is immediately solvated to produce H_3O^+, a hydronium ion.

Water itself is a very weak acid, in which the ion product $[H^+][OH^-]$ is 1.0×10^{-14} at 25°C. The equilibrium constant can be written

$$K = \frac{[H^+][OH^-]}{[H_2O]}$$

but because the concentration of H_2O is very large and nearly constant, the ion product K_w can be used instead:

$$K_w = [H^+][OH^-]$$

If the ion product K_w is 1×10^{-14}, the hydrogen ion concentration in pure water must be 1×10^{-7} at 25°C. Commonly, hydrogen ion concentration is expressed as pH, a term defined by S. P. L. Sörensen as the negative common logarithm of the hydrogen ion concentration. Or, if $H^+ = 10^{-x}$, then $x = pH$.

In water, the hydrogen ion concentration is 1×10^{-7}, and the pH is 7. In a 0.0001 M HCl solution, the hydrogen ion concentration is $1 \times 10^{-4}\,M$, and the pH is 4.

Mineral acids such as HCl ionize completely into H^+ and Cl^-, and we refer to them as strong acids. On the other hand, weak acids on solution in water remain mostly undissociated. For example, a 1 M solution of acetic acid is only 0.042 M with respect to hydrogen ions.

A convenient way of expressing acid strength of weak acids is as pK_a, which is the negative logarithm of the ionization constant of the acid. The equilibrium expression for the ionization of a weak acid HA in water may be written

$$HA = H^+ + A^-$$

$$K_a = \frac{[H^+][A^-]}{[HA]}$$

The value of K_a can be measured by the conductivity of the solution or by means such as potentiometric measurements with the glass electrode. The ionization constant K_a can be readily converted to pK_a by a simple calculation. For example, the K_a of acetic acid is 1.754×10^{-5}. The pK_a is

$$
\begin{aligned}
pK_a &= -\log K_a \\
&= -\log(1.75 \times 10^{-5}) \\
&= -(\bar{5} + 0.243) \\
&= 4.757
\end{aligned}
$$

The pK_a of a weak acid can also be determined by measuring the pH of a solution containing equimolar quantities of the acid and its salt. If, for example, 10 ml of 0.1 M acetic acid is titrated with 0.1 M NaOH, when 5 ml of NaOH has been added, half the acetic acid will be in the form of undissociated acid. The pH of the mixture at this point corresponds to the pK_a of acetic acid, as shown by the titration curve in Figure 2.1. The relationship between pH and pK of weak acids in the presence of their salts (buffers) is expressed by the equation†

$$pH = pK_a + \log\frac{[s]}{[a]}$$

If the ratio of salt $[s]$ to acid $[a]$ is 1, $\log [s]/[a] = 0$ and $pH = pK_a$. At any other ratios of $[s]/[a]$, the pH can be calculated from the above equation. ∎

The acid strength of amino acids can be measured in a similar manner, but because amino acids have more than one ionization, they present a different picture from that of acetic acid, for example.

Let us consider glycine again. According to the definition of acids, glycine has two hydrogens that can be ionized; in neutral solution glycine has the form of a zwitterion:

$$^+H_3NCH_2CO_2^- \rightleftharpoons H^+ + H_2NCH_2CO_2^-$$

and it can ionize in basic solution as shown, to yield a proton and the anion. The acid strength of the $-NH_3^+$ group can be measured, as before, by titration and the pK (designated pK_2) of glycine

---

† The equilibrium equation for the ionization of weak acids in water has been written

$$K = \frac{[H^+][A^-]}{[HA]}$$

When a weak acid is titrated with alkali, the salt of the acid formed is completely ionized; thus the concentration of anions A^- is almost the same as the concentration of salt s. Also, the concentration of undissociated acid HA is almost the same as the concentration of acid, which will be designated a. Substituting s and a in the equilibrium equation, we obtain

$$K_a = [H^+]\frac{[s]}{[a]}$$

or, expressed in terms of negative logarithms,

$$-\log K_a = -\log [H^+] - \log \frac{[s]}{[a]}$$

By definition, $-\log K_a = pK$, and $-\log [H^+] = pH$. Substituting,

$$pH = pK_a + \log \frac{[s]}{[a]}$$

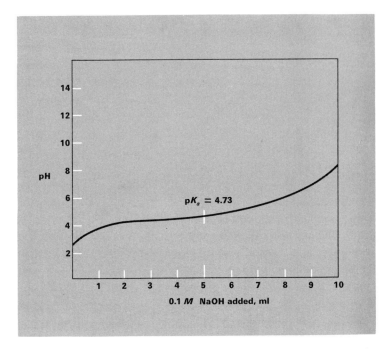

figure 2.1 ::
Titration of 10 ml of
0.1 *M* acetic acid.

determined by measuring the pH of the solution when it contains equimolar quantities of the two species, in other words, when $H_2NCH_2CO_2^-/H_3^+NCH_2CO_2^- = 1$. That p$K$ is 9.6, as shown by the titration curve in Figure 2.2.

When glycine is in an acid solution it exists as a cation:

$$^+H_3NCH_2CO_2H \rightleftarrows H^+ + {}^+H_3NCH_2CO_2^-$$

and it ionizes as shown to yield a proton and the zwitterion. The acid strength of the $-CO_2H$ group can also be measured, and the pK (designated pK_1) is 2.4, as shown by the titration curve. At this point the salt is represented by the zwitterion and the acid by the cation.

In sum, glycine in acid is fully protonated, has a charge of $+1$, and will migrate to the cathode in an electric field. In alkali glycine is fully ionized, has a charge of -1, and will migrate to the anode in an electric field. At a pH between 2.4 and 9.6 the net charge on glycine is zero. This is known as the *isoionic point* (pI) or isoelectric point. For all monoamino monocarboxylic acids, the isoionic point is readily calculated from the two pKs. For glycine, for example,

$$pI = \frac{pK_1 + pK_2}{2} = \frac{2.4 + 9.6}{2} = 6$$

It should be noted that glycine has a pK_1 of 2.4, which represents a much stronger acid than acetic acid, which has a pK_a of 4.75. Glycine is a much stronger acid, owing to the formal positive charge on the N, which exerts an electron-withdrawing effect. The weakness of the $-NH_3^+$ group is due to the strong pull on protons by the carboxyl group, bearing as it does its formal negative charge.

PROPERTIES DEPENDING ON GROUP R : The α-amino group and the carboxyl group of amino acids are, as we have already seen, engaged in peptide bonds in the protein molecule, while the rest of the amino acid molecule becomes a side chain of the protein. These side chains impart to the protein many of its chemical and physical properties. These will be discussed in more detail, and more appropriately, in relation to proteins.

Let us consider for the moment the acid-base properties of amino acids, which depend on the structure of R. In some amino acids the R group is a paraffinic chain with no ionizable hydrogens. In others, such as glutamic acid and aspartic acid, the R group has a carboxyl group; in lysine it has an amino group; in tyrosine a phenolic group; and in cysteine a thiol. All these groups are potential proton donors and in accordance with the definition they are acids.

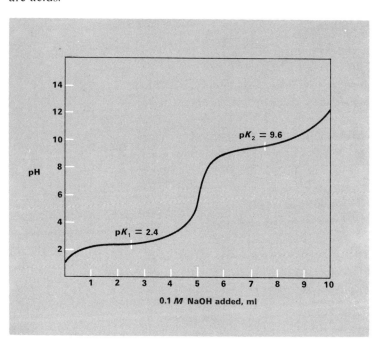

figure 2.2 ::
Titration curve of glycine hydrochloride.

If any of these amino acids is titrated, its titration curve will have three inflections, one for each ionization. In aspartic acid and glutamic acid, for example, three pK values are given for each amino acid:

$$\underset{\underset{pK_2}{\uparrow}}{HO_2C}CH_2\underset{\underset{NH_2 \leftarrow pK_3}{|}}{\overset{\overset{pK_1}{\downarrow}}{CH}}CO_2H \qquad \underset{\underset{pK_2}{\uparrow}}{HO_2C}CH_2CH_2\underset{\underset{NH_2 \leftarrow pK_3}{|}}{\overset{\overset{pK_1}{\downarrow}}{CH}}CO_2H$$

When glutamic and aspartic acid are part of a protein molecule, the ionization of the second carboxyl group (pK_2) is the one that contributes to the acid-base properties of the protein. The same is true for the ε-amino group of lysine and for any ionizable group in the R portion of the amino acid.

primary structure :: **2.3**

In 1902 Emil Fischer and Franz Hofmeister postulated, independently, the peptide bond in proteins. In their view a protein consisted of many amino acid units connected through amide or peptide bonds into a polymeric structure or polypeptide. They arrived at the peptide structure mainly by observing the changes that occur when a protein is hydrolyzed with mineral acids.

1. Proteins have few carboxyl groups and few amino groups that can be detected by titration.

2. As a protein is hydrolyzed, the number of titrable carboxyl and amino groups increases with time of hydrolysis.

3. Incomplete hydrolysis yields peptides containing few amino acids; these were found to be identical to peptides obtained by direct synthesis.

4. Proteins react with copper sulfate in alkaline solution, yielding a purple product. The same reaction is known for a substance called *biuret*, a compound with the structure $H_2NCONHCONH_2$. Other compounds with a similar structure give the same reaction.

On the basis of this information, Fischer and Hofmeister proposed the following general structure for proteins:

$$\underset{\underset{R_1}{|}}{H_2NCH}CONH\underset{\underset{R_2}{|}}{CH}CONH-$$

More recent evidence, obtained primarily by infrared spectroscopy, establishes firmly that in proteins the primary covalent bond is the peptide bond.

The term *peptide* is reserved for relatively small molecules containing few amino acids, and the term protein is arbitrarily used for polypeptides of molecular weight above 6,000. However, this does not mean that a protein must be constituted by a single polypeptide chain. In insulin, for example, two polypeptide chains are connected through covalent bonds. When two polypeptide chains make up the protein molecule, the two chains may be identical or may differ from one another.

The number and order of amino acids in the polypeptide(s) chain (primary structure) of a protein can be established by long and tedious analytical procedures.

It would be beyond the scope of an introductory text to describe in detail the methods employed in the analysis of protein primary structure. It is possible, however, to describe the principles involved and illustrate the general plan.

First, it is necessary to establish if the protein consists of one or more polypeptide chains. If more than one polypeptide chain makes up the protein molecule, they must be separated by chemical means that do not alter the nature of any of the amino acids. Insulin, for example, can be cleaved by oxidizing the $-S-S-$ group connecting the two chains. Performic acid is commonly used for this type of oxidation.

In the next step the amino acid composition is determined by chromatographic methods (see the Appendix). The information obtained by chromatography reveals which amino acids, and in what proportions, are present in the protein.

The most difficult step is the elucidation of the amino acid sequence in a polypeptide chain. Generally a long polypeptide is broken into smaller and more manageable fragments before applying any of the known analytical procedures. Ideally the fragmentation should be made by agents that attack specifically some peptide bonds; these specific agents are the *proteolytic enzymes*. For example, the enzyme trypsin catalyzes the cleavage of peptide bonds in which the $>$CO group belongs to the amino acid lysine or arginine. If a polypeptide is *digested* with trypsin, nearly all the peptides produced should have an arginine or lysine residue as the terminal amino acid:

↓   ↓

Ala-Glu-Leu-Ser-Lys-Tyr-Gly-Arg-Val-Try-Gly

Ala-Glu-Leu-Ser-Lys   Tyr-Gly-Arg   Val-Try-Gly

Other enzymes are known that catalyze the cleavage of other peptide bonds specifically.

The peptides resulting from the fragmentation are separated by chromatographic procedures and each is analyzed for its amino acid sequence. Two methods are widely used for this purpose: the Sanger and the Edman procedures.

After the structure of all the fragments is known, their position in the polypeptide molecule can be deduced from overlaps in amino acids. This can be illustrated as follows. Let us assume that two agents are used: I, attacking to the right of Tyr, and II, attacking to the right of Lys. A polypeptide Val-Tyr-Lys-Ser-Ser-Lys-Tyr-Val will yield the following peptides:

Digestion with agent I. Val-Tyr, Lys-Ser-Ser-Lys-Tyr, Val.

Digestion with agent II. Val-Tyr-Lys, Ser-Ser-Lys, Tyr-Val.

A knowledge of the structure of all six peptides and the specificity of the agents attacking the peptide bonds should be sufficient to reconstruct the original sequence.

Now we must turn our attention to the two most important chemical methods used in determining sequences.

METHOD OF SANGER : Peptides are readily dinitrophenylated by dinitrofluorobenzene—a reagent used extensively by F. Sanger in the study of insulin structure. Dinitrofluorobenzene reacts with the free amino group of a peptide.† It reacts also with the ε-amino group of lysine, but this is readily recognized.

---

† It is customary to write the structure of peptides starting with the amino group, which is called the N-terminal residue. The other end is the C-terminal residue.

The dinitrophenylated peptide can be hydrolyzed by acids to yield amino acids and the dinitrophenyl derivative of the N-terminal amino acid. This derivative, unlike amino acids, is ether-soluble and can be extracted from the reaction mixture. The identity of the N-terminal amino acid is thus revealed when the identity of the dinitrophenyl derivative is established by chromatographic methods. The main limitation of the method is that it allows only for the analysis of one terminal amino acid.

METHOD OF EDMAN : The Edman degradation has the advantage over the Sanger method that it allows for the determination of sequences of four or five amino acids in the same peptide sample.

Peptides react with phenylisothiocyanate through the N-terminal amino acid residue to form a phenylthiocarbamyl derivative; mild acid treatment releases the N-terminal amino acid residue as the phenylthiohydantoin derivative, leaving the amino group of the next amino acid in the sequence free:

$$C_6H_5-N{=}C{=}S + H_2N\overset{\overset{\displaystyle R_1}{|}}{C}HCONH\overset{\overset{\displaystyle R_2}{|}}{C}HCO- \longrightarrow$$

$$C_6H_5-NH-\underset{\underset{\displaystyle R_1}{\displaystyle HC}}{\underset{\displaystyle NH}{}}\overset{\displaystyle C{=}S}{\underset{\displaystyle OC}{}} \quad \xrightarrow{H^+} \quad C_6H_5-N{\longrightarrow}C{=}S + H_2N-\overset{\overset{\displaystyle R_2}{|}}{C}H-CO-$$

phenylthiohydantoin

The phenylthiohydantoin is readily extracted from the reaction mixture and identified by chromatographic procedures. The remainder of the peptide can be subjected to the same treatment again and the next amino acid in line identified, and so on.

secondary structure :: **2.4**

The primary structure of a protein only describes the order of amino acids in the polypeptide chain but tells us nothing of the shape of the chain. The polypeptide chain is not rigid; it can rotate freely around the α carbon of each amino acid. Let us then consider the following portion of a polypeptide:

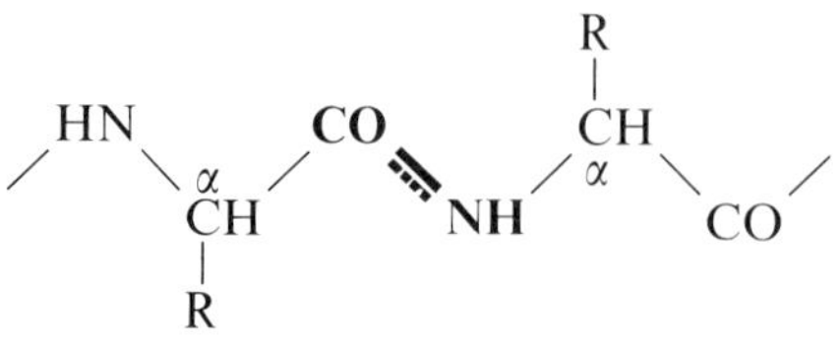

$$\text{HN}\diagdown_{\alpha}\text{CO}\diagdown\quad\overset{\displaystyle R}{\underset{\displaystyle}{\text{CH}}}$$

(structure of polypeptide portion showing HN, CO, CH, NH, CO groups around α carbons with R side chains)

The bonds to the α carbon are single bonds and allow rotation; the peptide bond, represented by a solid and a dashed line, has *partial double-bond character* and rotation is restricted. All atoms around the peptide bond must lie in a plane.

As a result of free rotation about the α carbon, the polypeptide chain can assume numerous shapes. The problem here is to find which shape is the most stable and therefore the most probable. If we examine the structure of the polypeptide backbone we see that one possible interaction can result in hydrogen bonding when two backbones come close together:

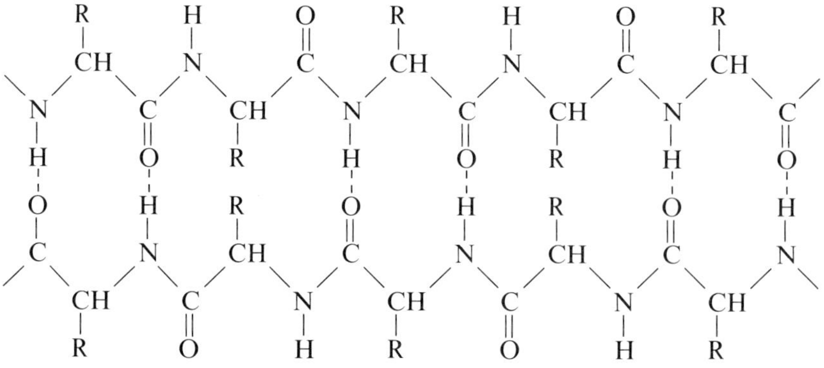

(diagram of two polypeptide backbone chains held together by hydrogen bonds, showing R, CH, N, H, C, O, CH groups in the β-sheet arrangement)

Such sheets of extended chains lying parallel to each other and held together by hydrogen bonds are known mainly in fibrous proteins; this type of structure is known as the β form, and it represents one type of secondary structure of proteins.

A single polypeptide chain, however, is capable of twisting a good deal. When it does so, it is conceivable that the $\diagup$CO group of one peptide bond comes close to the $\diagup$NH group of a distant peptide bond and interacts to form a hydrogen bond. Generally hydrogen bonds result when H is part of a dipole in which the negative pole is a small electronegative atom such as O or N:

$$\diagdown_\diagup C{=}O^{-}\text{-}\text{-}H^{+}{-}N^{-}\diagdown_\diagup$$

The two groups must come within 2.8 Å of each other before they interact. This is the case if the polypeptide is twisted into a spiral. The $>$CO of a peptide bond can be brought within 2.8 Å of the $>$NH of the third peptide bond and establish a hydrogen bond.

Linus Pauling and R. B. Corey proposed the spiral or α-helix shape as the secondary structure of some proteins (Figure 2.3). Their evidence was obtained mainly by X-ray diffraction techniques and the study of model compounds. The α helix is stabilized by the interactions just discussed, and even though a hydrogen bond is weak (5 kcal/mole), the sum of all the hydrogen bonds formed constitutes an adequate stabilizing force.

Not all proteins attain the helical structure. There are proteins, such as γ-globulin, in which there is no helical structure. In other proteins only some regions of the chain assume the helical shape, with the remaining part assuming random shapes.

Breaks or kinks in the α helix can be attributed in part to the presence of imino acids: proline and hydroxyproline. Both have a secondary nitrogen and neither can form hydrogen bonds:

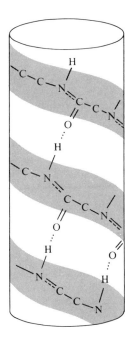

figure 2.3 :: α Helix with 3.7 amino acid residues per turn.

As a consequence, a polypeptide chain can assume the helical shape with interruptions or breaks at several places.

Stability of the helical shape is dependent upon a number of other factors, such as the nature of the amino acid side chains in the protein and the nature of the solvent. The solvent is of particular importance because in many instances it has a high capacity for hydrogen bonding, as is the case with water.

tertiary structure :: **2.5**

The nature of the side chains influences not only the stability of the α helix but also determines to a large extent the final shape assumed by the polypeptide chain, which in many proteins is that of a folded compact structure.

The folding is not random; it is dictated by the interactions of one amino acid with another, or with the backbone, or with the solvent. All these interactions impose a final shape on the molecule that is unique for each protein. This unique three-dimensional shape is known as the tertiary structure. The uniqueness of the tertiary structure is readily noted among the biological properties of proteins. For example, if the protein has catalytic activity (an enzyme), it can lose it in some cases by imposing a minor change in the tertiary structure.

Among the forces involved in maintaining the stability of the tertiary structure are those resulting from the interaction of non-polar side chains such as those present in valine, leucine, isoleucine, phenylalanine, and the like. Other intra- and interpeptide interactions also play a role, and in most instances the interactions result in covalent and noncovalent bonding.

HYDROPHOBIC OR APOLAR INTERACTIONS : The side chains of non-polar amino acids are insoluble in water; they repel and tend to avoid water (are hydrophobic). When two such hydrophobic chains come near each other they coalesce by excluding water, just as two droplets of oil in water coalesce on contact. The interaction of two nonpolar side chains imposes a strain on the polypeptide backbone. Nonpolar side chains should be expected to be found tucked in the internal regions of the molecule away from the surrounding water.

ELECTROSTATIC INTERACTIONS : Saltlike bonds may form when two groups with opposite charge come near each other. The side chains of glutamic acid and aspartic acid bear a carboxyl group, and the side chains of lysine and arginine bear amino groups, all of which are ionizable and are soluble in water. Interactions of these groups with water reduce the number of possible electrostatic interactions that could result from their contact. On the other hand, being water-soluble they tend to be on the outside portion of the molecule. This tendency also imposes a distorting force upon the polypeptide chain.

HYDROGEN BONDING : The side chains of several amino acids interact with each other or with the polypeptide backbone and establish hydrogen bonding. For example, the phenolic group of tyrosine and the $>$CO of the backbone, or the $-CO_2^-$ of glutamic acid, could form a hydrogen bond :

COVALENT BONDING : The only covalent bond known in the tertiary structure of proteins is the —S—S— bond that results from the interaction of two half-cystine residues located in the same polypeptide chain or on two or more polypeptide chains. The two situations are illustrated by ribonuclease and insulin, which are shown in Figure 2.4.

PROTEINS WITH KNOWN TERTIARY STRUCTURES : The approximate shape of proteins has been known from studies of their properties in solution. For example, proteins with several hundred amino acid residues give solutions of relatively low viscosity. Such protein molecules, being very long and very thin—in other words, very asymmetric—should give solutions of very high viscosity. The conclusion here is that in those proteins the polypeptide chain must be folded into a compact shape approaching that of a sphere.

By measurements of viscosity and other physical properties of protein solutions, it has been possible to approximate their shape, which for most soluble proteins is a relatively compact symmetric shape.

The tertiary structure of proteins, however, is not specified by an approximate shape. It should describe the precise foldings of the polypeptide(s) chains. This information is obtained with great

figure 2.4 :: Schematic representation of the structure of (a) insulin with intrapeptide bridge —S—S— (1) and interpeptide bridges (2 and 3) connecting the A chain to the B chain. (b) Ribonuclease with four intrapeptide bridges. The terminal amino acids in both structures are shown.

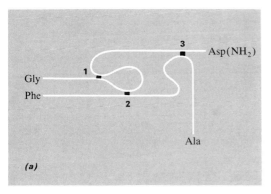

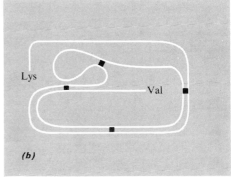

figure 2.5 :: Models of human deoxyhemoglobin (left) and horse hemoglobin (right). [*From H. Muirhead et al., J. Mol. Biol.*, **28**: *117–156* (*1967*).]

difficulty, and it is obtained mainly by the use of X-ray diffraction analysis. By this means the tertiary structure of myoglobin, hemoglobin, lysozyme, and ribonuclease have been deduced. In Figure 2.5 are reproduced three-dimensional models of hemoglobin.

quaternary structure :: **2.6**

A number of proteins exist in nature as aggregates of several protein subunits. A subunit, commonly called a *monomer*, has its own tertiary structure, but often it reveals no biological properties until several subunits aggregate into a polymer. The polymeric structure is considered a fourth level of complexity in protein structure and is called the quaternary structure.

The forces binding the monomers in the aggregate are mainly surface interactions between the side chains of the monomeric units.

denaturation :: **2.7**

The importance of the tertiary structure of proteins in biological phenomena is readily recognized when the native conformation is disrupted by physical or chemical means. Enzymes, for example, lose their activity when heated even for very short periods of time. Heat in this case causes changes in the native tertiary structure of the protein, and these changes are attended by loss of biological activity. Other properties of the native protein also change as a result of thermal action. Physical and chemical agents, such as radiation, violent shaking, acids, bases, and organic solvents, can also modify the native structure of proteins. The changes that take place as a result of their action are known as *denaturation*.

Denaturation of a protein is accompanied by changes in solubility, viscosity, reactivity of functional groups, and loss of biological activity. When a protein is denatured, the conformation is disrupted; an α helix uncoils partially, leading to random shapes. A globular protein becomes less symmetric as a result of uncoiling, and this is reflected in increased viscosity; solutions of denatured proteins are more viscous than the corresponding solution of the native proteins. Solubility also decreases, and in many cases the denatured protein will coagulate.

In a native protein many of the functional groups, such as —SH or —OH, are not readily detectable by chemical means. As the protein denatures, the functional groups are made accessible to chemical detection. This is also in agreement with the idea that denaturation is best represented by a partial disruption of the secondary and tertiary structures (Figure 2.6).

In some instances, denaturation can be reversed. For example, the addition of a concentrated urea solution to a solution of native protein will cause changes in the protein solution similar to those discussed above, including loss of biological activity. If the urea

figure 2.6 :: Denaturation. (*a*) Native protein with its tertiary structure intact. (*b*) Initial unfolding with partial loss of hydrogen bonding. (*c*) Denatured protein.

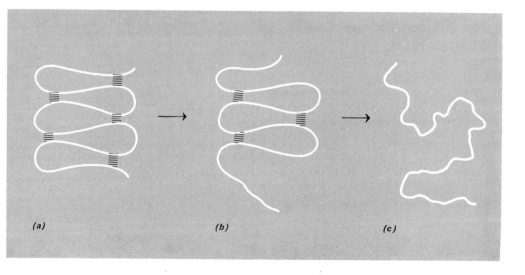

(a)   (b)   (c)

is then removed by dialysis, certain proteins will "renature" and recover their original properties.

It is not always easy to establish when a protein is denatured. The criteria above are not in all cases unequivocal. For example, an increase in the viscosity of a protein solution can result when globular molecules aggregate into a linear shape without changing their tertiary structure. It is also possible to imagine that a globular protein uncoils for a brief period of time and then rapidly regains a globular shape. Here the viscosity remains the same, but in the recoiling process the original conformation could easily be lost.

More than one criterion must be applied to decide that a protein has undergone denaturation. Also, the stability of proteins toward denaturating agents varies widely. Some proteins withstand temperatures at which other proteins would be completely denatured.

properties :: **2.8**

Proteins are macromolecules that form true solutions. Because their molecular dimensions are in the range of colloidal particles, protein solutions are regarded as colloidal solutions and behave as colloids. For example, proteins will not diffuse through semi-permeable membranes through which smaller molecules will.†
Proteins, like other macromolecules, should be called molecular colloids to distinguish them from organic dispersions. The difference is that in a protein solution the particle is a molecule that cannot be broken down without changing its identity. In organic dispersions, the particle is made up of many identical molecules. Soap in water, for example, tends to form aggregates of many soap molecules. The aggregates can be broken down, but soap does not change chemically.

Colloidal particles are 100 to 1,000 Å in diameter. Most protein molecules fall within this range.

MOLECULAR WEIGHT OF PROTEINS : Proteins were defined earlier as polypeptides ranging in molecular weight from 6,000 to several

† Semipermeable membranes are made of materials such as cellophane or collodion. They have small pores that are large enough to let small molecules through but too small for macromolecules to cross. The separation of large molecules such as proteins from smaller organic molecules or inorganic ions is accomplished by *dialysis*. The mixture of large and small molecules in solution is placed in a cellophane bag which is submerged in a large volume of water. Because small molecules diffuse in and out of the membrane, they are eventually removed if the outside water is constantly replaced by fresh water. The macromolecules, not being able to cross the walls of the membrane, remain inside the bag.

million. The molecular weights of some well-known proteins are listed in Table 2.2.

The molecular weights of proteins are determined by several methods, including osmotic pressure, sedimentation in the ultracentrifuge, and light scattering. The ultracentrifuge method is the most widely used.

The ultracentrifuge is an instrument that attains speeds of over 65,000 rpm, developing centrifugal forces of over 200,000 times gravity. The instrument is so designed that a very small quartz cell containing the protein solution can be observed by optical and photographic systems while the instrument is in operation.

At the start of the measurement, all the protein molecules in solution are uniformly distributed in the cell, but as the centrifuge attains high velocity the particles are forced toward the bottom of the cell, leaving clear solvent at the top and forming a boundary. The rate at which the particles sediment can be measured over a period of time, and from this rate the sedimentation constant can be calculated.

The molecular weight is related to the sedimentation constant by the equation

$$M = \frac{RTs}{D(1 - V\rho)}$$

in which M is the molecular weight, R is the gas constant, T the absolute temperature, and s the sedimentation constant. The other terms, D, V, and ρ, must be also measured and are the diffusion constant, the partial specific volume of the protein, and the density of the solution, respectively.

PROTEIN	M.W.
Insulin	5,800
Ribonuclease	13,700
Myoglobin	17,000
Papain	20,900
Pepsin	36,400
Egg albumin	44,000
Serum albumin	69,000
Serum γ-globulin	180,000
Catalase	250,000
Fibrinogen	450,000
Thyroglobulin	630,000
Hemocyanin	2,800,000

table 2.2 :: Molecular weights of some proteins

Some difficulties are encountered when protein molecules have a tendency to aggregate into larger particles. Insulin, for example, has a molecular weight of 6,000, which corresponds to the A and B chains linked through $-S-S-$ bonds. Under certain conditions of pH and salt concentration, three or four insulin molecules aggregate to form a particle with a molecular weight of 18,000 to 24,000. Sometimes it is difficult to recognize aggregates, and the molecular weight determined frequently represents a multiple of the true molecular weight.

REACTION WITH ACIDS AND BASES : Proteins have ionizable groups that correspond to some of the R groups of the component amino acids. In Table 2.3 are listed the ionizable groups of proteins, both acidic and basic. Proteins can react with acids and bases and, like amino acids, are amphoteric substances.

At neutral pH the carboxyl groups and amino groups of most proteins are charged. The reason is the same as that given for amino acids: The carboxyl groups are dissociated ($-CO_2^-$), bearing the negative charges; the amino groups, being protonated ($-NH_3^+$), bear the positive charges. When acid is added, the dissociation of carboxyl groups is repressed and the negative charges are reduced. By adding base the protons of the $-NH_3^+$ group react, leaving an uncharged $-NH_2$ group.

At some pH the number of dissociated and combined protons is equal and the net charge in the protein is zero. At this pH, called the *isoelectric point*, the protein is least soluble and will not migrate in an electric field. At pHs below the isoelectric point, the protein exists as a cation, because there is an excess of positive charges. At pHs above the isoelectric point the protein exists as an anion.

ELECTROPHORESIS : As explained above, proteins migrate in an electric field toward the pole of opposite charge. The direction and

NAME	IONIZABLE GROUP	pK
Aspartic	β-CO$_2$H	3.65
Glutamic	γ-CO$_2$H	4.25
Cysteine	$-SH$	8.33
Tyrosine	$-OH$	9.10
Histidine	NH	5.97
Lysine	$-NH_3^+$	10.3
Arginine	$-NH_3^+$	13.2

table 2.3 :: pK values of acidic and basic groups in proteins

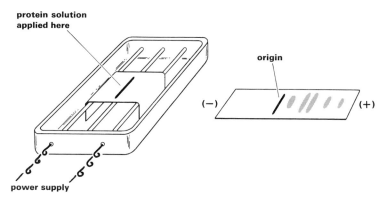

protein solution
applied here

origin

(−)   (+)

power supply

figure 2.7 :: Paper electrophoresis. The mixture of proteins in solution of buffer pH 8.5 is applied on the paper. As the current flows, proteins migrate toward the pole of opposite charge (at pH 8.5 most known proteins carry a negative charge). At the end of the run, the paper is treated with a dye that combines with protein (right). The fast-moving protein carries the greatest negative charge.

rate of movement depends largely on the net charge of the protein, which varies according to pH.

The procedure known as electrophoresis is useful to separate proteins from one another and as a check of purity. In practice there are two general systems of electrophoresis: free boundary and zone electrophoresis. In free boundary, proteins move in a buffered liquid medium contained in a U tube. In zone electrophoresis proteins migrate in a solid or semisolid material such as filter paper, starch gel, or agar gel (Figure 2.7).

In principle, proteins can be separated even when the difference in net charge is not very great. The pH of the solution must be carefully adjusted, since net charge depends on pH.

In the separation of blood plasma proteins it has become customary to adjust the pH to approximately 8. At this pH, all the plasma proteins are negatively charged (their isoelectric pH is below 8), and all move toward the anode (+). Although the direction of movement is the same, their rates vary considerably, because at pH 8 some proteins are more negatively charged than others.

REACTIVE GROUPS : Reactivity of proteins and some of their chemical properties are largely determined by the nature of groups R of the component amino acids. The acidic and basic properties of proteins, as already discussed, are mainly due to the ionizable groups of the dicarboxylic and dibasic amino acids. Other groups in the side chains of proteins are responsible for other typical protein reactions and physical properties.

Protein solutions, for example, absorb light in several ultraviolet ranges, but absorption in the range of 279 mμ is of particular interest. This characteristic absorption derives principally from the indol group of tryptophan, the phenolic group of tyrosine, and to a much lesser extent the phenyl group of phenylalanine.

Several compounds that react with the —SH group of cysteine, as exemplified by iodoacetic acid (ICH_2CO_2H) and some of its derivatives, react also with the —SH groups in proteins. Others in the category of organometallo compounds, of which p-chloro-mercuribenzoate is the best known, form mercaptides. The thiol group also tends to oxidize readily to a disulfide (—S—S—) and, as already shown, this is important in establishing intra- and interpeptide bonds.

The —OH groups in serine and tyrosine are susceptible to esterification with acetic anhydride and similar reagents. Acylation of the free —NH_2 group of lysine is also possible with a variety of acylating agents.

Not all the reactions of proteins with small molecules are readily explained in chemical terms. Proteins, for example, have the capacity to form tightly bound complexes with ions. The acid dyeing of wool and cytological staining are two well-known examples of the reaction of proteins with small molecules. The capacity of proteins to react with small charged or uncharged molecules is an important property of proteins which is unfortunately not totally understood.

SOLUBILITY : The solubility of proteins is influenced by pH as well as by the presence of salts. Proteins are least soluble at their isoelectric point and might precipitate when the pH of the solution is adjusted to the pH of the isoelectric point.

Proteins in solution precipitate when large amounts of a salt are added. The reason is that the interaction between water and protein is reduced as the interaction between water and salt ions increases. Consequently, interaction between protein molecules increases, resulting in associations and precipitation. The process is known as *salting out*.

Some proteins normally not soluble in water can be made soluble by adding salts. In this case, the protein-protein interaction is reduced as the protein-water interaction increases. The protein becomes soluble and the process is known as *salting in*.

Salting out is very useful to isolate and separate proteins from mixtures, because different proteins are salted out at different salt concentrations. Taking advantage of the difference, one can build a system of fractionation of proteins.

One of the most commonly used salts is ammonium sulfate, which is very soluble in water, making it possible to attain very high concentrations of salt when needed.

BIOLOGICAL ROLE OF PROTEINS : Proteins make up nearly 80 percent of the solid matter of the living cell, and they represent one of its major structural components. Proteins such as collagen are quite insoluble and ideally suited to serve as support material. Globular proteins, being soluble, function in a variety of ways. Those in the blood plasma of animals, for example, serve to regulate water movement between the capillary blood vessels and tissues. This is possible because proteins cannot cross the walls of the capillaries, whereas water and ions can. The osmotic pressure developed will force water toward the capillaries.

The respiratory protein hemoglobin contains a pigmented prosthetic group belonging to the group of compounds known as ferroporphyrins. The prosthetic group has the ability to bind molecular oxygen and to release it without difficulty. What is interesting here is that the ferroporphyrin alone does not have the oxygen-binding capacity; it does so only when present in hemoglobin. All the respiratory proteins known in nature are of a similar type.

Other globular proteins have the ability to catalyze chemical reactions in the cell. Every cell contains a large number of catalysts, the enzymes. Enzymes speed up reactions that ordinarily would be too slow to serve any useful function. Also they are specific for a given reaction or a given compound. To date no enzyme has been found that is not a protein.

The contractile elements of muscle are protein of a special type. They have the ability to transform chemical energy into mechanical energy, leading to muscle contraction and movement.

There are in nature a number of peptides and proteins that regulate biological systems and are classified as *hormones*. Insulin, for example, is a regulator of glucose metabolism. The pituitary gland of vertebrates produces a variety of hormones that regulate growth of the animal, balance of fluids, reproductive cycles, and other important biological functions. It is not clearly understood how protein hormones "regulate."

A foreign protein, one not present in an organism, evokes the formation of antibodies if the foreign protein is introduced into the organism without first breaking down. The protein is said to be *antigenic*, and the antibody produced specifically reacts with its antigen. The reaction takes several forms, but it may be described broadly as a neutralization of the antigen by the antibody. An organism becomes immune to a second invasion of the same foreign protein because it can be neutralized by the antibodies that already exist. Antigen–antibody reactions are highly specific, and immunological tests have become one of the most valuable methods to characterize proteins.

references ::

DOTY, P., "Proteins," *Scientific American*, September, 1957.

HAUROWITZ, F., *The Chemistry and Function of Proteins*. New York: Academic Press, Inc., 1963.

PERUTZ, M. F., "The Hemoglobin Molecule," *Scientific American*, November, 1964.

STEINER, R. W., *The Chemical Foundation of Molecular Biology*. Princeton, N.J.: D. Van Nostrand Company, Inc., 1965.

nucleic acids ::: 3

NUCLEIC ACIDS, LIKE PROTEINS, ARE MACROMOLECULES RANGING in molecular weight from about 30,000 to several million. They occur in all living cells as a major component of the nucleus and also as a component of cytoplasmic structures such as the ribosomes.

Two types of nucleic acids have been known for a long time, each from a different source: deoxyribonucleic acid (DNA) from animals

DNA	RNA
Adenine	Adenine
Guanine	Guanine
Cytosine	Cytosine
Thymine	Uracil
D-Deoxyribose	D-Ribose
H_3PO_4	H_3PO_4
Less common:	
5-Methylcytosine	
5-Hydroxymethylcytosine	

table 3.1 :: Hydrolysis products of DNA and RNA

and ribonucleic acid (RNA) from plants. The classification into animal and plant nucleic acid was discarded, when it became clear that both DNA and RNA are present in all living cells. The difference between DNA and RNA was made on the basis of the products released by complete hydrolysis, as shown in Table 3.1 on page 39.

In more recent times it was discovered that DNA is mainly located in the nucleus of the cell and that the major portion of the cell's RNA is located in the cytoplasm, where it is intimately involved with protein synthesis.

nucleotides as components of RNA and DNA :: 3.1

Nucleic acids are polynucleotides, that is, polymeric structures in which the repeating units are ribonucleotides (in RNA) and deoxyribonucleotides (in DNA):

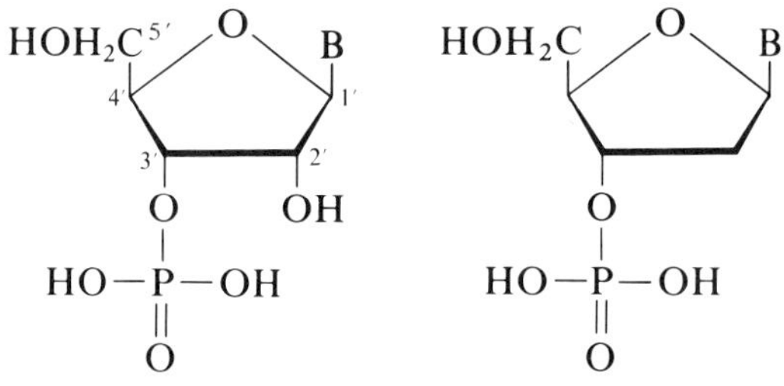

The difference between the two structures is that in deoxyribonucleotides there is no —OH in position 2'.† The presence of three esterifiable —OH groups in the ribose portion or two in the deoxyribose portion gives rise to several possible phosphoesters. The structures shown in the paragraph above are the 3'-phosphoesters.

Structurally a nucleotide can be regarded as a phosphoester of a nucleoside. A nucleoside is a N-glycoside in which the sugar component is ribose or deoxyribose and the aglucon is a pyrimidine or purine base. A more detailed discussion on the structure of sugars will be given in Chapter 4. Here the discussion will be confined to the structure of the pyrimidine and purine bases.

† The five carbons of the pentose are numbered with prime numbers to distinguish them from numbers used for the atoms of the pyrimidine and purine bases represented by B in the above structures and to be discussed shortly.

Pyrimidines are derivatives of the heterocyclic compound, 1,3-diazine, and purines are derivatives of the fused pyrimidine-imidazol ring system called purine:

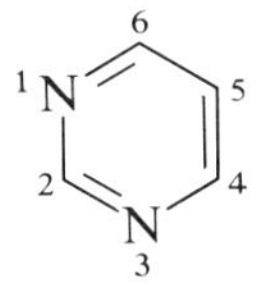

pyrimidine 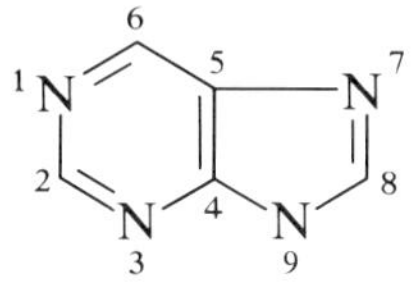   purine

The pyrimidine and purine bases occurring in nucleic acids and their structures are listed in Table 3.2.

table 3.2 :: Structures of purines and pyrimidines

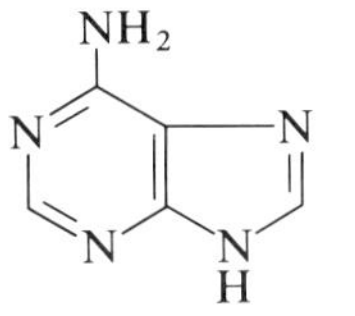

adenine 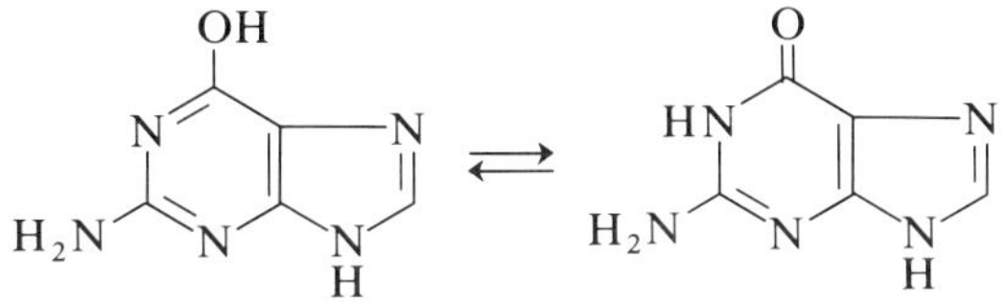   guanine

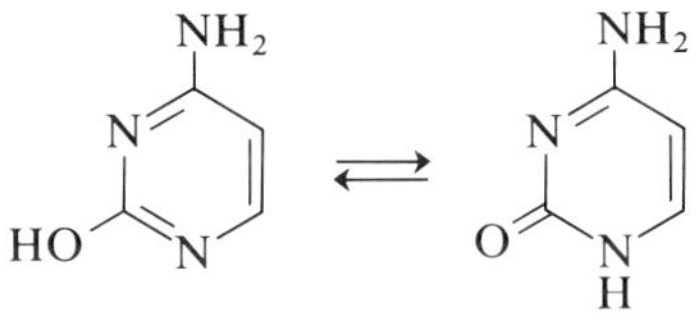

cytosine 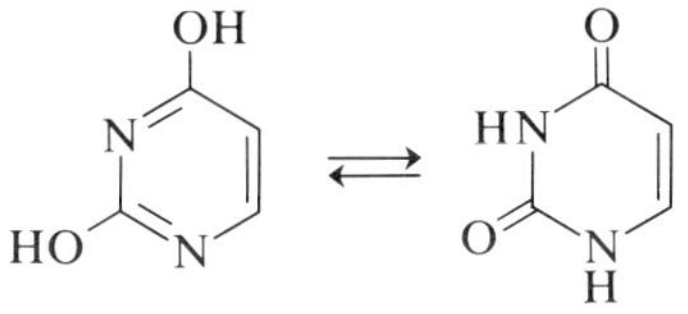   uracil

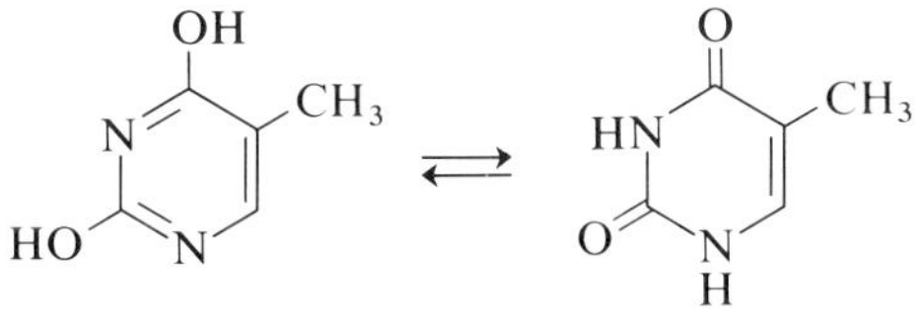

thymine

Found less frequently:

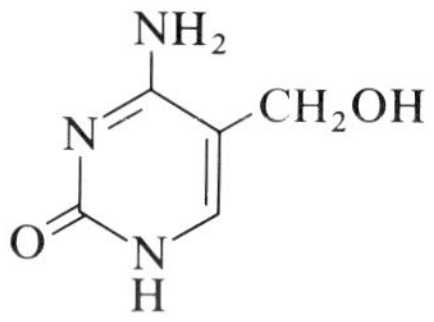

5-hydroxymethylcytosine 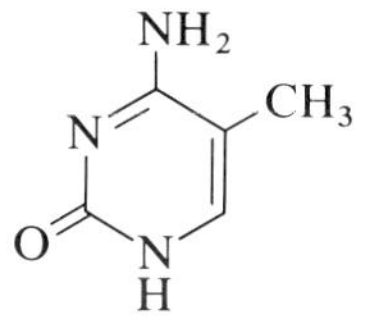   5-methylcytosine

Pyrimidines or purines with —OH substituents can exist in tautomeric forms, as already shown in Table 3.2:

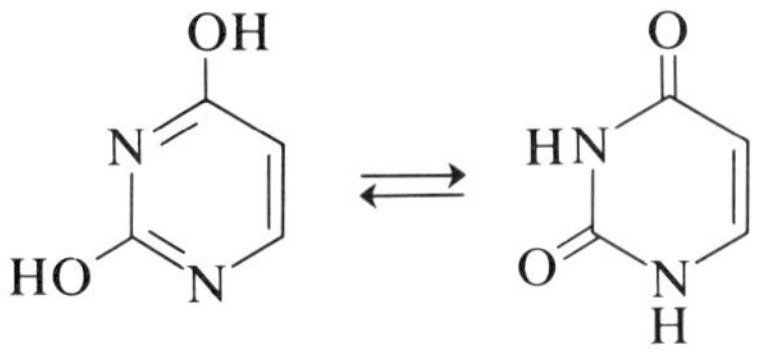

enol or lactim   keto or lactam

The position of the N-glycosidic bond between the pentose and the pyrimidines is established through N_3, and with purines through N_9. It has also been established that of the two possible isomers with respect to the glycosidic bond (α or β) only the β form exists in nucleosides:

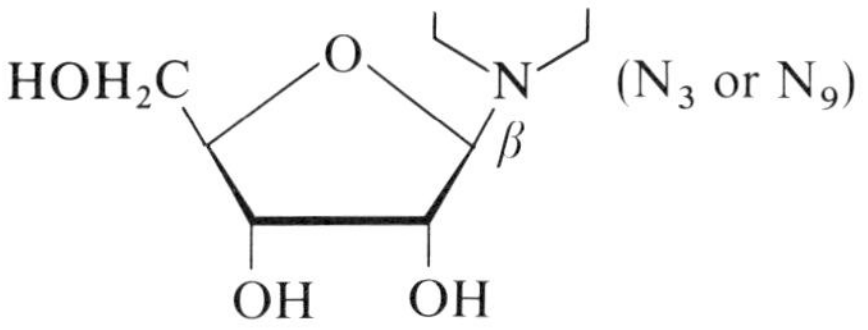

The formation of phosphomonoesters of nucleosides can be through any of the —OH groups of the pentose. For example, adenosine can give rise to the following phosphoesters: adenosine-2'-monophosphate, adenosine-3'-monophosphate, or adenosine-5'-monophosphate; and deoxyadenosine can give rise to only the 3'- and 5'-monophosphates.†

Of particular interest are 5'-phosphoesters, because several compounds of supreme biological importance belong to this group: adenosine diphosphate (ADP) and adenosine triphosphate (ATP):

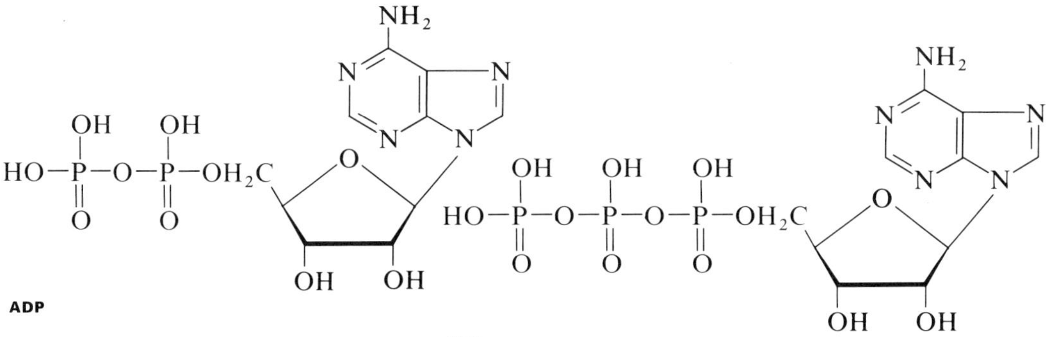

ADP

ATP

† Nucleotides are also named as acids: for example, 2'-adenylic acid. The names of other nucleosides and nucleotides are listed in Tables 3.3 and 3.4.

PROPERTIES OF NUCLEOTIDES : The method used to hydrolyze nucleic acids determines which phosphoesters are produced. Enzymes that attack certain specific bonds produce 3'- or 5'-phosphoesters, depending on whether the enzyme attacks the 5'- or the 3'-phosphoester bond.

Mixtures of nucleotides produced by the hydrolysis of nucleic acids can be resolved into individual components by paper chromatography, electrophoresis, or ion-exchange chromatography. Separation is made possible mainly because nucleotides differ from one another in their acid-base properties. All have a phosphate group with a pK_1 of about 1.6 and a pK_2 of about 6.5. Phosphates of guanosine, adenosine, and cytidine have in addition to the phosphate group an $-NH_2$ group that can be protonated. These substances behave as zwitterions in aqueous solutions.

Since the net charge on nucleotides is dependent upon the pH of the solution, it is possible to adjust the pH to a point where differences in charge makes their separation by electrophoresis possible.

Nucleotides can be hydrolyzed by acids to yield a nucleoside and phosphoric acid and also pentose phosphate and the pyrimidine or purine. The nature of the product depends on the conditions used.

table 3.3 :: Nucleosides

Adenosine	Adenine and ribose
Deoxyadenosine	Adenine and deoxyribose
Guanosine	Guanine and ribose
Deoxyguanosine	Guanine and deoxyribose
Cytidine	Cytosine and ribose
Deoxycytidine	Cytosine and deoxyribose
Uridine	Uracil and ribose
Deoxyuridine	Uracil and deoxyribose
Thymine riboside	Thymine and ribose
Thymidine	Thymine and deoxyribose

table 3.4 :: Nucleotides

Guanosine-2'-phosphate	Deoxyguanosine-3'-phosphate
Guanosine-3'-phosphate	Deoxyguanosine-5'-phosphate
Guanosine-5'-phosphate	
Cytidine-2'-phosphate	Deoxycytidine-3'-phosphate
Cytidine-3'-phosphate	Deoxycytidine-5'-phosphate
Cytidine-5'-phosphate	
Uridine-2'-phosphate	Deoxyuridine-3'-phosphate
Uridine-3'-phosphate	Deoxyuridine-5'-phosphate
Uridine-5'-phosphate	Thymidine-5'-phosphate

Treatment of nucleotides with dilute alkalies causes migration of
the phosphate group when a vicinal —OH group is present. The
reason for the migration is the formation of a cyclic phosphodiester:

In the phosphodiester the two ester bonds are equally reactive,
and further attack by a base yields the two isomers

5'-Phosphoesters do not undergo this change, because the orientation of the free —OH groups is unfavorable and no reaction
takes place. Deoxyribonucleotides cannot undergo change with
alkali because there is no —OH group in position 2'.

internucleotide bond :: 3.2

Nucleotides can conceivably combine in many ways to produce
polymeric structures, but all the evidence favors one type of combination in nucleic acids, a 3'-5'-phosphodiester bond:

The same type of phosphodiester bond exists in both RNA and DNA, as shown by the experimental evidence, to be discussed next.

INTERNUCLEOTIDE BOND IN RNA : When RNA is hydrolyzed with dilute alkalies, a mixture of 2'- and 3'-phosphoesters is obtained. It is already known that alkalies cause cyclization of the phospho-ester in nucleotides; in RNA cyclization precedes hydrolysis, as shown here:

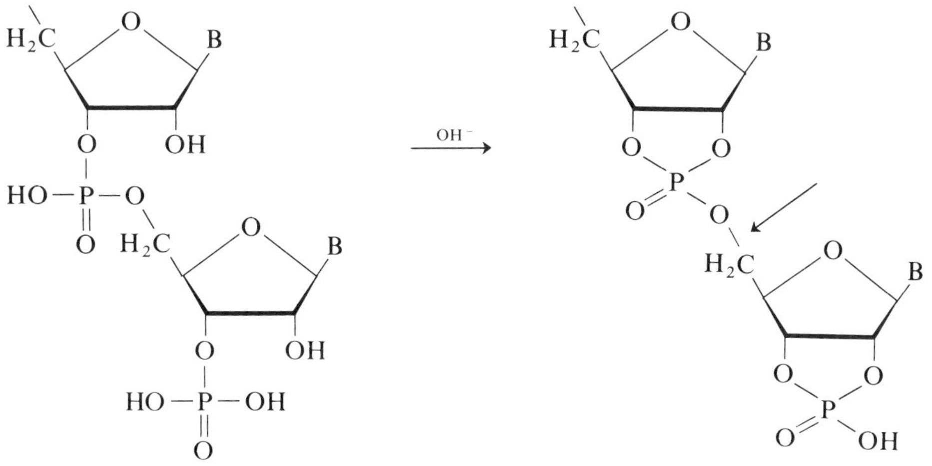

Further attack by alkali cleaves the bond connecting $C_{5'}$ to the phosphate, to yield a mixture of cyclic nucleotides:

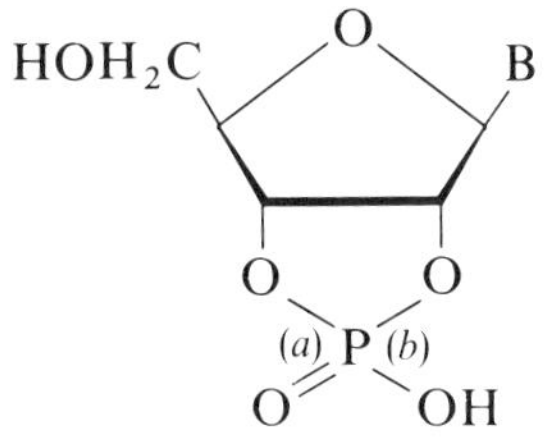

As already seen, cleavage at (a) will yield 2'-phosphoesters, and cleavage at (b) will yield 3'-phosphoesters. Since the two bonds are equally reactive, a mixture of the isomers is produced.

Formation of a cyclic phosphotriester is a prerequisite for the hydrolysis of RNA, as shown above. Cleavage of the ester bond at $C_{5'}$ is predicted from experience gained with model compounds; it is evident that this bond is more unstable than either of the two other ester bonds.

The absence of 5'-phosphoesters in the alkaline hydrolysis products of RNA is explained by the failure of the —OH in $C_{5'}$ to form cyclic phosphoesters—as explained earlier. The formation of 2'- and 3'-phosphoesters is in harmony with the postulated mechanism of hydrolysis, and it is proof that the —OH in either the 2' or 3' positions must be esterified. It is therefore concluded that the internucleotide bond in RNA must be either 2'-5' or 3'-5'. The choice between these two possibilities has been made in favor of the 3'-5', for several reasons.

One reason is the additional evidence gained from enzymatic hydrolysis of RNA. The specificity of enzymes is such that only one particular bond is attacked—and this can be learned from observations made on the enzymatic action upon model compounds. Pancreatic ribonuclease, for example, is known to form cyclic phosphodiesters with 3'- but not with 2'-phosphates. It also cleaves the cyclic phosphodiesters unidirectionally to yield 3'-phosphates exclusively.

+ ROH

The products obtained when ribonuclease attacks RNA are mixtures of oligonucleotides (a few nucleotides linked through phosphoester bonds) and nucleotides. The position of the phosphate is in all instances 3'. This can only happen if the internucleotide linkage is 3'-5' in RNA.

INTERNUCLEOTIDE BOND IN DNA : The absence of an —OH group in position 2' of deoxynucleotides makes it impossible for them to form cyclic phosphoesters. A consequence of the failure to form cyclic phosphoesters is that DNA is stable to the action of dilute alkalies.

Because DNA is stable to alkalies, other methods of hydrolysis must be employed. One effective method is hydrolysis by specific enzymes that should yield predictable products. Fortunately two *nucleases* have been found—one in pancreas and the other in spleen—which catalyze specifically the cleavage of one or the other phosphoester bonds:

pancreatic nuclease ———————→ ——————— spleen nuclease

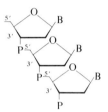

figure 3.1 ::
Schematic representation of a segment of DNA. The 3'–5' phosphodiester bond is represented by P.

The products obtained when pancreatic nuclease attacks DNA are mainly 5'-phosphoesters; with spleen nuclease the products are mainly 3'-phosphoester. This can only happen if the ester bond between deoxynucleotides in DNA is 3'-5'.

In summary: The internucleotide bond in both RNA and DNA is a phosphodiester bond connecting $C_{3'}$ of one nucleotide to $C_{5'}$ of the next, as shown in Figure 3.1.

structure of DNA :: **3.3**

An average DNA molecule has thousands of nucleotides; with four types of nucleotides predominantly occurring in DNA, the number of theoretically possible combinations is staggering.

The task of unraveling the nucleotide sequence in a DNA molecule is complicated by the inadequacy of the chemical methods of degradation; there is nothing in nucleic acid chemistry that compares favorably to the Sanger or Edman degradation procedure for proteins. Because of this difficulty, the primary structure of DNA remains largely unknown.

Not knowing the primary structure of DNA has not prevented investigation of its macromolecular shape; the progress made in the last few years has been impressive. In fact, one of the fundamental concepts of modern biology was born from the brilliant theories of J. H. Watson and F. H. C. Crick on the structure of the

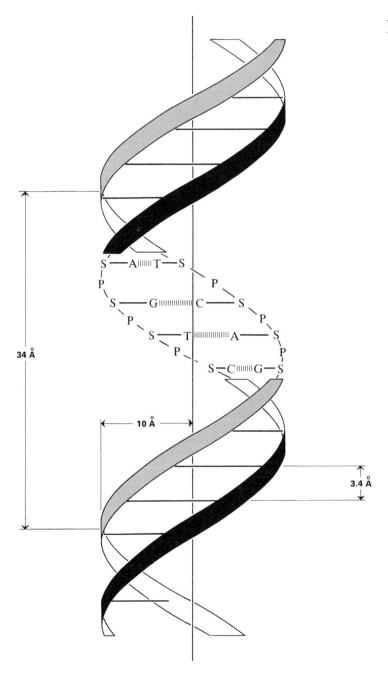

figure 3.2 ::
Watson-Crick model of
DNA.

DNA molecule—this fundamental concept is that of molecular replication.

To explain how a DNA molecule can replicate, Watson and Crick first constructed a model to represent the macromolecular shape of DNA.

WATSON-CRICK MODEL : The DNA molecule, according to the model illustrated in Figure 3.2, consists of two polynucleotide chains interwoven into a helical structure. The width of the double-stranded helix is 20 Å, which conforms with the theoretically predicted dimensions. Each turn of the helix is 34 Å, or the equivalent of 10 nucleotides arranged linearly.

Each strand has a backbone of deoxyribose phosphates linked through 3'-5' phosphodiester bonds; they run in opposite directions (antiparallel) in relation to their ester bonds, as shown in Figure 3.3. The deoxyribose and phosphate units are about on the same plane and interconnected into strands running parallel to the long axis of the molecule.

The plane relationship of the deoxyribose to the purine or pyrimidine bases is approximately 90 degrees. Thus the bases in DNA project at near right angles to the long axis.

Within the limits of the width of the double-stranded helix, the bases can be brought close enough to form hydrogen bonds. But

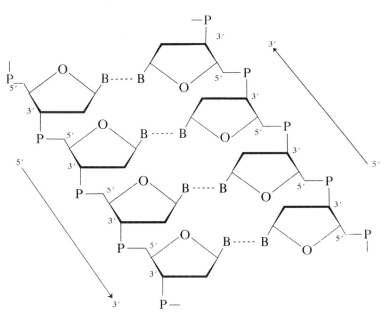

figure 3.3 ::
Antiparallel orientation of the phosphodiester bond in DNA.

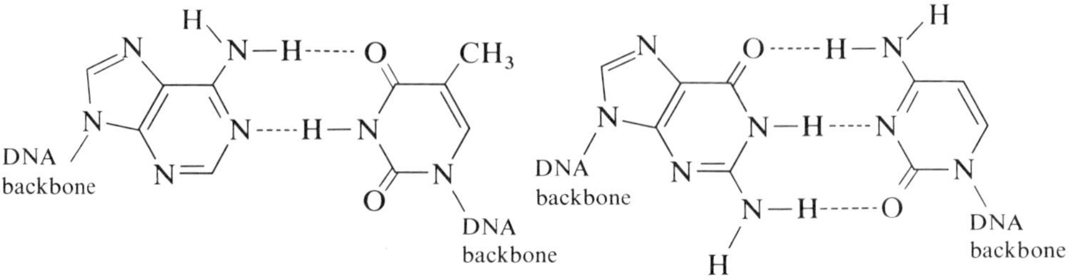

figure 3.4 :: Pairing of A-T and G-C by forming hydrogen bonds.

the bases must be arranged so that the adenine (A) from one strand is in front of the thymine (T) of the other; the guanine (G) of one strand must also be opposite the cytosine (C) of the other. This is the only possible distribution of the bases that allows hydrogen-bond formation within the experimentally determined dimensions of the helix. If two purines were arranged to face each other, they would not fit into the allowable space; two pyrimidines would be too far to establish hydrogen bonds. The only arrangement possible is shown in Figure 3.4. The G-C pair can form three hydrogen bonds, and the A-T pair two—which is the reason the G-C pairs are more stable than the A-T pairs.

The bases are stacked in the inner portion of the molecule with the phosphates outside. Since the bases are hydrophobic (they repel water), their tendency is to be away from the surrounding water and attain more stability by tucking into the inner region of the molecule.

The model predicts that in DNA the molar ratios of purines to pyrimidines should be 1, because for every purine on one strand there should be a pyrimidine on the other; it also predicts that the ratios A/T and G/C should be 1. DNA can thus be of an A/T or a

SOURCE OF DNA	A	T	G	C	$\dfrac{A+G}{T+C}$	$\dfrac{A+T}{G+C}$
Human liver	30.3	30.3	19.5	19.9	0.99	1.53
Ox thymus	29.0	28.5	21.2	21.2	1.01	1.36
Pig spleen	29.6	29.2	20.4	20.8	1.00	1.43
Horse spleen	29.6	27.5	22.9	20.1	1.10	1.53
Sheep liver	29.3	29.2	20.7	20.8	1.00	1.41
Rat bone marrow	28.6	28.4	21.4	20.4	1.02	1.33
Serratia marcescens	20.7	20.1	27.2	31.9	0.94	0.69
Mycobacterium tuberculosis	18.0	20.0	28.5	33.5	0.87	0.61

table 3.5 :: Base composition† of DNA

† In mole percentages.

G/C type, depending on which bases predominate, and the ratio (A + T)/(G + C) is expected to vary from one DNA to another. This is in fact the case, as shown in Table 3.5.

The constancy of these ratios was observed by Erwin Chargaff sometime before the DNA model was proposed. The model was constructed using this information as a fundamental fact.

The replication of DNA can be explained most simply by assuming that the two strands separate by breaking the hydrogen bonds: each strand becomes a template for the synthesis of a new DNA strand from nucleotides. If the basic arrangement is maintained, that is, thymine lines up with adenine and cytosine with guanine, a complementary chain to the template is formed. For example, if a segment of the template has the arrangement ATTGACCA from the free 5′ to the free 3′ end, the newly synthesized chain will be TAACTGGT from the free 3′ to the free 5′ end. Since each strand produces its complementary strand, the two newly formed strands combine into a DNA molecule identical to the original. More will be said about DNA replication in Chapter 13.

properties of DNA :: 3.4

SIZE AND SHAPE : Based on the Watson-Crick model, a DNA molecule with a molecular weight of, for example, 7,000,000 would correspond to a rigid gently curved rod 30,000 Å in length and 15 to 20 Å in width. The rather asymmetric molecule should give extremely viscous solutions, which is in agreement with experimental observations.

Most DNA so far isolated have molecular weights in the millions. For example, it is estimated that the molecular weight of DNA isolated from the bacterium *Escherichia coli* is 1 or 2×10^9. Molecular-weight determinations in this range are difficult, and in most cases the values obtained are approximations.

Another difficulty in assessing the molecular weight of DNA is that during its isolation from the cell it is apt to denature, and this could conceivably be attended by a reduction in molecular weight. As the methods of isolation improve, the molecular weights assigned to DNA are being revised, mostly upward.

OPTICAL PROPERTIES AND DENATURATION OF DNA : Solutions of DNA strongly absorb ultraviolet light in the 260-mμ region. Absorption is related to the purines and pyrimidines, all of which absorb light in that region. It is of interest that the extent to which

DNA absorbs ultraviolet light falls short of the extent of absorption expected if the absorption of all the bases were added. This effect, known as *hypochromism*, has been useful in the interpretation of DNA structure. On theoretical grounds not to be discussed here, the absorption of ultraviolet light is expected to be less when the purines and pyrimidines are stacked in an orderly fashion than in a disorganized solution of the bases.

When DNA solutions are heated, the absorption of ultraviolet light increases sharply when the temperature reaches a point characteristic for each DNA sample. This phenomenon is believed to result from the separation, hence disorganization, of the two chains in the DNA molecule; at a given temperature, usually above 50°C, and in solutions of certain ionic strength the two chains separate, the separation being complete within a range of 5°C. The temperature midpoint (T_m) is analogous to the melting point of a crystal and varies for different types of DNA (Figure 3.5).

One reason for the variation in T_m of different DNA samples is the difference in content of the pairs guanine-cytosine. As shown in Figure 3.5, guanine forms three hydrogen bonds with cytosine but adenine forms only two with thymine. Logically, guanine-cytosine pairs are more difficult to break than adenine-thymine pairs. The T_m values of several DNA types have been plotted against their

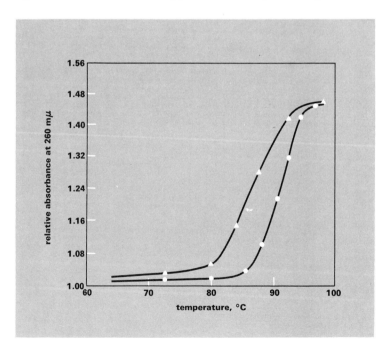

figure 3.5 :: Effect of temperature on the relative absorbance of two DNA samples.

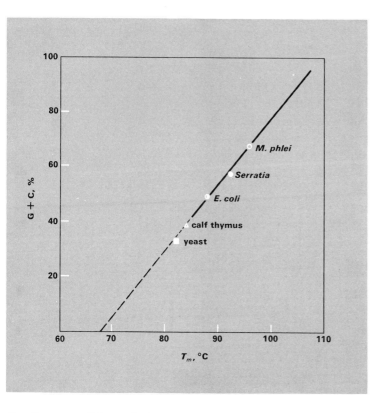

figure 3.6 ::
Melting temperature T_m
related to the G + C
content of DNA from
various sources.

G + C content (Figure 3.6). The linear relationship between T_m and G + C is the basis for an excellent method to determine the base composition of any DNA using very small samples to determine T_m.

The separation of the DNA chains is in a way comparable to the denaturation of proteins, and here too the process is called denaturation. When the two chains separate, they can recombine by base pairing if the solution is cooled slowly; this is called *annealing*. But if the solution is cooled rapidly, irreversible changes occur; random coils are formed from individual chains and the change is reflected in a decrease in viscosity of the solution. The reason is that an organized double helix is a very long rod giving viscous solutions, but a random coil, being more symmetric, should give less viscous solutions.

Heat is not the only agent that denatures DNA. Extreme pH and very low salt concentration of the solution can also cause denaturation. This is understandable, because hydrogen bonds can be broken at extreme pH values, owing to tautomeric changes occurring in the purines and pyrimidines.

RNA is also a polynucleotide, but the pentose ribose has a free hydroxyl group in position 2'. The possibility of branches has been considered but there is little evidence in support of a branched structure. RNA is, according to the best assessment, a long-chain polynucleotide. It does not exist in a regular conformation like a double-chain DNA. It is more likely a single chain with the potential for forming a double chain by base pairing, but in this case uracil replaces thymine in the A-T pair. The base composition of most RNA has none of the regularity in purine to pyrimidine ratios characteristic of DNA. It is understandable that on a single chain the molar proportion of purines and pyrimidines can vary considerably. Only when a double chain is formed is a constant ratio of purine to pyrimidine to be expected. The constancy is dictated by the already established fact that pairing is restricted to the two combinations A-T (or A-U in RNA) and G-C.

A single-chain RNA molecule could exist in a folded conformation. The folds would be like regular loops, and hydrogen bonds could be established between complementary bases of the single chain. Models for low-molecular-weight RNA (known as soluble RNA) depict the molecule as a folded structure. A possible folding is illustrated in Figure 3.7.

PROPERTIES OF RNA : There are different types of RNA known in living cells. The soluble RNA found in the cytoplasm is of low molecular weight, consisting of less than 100 nucleotides. The structure of one such molecule, *alanine transfer RNA*, has been unraveled by Robert W. Holley and his associates (Figure 3.7). It consists of a single polynucleotide chain of 77 subunits. The name transfer RNA is applied to some soluble RNA because of its role in the "transfer" of amino acids in the process of protein synthesis.

Other RNA species are found in the ribosomes, which are very small particles in the cytoplasm and are composed mainly of RNA and protein. It is here, in the ribosomes, where most protein biosynthesis occurs. There is little known about the structure of ribosomal RNA.

A solution of RNA absorbs ultraviolet light in the region 260 mμ and to about the same extent as a comparable solution of DNA. Hypochromism is also evident in RNA solutions and, as is the case in DNA, heat reduces the hypochromic effect in RNA solu-

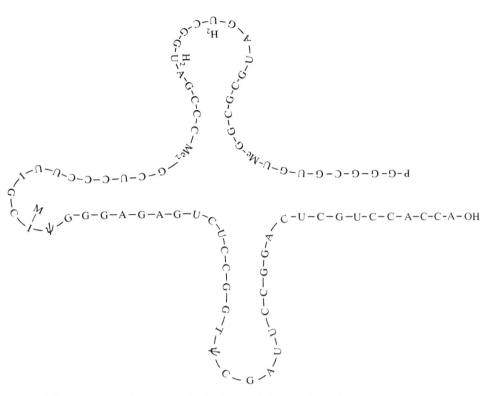

figure 3.7 :: Nucleotide sequence in alanine tRNA. The conformation shown is one of several possible. In addition to the more common bases, alanine tRNA also contains: ψ, pseudouracil; Me, 1-methyl guanine; Me$_2$, N-dimethyl guanine; I, xanthine; M—I, 1-methyl xanthine; UH$_2$, 5,6-dihydrouracil. [*From R. W. Holley et al., Science,* **147**: *1462* (*1965*).]

tions. The increase in absorption of light in the range 260mμ when RNA solutions are heated also follows the pattern already observed for DNA. There is a midpoint temperature, and it is believed that the observed effect is also due to the breaking of hydrogen bonds. If this is the case, then some secondary structure must be attributed to RNA to explain this effect.

Also, RNA molecules containing a high proportion of guanine and cytosine are more resistant to heat than those containing a lower proportion of these bases. As already shown, guanine and cytosine have a potential to establish three rather than two hydrogen bonds, giving more stable structures. In view of these facts, it appears that in RNA there is some organization or secondary structure. This is supported by observations made on synthetic polynucleotides in which secondary structure is generated as a result of hydrogen bonding.

Most nucleic acids probably do not exist in the cell as free chemical entities (except for the low-molecular-weight soluble RNA). Their isolation from the cell is normally in the form of nucleoprotein, in which the nucleic acid is bound to the protein by saltlike bonds easily cleaved by mild treatment such as by adding electrolytes or changing the pH of the solution.

The type of protein can vary from one sample to another, but the most commonly found proteins are of relatively low molecular weight and rich in the basic amino acids lysine and arginine. The proteins are given special names such as histone and protamine. The histones contain a high proportion of lysine and arginine and range in molecular weight from 10,000 to 20,000; protamines are generally smaller polypeptides (molecular weight of 5,000) and are made up largely of arginine.

The structure of nucleoproteins, except for some viruses, is not known, and there is no satisfactory model showing the way a protein fits into a nucleic acid molecule. Both histones and protamines carry positive charges and should neutralize the negative charges on the nucleic acid.

Viruses are particles made up entirely of nucleoprotein. The viruses are infective agents responsible for many diseases in plants and animals attacking specifically a type of cell in a given organism; there are some viruses (bacteriophage) that attack bacteria. Several viruses have been isolated in pure form and crystallized. As they are substances definable in chemical terms, they can be regarded as nucleoproteins possessing the potential to promote in the host cell the synthesis of more virus molecules that are identical to the original.

All plant viruses known are made up of RNA and protein, whereas viruses that attack animals are made up of either RNA or DNA and protein. Bacteriophages are mostly DNA and protein, but a few RNA bacteriophages are known. Viruses cannot be cultivated like bacteria; they reproduce only in a specific environment within a given cell. The tobacco mosaic virus, the first virus to be crystallized, can multiply only in the tobacco leaf. The virus depends on the energy of the host cell and its catalysts to synthesize new virus. The nucleic acid in the virus contains the information to direct its synthesis.

A great deal of research into the structure of viruses has been done. One that has received much attention is the tobacco mosaic virus. It has a particle weight corresponding to 40 million; it has a rod shape 260 mμ long and 15 mμ thick. The internal structure is represented by a thread of nucleic acid looped in a protein matrix (Figure 3.8). The nucleic acid can be separated from the protein, and by so doing one of the most significant principles of recent times has been discovered: The nucleic acid alone has the potential to infect.

Another group of viruses has received much attention: the bacteriophage. A typical bacteriophage is represented schematically in Figure 3.9. An hexagonal head and a tail can be distinguished, both of which are proteins. The DNA in bacteriophage is packed inside the head. When a bacteriophage comes in contact with the membrane of a specific bacterium, the DNA is injected into the host cell, where it can replicate very fast. The newly formed virus

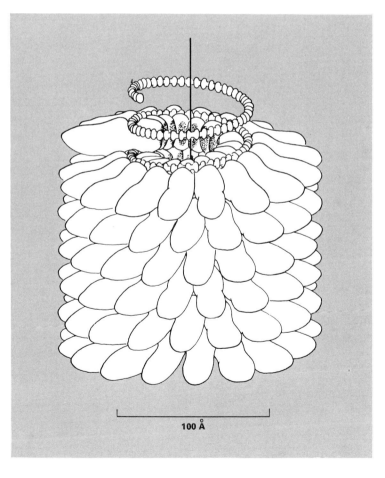

100 Å

figure 3.8 ::
Structure of tobacco mosaic virus. [*From A. Klung and D. L. D. Caspar, in K. M. Smith, ed., Advances in Virus Research, Vol. 7, p. 225. (New York: Academic Press, Inc., 1960.)*]

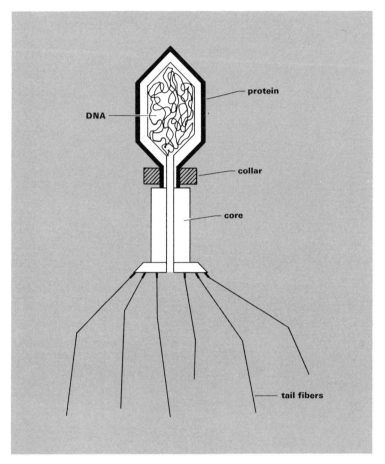

figure 3.9 ::
Schematic representation
of bacteriophage.

particles cause the bacterium to burst, and the virus particles stream
out.

references ::

CHARGAFF, E., *Essays on Nucleic Acids.* Amsterdam: Elsevier Publishing Company,
1963.
DAVIDSON, J. N., *The Biochemistry of the Nucleic Acids* (3rd ed.). London:
Methuen & Co., Ltd., 1960.
POTTER, V. R., *Nucleic Acid Outlines.* Minneapolis: Burgess Publishing Company,
1960.
STEINER, R. F., *The Chemical Foundations of Molecular Biology.* Princeton, N.J.:
D. Van Nostrand Company, 1965.
WATSON, J. D., *Molecular Biology of the Gene.* New York: W. A. Benjamin, Inc.,
1965.

polysaccharides ::: 4

POLYSACCHARIDES ARE HIGH-MOLECULAR-WEIGHT CARBOHYDRATES.
They are either linear or branched molecules consisting of simple
sugars joined by glycosidic bonds. Originally the term carbohydrate implies that only C, O, and H are present in these molecules and in a proportion corresponding to a hydrate of carbon:
$C(H_2O)$. However, not all carbohydrates are composed entirely of
C, O, and H and in the proportion indicated. The term carbohydrate, as currently used, describes a group of related polyhydroxy aldehydes and ketones occurring in nature. They share in
common some chemical properties and some biological functions.
  The polysaccharides comprise a large group of high-molecular-
weight carbohydrates present in microorganisms, plants, and
animals, where they serve as structural materials or as nutrients.

nomenclature and classification :: 4.1

A simple sugar or monosaccharide is named according to the
number of carbons in the molecule and the ending *ose*. The prefix
aldo or *keto* is used to indicate the presence of aldehyde or ketone

groups in the sugar. For example, four carbons may constitute an aldo- or ketotetrose, five carbons, aldo- or ketopentose, and six carbons, aldo- or ketohexose. The term *glycose* is used to denote any monosaccharide. Polysaccharides are named according to the repeating unit and by changing the *ose* ending of the monosaccharide to *an*. Thus a polymer of glucose becomes a *glucan*, and, in keeping with the general term glycose, any polymer of any one sugar becomes a *glycan*. If more than one sugar enters into the polysaccharide molecule, the two are named in alphabetical order. For example, if a polysaccharide consists of D-glucose and D-mannose, the name is D-*gluco*-D-*mannoglycan*.

Many polysaccharides were discovered and named a long time ago. These names, which reveal nothing about the composition of the polysaccharide, still remain and are the accepted nomenclature for polysaccharides, such as starch, cellulose, chitin, and others.

Polysaccharides can be classified into *homopolysaccharides* or *homoglycans*, and *heteropolysaccharides* or *heteroglycans*. Those of the second group are polymers consisting of at least two different glycoses. In this group are also included the *mucopolysaccharides*, which are heteroglycans, containing nitrogen and sulfur in addition to C, O, and H.

sugars as components of polysaccharides :: 4.2

The term sugar includes any of a class of sweet soluble crystalline carbohydrates, of which sucrose is the best known. The term has also become almost synonymous with hexoses and pentoses, which are the most commonly found monosaccharides in nature. They are produced when polysaccharides are heated with acid or treated with specific enzymes. Pentoses and hexoses are by definition tetrahydroxy- and pentahydroxyaldehydes or ketones, respectively :

CHO	CH_2OH	CHO	CH_2OH
$(CHOH)_3$	C=O	$(CHOH)_4$	C=O
CH_2OH	$(CHOH)_2$	CH_2OH	$(CHOH)_3$
	CH_2OH		CH_2OH
aldopentose	**ketopentose**	**aldohexose**	**ketohexose**

Like all other aldehydes and ketones, they are reducing substances. Their structures were established almost entirely by the extensive work of the distinguished German chemist Emil Fischer (1852–1919). He made great efforts to establish the configuration of glucose first, and then the structure of all pentoses and hexoses were readily determined. The structure of glucose was already established as a straight-chain polyhydroxy aldehyde:

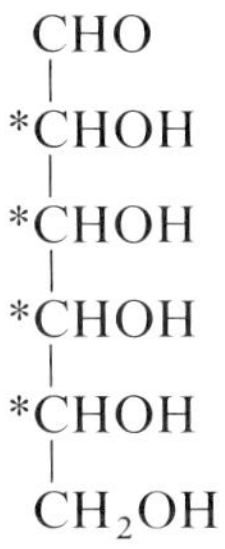

```
 CHO
  |
*CHOH
  |
*CHOH
  |
*CHOH
  |
*CHOH
  |
 CH₂OH
```

The four carbons marked with an asterisk are asymmetric carbons (they bear four different groups). Accordingly, there should be $2^4 = 16$ stereoisomers of the above structure. How Fischer chose the correct structure of glucose from the 16 possible structures is a subject that should be reviewed in an organic chemistry text. Fischer established the structure of glucose as†

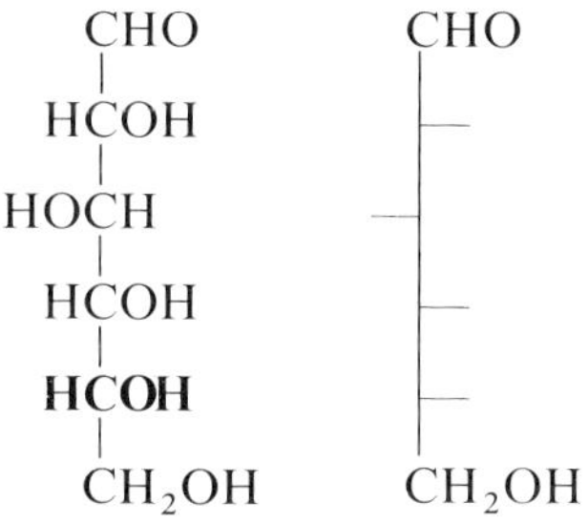

```
 CHO            CHO
  |              |
HCOH           ——
  |              |
HOCH           ——
  |              |
HCOH           ——
  |              |
HCOH           ——
  |              |
 CH₂OH          CH₂OH
```

and gave it the same configuration as the reference compound, D-glyceraldehyde; that is, the hydroxyl of C_5 is written to the right in the projection formula:

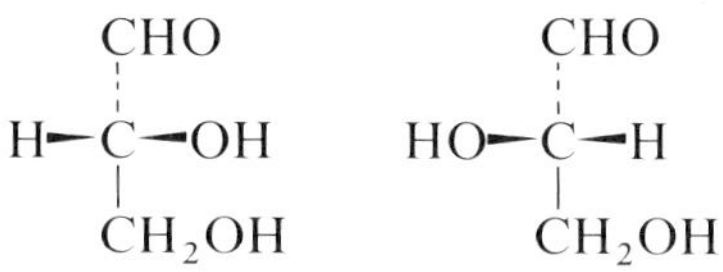

```
     CHO              CHO
      |                |
 H—C—OH          HO—C—H
      |                |
     CH₂OH            CH₂OH
```

D-**glyceraldehyde**   L-**glyceraldehyde**

† On the right is the shorthand method used to represent glucose and other glycoses. The orientation of the —OH groups is symbolized by the horizontal lines.

Naturally occurring monosaccharides are of the D configuration, and, unless indicated, all the compounds discussed here are assumed to be of the D configuration.

PROPERTIES OF MONOSACCHARIDES : Some properties of monosaccharides can be discussed using glucose as the prototype. When glucose is in solution, it undergoes an intramolecular reaction between the aldehyde group and one of the hydroxyls, preferentially the hydroxyl group of C_5. The product is a hemiacetal.

When C_1 forms the hemiacetal, the carbon becomes asymmetric; therefore, two possible isomers are produced : an α isomer, in which the —OH of C_1 is of the same configuration as C_5, and a β isomer, in which the —OH of C_1 is of the opposite configuration to that of C_5 :

$$
\begin{array}{ccc}
\text{H} \quad \text{OH} & \text{H} \quad \text{O} & \text{HO} \quad \text{H} \\
\text{C} & \text{C} & \text{C} \\
\text{HCOH} & \text{HCOH} & \text{HCOH} \\
\text{HOCH} & \text{HOCH} & \text{HOCH} \\
\text{HCOH} & \text{HCOH} & \text{HCOH} \\
\text{HC} & \text{HCOH} & \text{HC} \\
\text{CH}_2\text{OH} & \text{CH}_2\text{OH} & \text{CH}_2\text{OH} \\
\alpha\text{-D-glucose} & & \beta\text{-D-glucose}
\end{array}
$$

Neither reducing properties nor any other property of the aldehyde group is lost in solution despite the conversion to a hemiacetal. The reason is that an equilibrium is reached in which all three forms exist but the aldehyde form is in low concentration. When the aldehyde group reacts, it is removed from the equilibrium mixture. According to the law of mass action, the equilibrium is maintained by the conversion of the other forms to the aldehyde form. The reaction can proceed to completion if the compound reacting with the aldehyde is in sufficient concentration.

A more accurate way to write the hemiacetal structure of glucose and other sugars is as shown here in the form of the cyclic structure first proposed by Haworth. Ketohexoses and pentoses normally form five-membered ring structures, as at the top of page 63. It is customary to write only the hydroxyl groups, or just lines as in

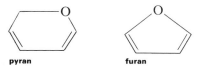

α-D-**glucose**

β-D-**fructose**

the simplified structures on the right. The position of the hydrogens is self-evident. The two heterocyclic rings are considered to be derived from pyran and furan. Hence the names *pyranose* and *furanose* are given to the monosaccharides with a six-membered and a five-membered ring, respectively:

pyran   **furan**

Of the two rings, pyranose is more common among the hexoses. Glucose is a pyranose and should be named α-D-glucopyranose or β-D-glucopyranose, according to the configuration of the hemiacetal.

Glucose reacts with methanol in the presence of hydrogen chloride to form two isomeric glycosides. The glycosides react with dimethyl sulfate in alkaline solution to yield a completely methylated glucose:

glucose   α-**methyl glucoside**   β-**methyl glucoside**

α-**methyl glucoside**   **pentamethyl glucose**

The glycosidic methyl is in an acetal and is readily hydrolyzed by acids, but it is resistant to alkalies. The other methyl groups in pentamethylglucose are in stable ether bonds and not hydrolyzed by acids. Exhaustive methylation is a very useful procedure in the study of the structure of polysaccharides.

Glycosides of glucose can be formed with any number of compounds with the general structure R—OH. A second glycose molecule or any hexose with several free hydroxyl group satisfies this requirement. In this case also two isomers are possible: α or β. For example, maltose is formed by joining two glucose molecules through a glycosidic linkage:

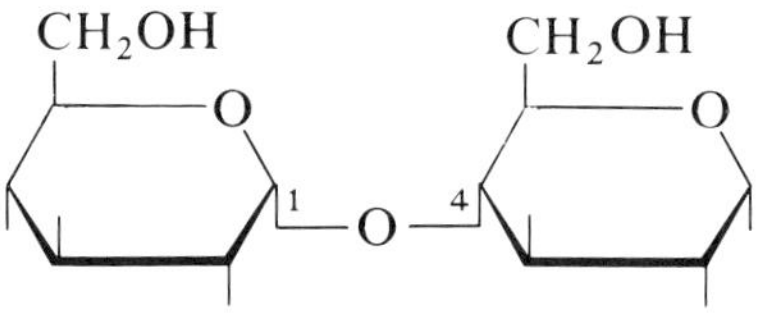

maltose

The resulting glycosidic bond in this case is designated as an α-1,4 linkage. The glycosidic bond can be formed with any one of the free hydroxyl groups, but most naturally occurring oligo- and polysaccharides have the 1,4 linkage.

STRUCTURE OF SOME MONOSACCHARIDES : A list of pentoses and hexoses frequently found as polysaccharide components is presented in Table 4.1. In addition to the sugars, some sugar derivatives are also found in some polysaccharides. For example, in the uronic acids, C_6 is oxidized to a carboxylic acid; in the amino sugars, the —OH group of C_2 is substituted by an —NH$_2$ group.

methods for the study of polysaccharide structure :: 4.3

Polysaccharides are seldom obtained in pure form, that is, free of traces of other substances originally present in the cell. Even when they are pure, they do not always constitute homogeneous substances but mixtures of several molecules of different molecular weight. The molecular weight of the mixture is usually determined as the average molecular weight. The average molecular weights of polysaccharides lie in extremely wide ranges and depend largely on their source, the method of extraction, and the method of purification.

Although a polysaccharide is not usually a homogeneous substance, the chemical structure of all the component molecules in a given polysaccharide is the same except for size. The structure of a polysaccharide is established by determining (1) the type of component glycose, (2) the nature of the glycosidic bond, (3) the presence or absence of branches, and (4) the average molecular weight.

table 4.1 :: Structures of common glycoses†

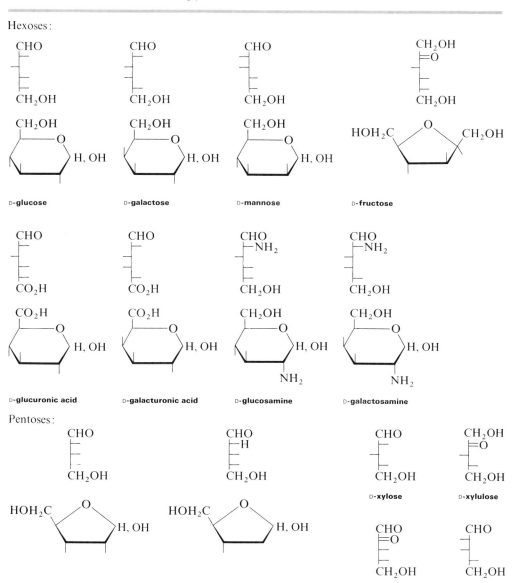

Hexoses:

D-glucose D-galactose D-mannose D-fructose

D-glucuronic acid D-galacturonic acid D-glucosamine D-galactosamine

Pentoses:

D-xylose D-xylulose

† H, OH means either the α or β anomer.

TYPE OF GLYCOSE : The structure of most polysaccharides known in nature is that of either linear polymers or polymers with cross-linkages of glycoses. To identify the component glycoses in a polysaccharide, it is first hydrolyzed with acids. Complete hydrolysis releases the sugar components of the polysaccharides. The identification of the component glycoses offers no problem, and they are readily determined by chromatographic procedures. The task is made easier because most known polysaccharides contain one or two, less commonly three, types of glycose units.

It is desirable to obtain by hydrolysis fragments of the polysaccharide molecule so that the type of bond uniting the sugar units in the polysaccharide can be established. A disaccharide is the smallest fragment that can still reveal the bond. Disaccharides are obtained by partial acid hydrolysis or by hydrolysis with specific enzymes that have the capacity to break polysaccharides into disaccharides. Determination of the type of bond in the disaccharide can be related to the type of bond in the original polysaccharide.

NATURE OF THE GLYCOSIDIC BOND : A sugar can combine with another sugar, either identical to or different from itself, by establishing a glycosidic bond. It has already been said that the hemiacetal —OH of sugars combines with a variety of compounds of the general type R —OH. Sugars themselves fall under this category. There are, however, several —OH groups in a sugar molecule that can theoretically combine with the hemiacetal —OH.

The position of the glycosidic bond in a polysaccharide is established by examining the hydrolysis products of the exhaustively methylated polysaccharide. Let us consider a polyglycan :

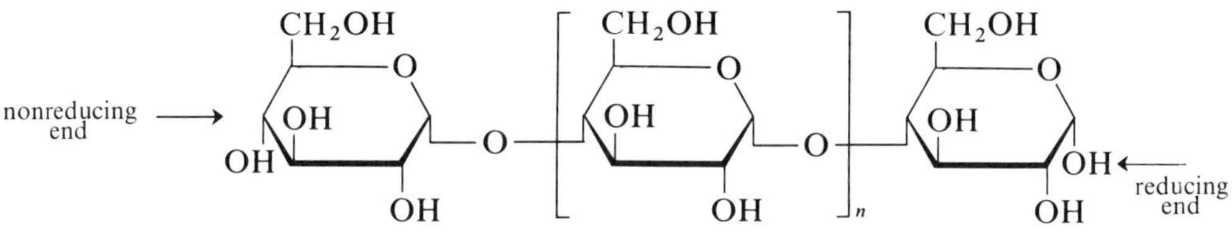

Disregarding momentarily the type of sugar and its configuration, we can observe that the first and last units have four reactive —OH groups; all others have only three. The glycosidic bond has been placed on position 4 in this example. If the polysaccharide is methylated and hydrolyzed, the expected products will be

2,3,4-tetramethyl glycose   2,3,6-trimethyl glycose

The tetramethyl glycose is from the first unit only. The last unit loses its methyl group in position 1 because it is an acetal and unstable to acids. In the terminology of carbohydrate chemistry the hemiacetal end is referred to as the reducing end; the other end of the molecule is the nonreducing end. The absence of a methyl group in position 4 suggests that this $-OH$ group was engaged in a bond in the original polysaccharide.

The position of the linkage is not sufficient to describe the structure of a polysaccharide. Glycosidic bonds, as we have already observed, can exist in two configurations, depending on the arrangement of atoms bonded to C_1. In polysaccharides, the glycosidic bonds are either in the α or β configuration. The decision between the two stereoisomers is made on the basis of their behavior toward specific enzymes. *Emulsin* is an enzyme found in many plants and hydrolyzes β-glycosides but has no effect whatever on α-glycosides. There is also an enzyme in most cereals, *maltase*, that specifically attacks α-glycosides. The enzymes do not attack the polysaccharides themselves, but polysaccharides can be cleaved into disaccharides by partial acid hydrolysis or by the action of other specific enzymes.

The existence of the two configurations in nature is of interest to biochemists because many organisms have enzymes that attack only one type of bond. For example, cellulose and starch are polyglucans but differ in the configuration of their glycosidic bonds. Starch is a valuable foodstuff because its α-glycosidic bonds are readily cleaved by the action of digestive enzymes present in most animals; on the other hand, cellulose has no food value for most animals, because they do not have enzymes that cleave β-glycosidic bonds.

DETERMINATION OF BRANCHES : Polysaccharides exist also as cross-linked polymers of sugars. The branches or cross-linkages can be made through any of the free hydroxyl groups still present in the sugar units of a linear polyglycan. Most commonly found branches are located on the —OH of C_6, which establishes a 1,6-glycosidic bond. Hydrolysis of the exhaustively methylated polysaccharide should yield 2,3-dimethyl glucoses from the original glycose units bearing a 1,6 branch. From a polyglucan, for example, 2,3-dimethyl glucose is obtained, in addition to tri- and tetramethyl glucose:

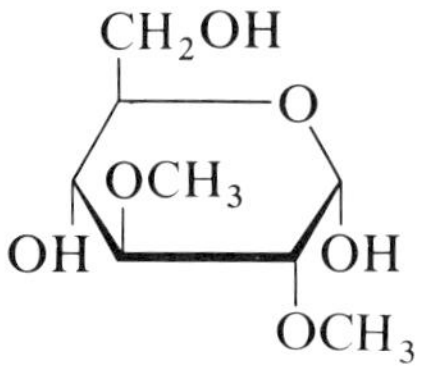

2,3-dimethyl glucose

It follows from this that the proportion of dimethyl glycose to trimethyl glycose is a measure of branching in a polysaccharide. The properties of branched polysaccharides are expected to be different from those of linear molecules.

DETERMINATION OF MOLECULAR WEIGHT : The molecular weight of polysaccharides is determined by physical means similar to those listed for proteins: ultracentrifugation, light scattering, and osmotic pressure.

Molecular-weight determination by chemical means is also possible by the analysis of the products of hydrolysis of the methylated polysaccharide. In a linear glucan, for example, the ratio of tetramethyl glucose to trimethyl glucose should reveal the length of the molecule (or the average of the molecular species). This is so because only one tetramethyl glucose per molecule is formed from the nonreducing end of the molecule. One difficulty with this type of analysis is that it is not always easy to determine accurately the proportion of tetramethyl glucose in the presence of a very large proportion of trimethyl glucose.

homopolysaccharides :: 4.4

Homopolysaccharides, or homoglycans, are polymers of a single type of sugar. It should be emphasized, however, that the definition applies to homoglycans containing at least 95 percent of a single sugar because it is only rarely that a polysaccharide can be obtained in pure form.

The most common homoglycans are polymers of D-glucose (glucans). In Table 4.2 are listed some of the better known homoglycans.

Homoglycans such as cellulose in plants and chitin in some invertebrates serve as structural polysaccharides. Starch and glycogen, on the other hand, are found as deposits in the cells, where they serve as food. Most homopolysaccharides fall in one of two categories: structural or nutrient polysaccharides. Of the structural polysaccharides, cellulose and chitin have been studied extensively and will be discussed next.

CELLULOSE AND CHITIN : *Cellulose* is a linear polymer of β-glucopyranose. It is the most abundant organic compound found in nature. It is estimated that of all the carbon dioxide in nature half is fixed in the cellulose of plants; this is equivalent to roughly 1×10^9 kilograms (kg) of cellulose.

The mechanical strength of cellulose is attributed to its micellar structure. The linear chains form microfibrillae or bundles of parallel chains held together by hydrogen bonds. One hundred or more chains constitute a micelle.

The molecular weight of cellulose is estimated at 1,000,000. One difficulty in obtaining accurate molecular weights in cellulose and other polysaccharides is that there is some degradation of the original substance during the process of extraction.

Cellulose is obtained from plants after destroying or dissolving the noncellulosic substances. Cellulose itself is insoluble in most of the ordinary solvents, but it can be brought into solution in ammoniacal cupric hydroxide (Schweizer's solution).

The cellulose molecule is a long chain of D-glucose units connected through β-1,4-glycosidic bonds. The smallest unit representing the bond is cellobiose, which can be obtained together with cellotriose and cellotetrose by partial acid hydrolysis. The position of the glycosidic bond has been established by analyzing the hydrolysis products of methylated cellulose acetate since cellulose itself resists methylation with dimethyl sulfate and alkali. The products of hydrolysis, trimethyl glucose and tetramethyl glucose, are found in ratios indicating that cellulose must be a linear structure of glucose units. From the evidence presented the

table 4.2 :: Some known glycans

Glucans:	cellulose, amylose, glycogen, amylopectin, chitin
Galactans:	agar, pectin, galactan from snails
Mannans:	yeast mannan
Xylans:	hemicellulose xylan
Fructans:	inulin

structure of cellulose is

The presence of numerous —OH groups in the cellulose molecule is evident. Cellulose can be modified chemically by modifying the reactive groups, and it can be converted into several derivatives.

Although cellulose is primarily a product of the higher plants, it is found also in a few microorganisms and lower animals.

Chitin is a polysaccharide similar to cellulose in many ways; it is found in the cuticle or the exoskeleton of insects and crustacea, where it is intimately combined with calcium carbonate deposits and protein.

Chitin is a polyglycan consisting of N-glucosamine units connected through β-1,4-glycosidic linkages. The fine structure of chitin resembles that of cellulose, as established by X-ray diffraction analysis. Parallel chains of the chitin molecule are held together in bundles by hydrogen bonds established between chains.

Like cellulose, chitin is difficult to dissolve in ordinary solvents; it dissolves in concentrated acids but some breakdown of the chitin is to be expected.

The glycose in chitin, 2-amino-2-deoxyglucose (glucosamine), is acetylated. The structure of chitin is

The resemblance between chitin and cellulose is not only in the fine structure but in the chemical structure as well. Both are β-1,4-glycosides.

STARCH AND GLYCOGEN : *Starch* is the main nutrient polysaccharide of plants; its counterpart in animals is glycogen. Both are readily isolated from tissues without undergoing significant change. Chemically starch and glycogen are analogous; both are polyglucans linked through α-1,4-glycosidic linkages. Their difference is mainly in their molecular weight and degree of branching.

Starch exists in two forms: amylose and amylopectin. The two forms can be separated from one another by treating starch with hot water. Amylose, representing 10 to 20 percent, dissolves and amylopectin remains. Both react with iodine to produce intensely colored compounds; amylose becomes intensely blue and amylopectin violet to red when iodine is added.

Structurally, amylose is a straight-chain polyglucan (200 to 300 glucose units) that yields maltose in partial hydrolysis:

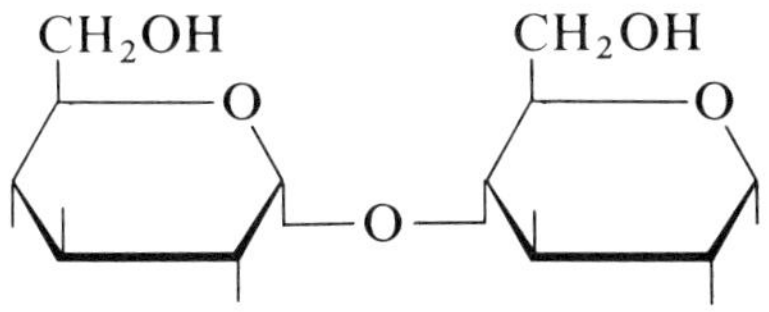

Methylated amylose yields on hydrolysis a large proportion of trimethyl glucose and some tetramethyl glucose, which are the products expected from a linear polyglucan.

Amylopectin by contrast has over 1,000 glucose residues and yields on hydrolysis some isomaltose in addition to maltose:

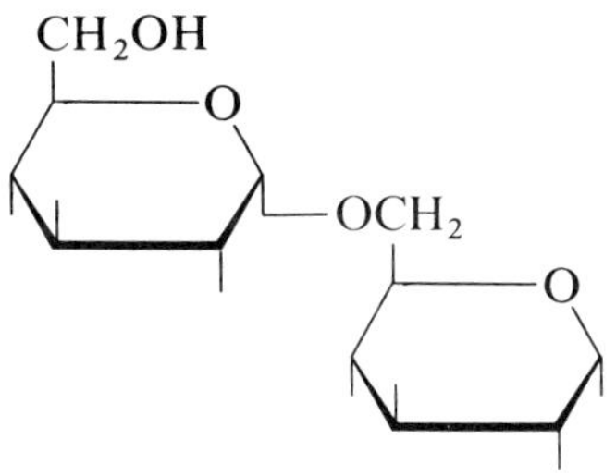

isomaltose

The isomaltose is produced when the glycosidic linkages neighboring the branching points are cleaved. Methylated amylopectin yields on hydrolysis a significant amount of dimethyl glucose, the expected product from the cross-linked units.

The structures of amylose and amylopectin are partially represented here:

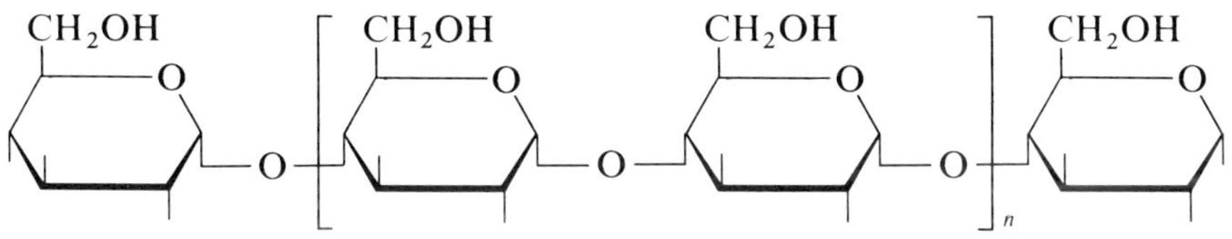

amylose

amylopectin

Glycogen is similar to amylopectin in that it is highly branched. The molecular weight of glycogen varies over an extremely wide range depending on the source and on the method used for its isolation. If it is isolated by using acids, which are often needed to precipitate protein, the glycogen undergoes some degradation and the molecular weight is low. Mild procedures yield less degraded preparations, and the molecular weight ranges from a few million to several hundred million.

OTHER HOMOPOLYSACCHARIDES : The plant kingdom is rich in polysaccharides. In addition to starch and cellulose, plants produce a variety of substances that fall under the general categories of hemicelluloses, gums, mucilages, and others. From the standpoint of chemistry they are difficult to classify, because they are seldom obtained in pure form. Most of the plant homopolysaccharides are structural components of the cell, but some serve as reserve food also. A few examples will be cited and discussed briefly.

Hemicelluloses. The term hemicelluloses applies to a group of ill-defined polysaccharides obtained from wood and cereal residues (husks, cobs, and the like). They form part of the cell wall of all land plants. In the strictest sense, hemicelluloses should be considered heteropolysaccharides, as they contain more than one sugar component. There are some that yield only one sugar on hydrolysis, as, for example, *xylan*, which consists of D-xylose units linked through β-1,4-glycosidic bonds. Other hemicelluloses yield arabinose and glucuronic acid.

Inulin. Found in some tuberous plants, inulin yields D-fructose on hydrolysis. It is a fructan (2,1-glycosidic linkages). Inulin is soluble in water, and its molecular weight is relatively low as compared to starch. Inulin is a nutrient polysaccharide.

Pectin. Pectin or pectic substances are mainly polymers of D-galactose and galacturonic acid. They are present in the cell wall and between the cells of plants. They are noted for their ability to form gels quite readily. Agar, the well-known bacteriological culture medium, is a galactan consisting of both D- and L-galactose. Pectin or pectinic acid is a polymer of galacturonic acid and is abundantly found in fruits, particularly in the rind of oranges and lemons. There are in this group other polysaccharides with the same property of forming gels readily.

These are only a few of the many homopolysaccharides found in plants. Most sugars have the potential to make glycosidic bonds and to produce a wide array of structures. They are listed as homopolysaccharides but only as a matter of convenience. It is not a simple matter to decide between a structure containing one single type of sugar but contaminated with other polysaccharides and a structure containing more than one sugar.

heteropolysaccharides :: 4.5

Two major groups of heteropolysaccharides are distinguished: those consisting of neutral sugars, and mucopolysaccharides, consisting of amino sugars, uronic acids, and some of their derivatives. The polysaccharides of the first group yield on hydrolysis more than one type of sugar and sometimes nonsugar components. Here one finds some of the hemicelluloses of softwood, some gums, mucilages, and pectic substances. The biochemistry of this group of compounds is still very limited.

The mucopolysaccharides are structural polysaccharides found mainly in the connective tissue of most animals and in some cases as blood components. They are linear polymers of uronic acids linked to acetylated or sulfated amino sugars. The simplest unit in a mucopolysaccharide is a disaccharide containing a uronic acid linked through a 1,3-glycosidic bond to an amino sugar. Some of the better known mucopolysaccharides will be discussed next.

HYALURONIC ACID : The simplest mucopolysaccharide known is a linear polymer of a disaccharide consisting of glucuronic acid linked to N-acetyl glucosamine by a β-1,3-glycosidic linkage:

The structure of hyaluronic acid is partially represented by

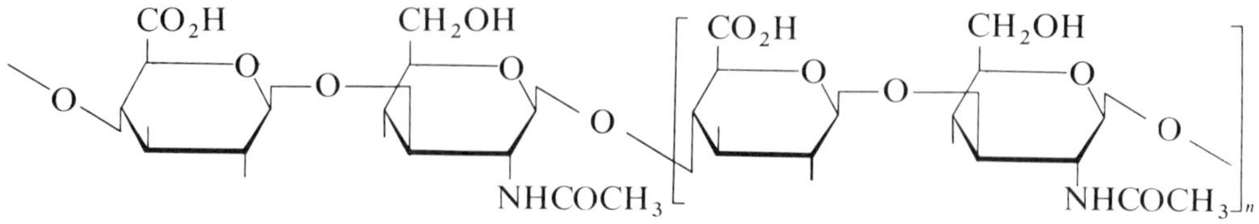

in which the disaccharides are linked through β-1,4 linkages.

The molecular weight of hyaluronic acid is in the millions. (As is the case with other complex macromolecules, it is often isolated from its source accompanied by protein.) The isolation procedure used to remove protein is apt to degrade the hyaluronic acid, making it difficult to conclude that the isolated material truly represents the material of the cell. There is also the possibility that the protein is not associated with hyaluronic acid but becomes so during the extraction procedure since hyaluronic acid with its multiple negative charges can react with other charged molecules such as proteins.

Hyaluronic acid is found in the ground substance, the material cementing cellular structures. It was first isolated from the vitreous humor and later found in umbilical cord, joint fluids, skin, bone, and heart valves.

The ground substance can be "depolymerized" by the action of enzymes known as hyaluronidases or *spreading factors*. Pathogenic bacteria possessing hyaluronidase penetrate through connective tissue as the cementing substance is loosened by its action.

CHONDROITIN SULFATES : Two types of sulfate esters are known in this group: chondroitin-4-sulfate and chondroitin-6-sulfate, also labeled types A and C. They are linear polymers of disaccharides consisting of glucuronic acid linked through β-1,3-glycosidic linkage to the 4- or 6-sulfate ester of N-acetyl galactosamine:

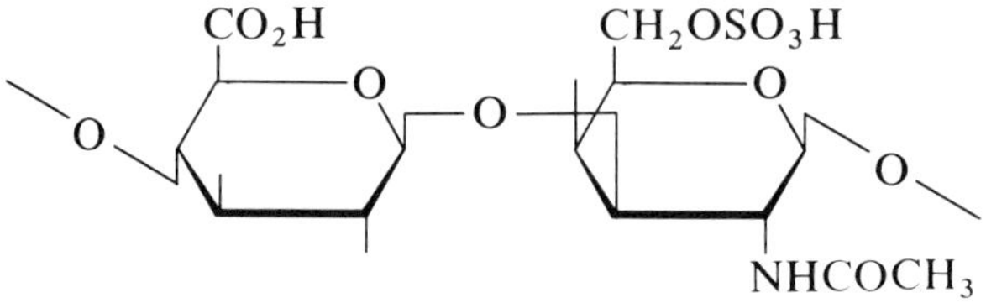

The disaccharides are linked through β-1,4-glycosidic linkages. Chondroitin-6-sulfate is partially represented here:

A third type, B, has been described containing iduronic instead of glucuronic acid.

The molecular weight of the chondroitin sulfates is estimated at about 50,000. It is often obtained in association with protein, but in this case the protein is not a mere artifact but part of a larger unit. As a strong polyanion it reacts with calcium, sodium, and potassium and it probably exists in tissues as their salt.

Chondroitin sulfates are predominantly found in cartilage and also in tendons, skin, heart valves, and saliva.

HEPARIN : Closely related chemically to the chondroitin sulfates is the blood anticoagulant *heparin.* It is found in tissues but mainly in the liver. The structure of heparin has not been conclusively established. It is a polymer of glucosamine and glucuronic acid, but the position of the sulfate groups is uncertain.

OTHER HETEROPOLYSACCHARIDES : The limited discussion of other heteropolysaccharides is only a reflection of our limited knowledge of their chemistry. Substances that are undoubtedly of great interest include the following.

Blood group substances are found in erythrocytes and are responsible for the well-known phenomenon of agglutination. The human types A, B, O, and Le have been obtained in relatively pure form. On hydrolysis they yield amino acids and the sugars D-galactose, glucosamine, galactosamine, and L-fucose:

$$
\begin{array}{c}
\text{CHO} \\
|\\
\text{HOCH} \\
|\\
\text{HCOH} \\
|\\
\text{HCOH} \\
|\\
\text{HOCH} \\
|\\
\text{CH}_3
\end{array}
$$

L-**fucose**

Bacterial cell walls are complex structures that are of great interest. They are rich in polysaccharide combined with protein; the exact type of combination is only suspected, but sound experimental facts are still lacking. The cell wall from some Gram-negative bacteria, for example, yields on hydrolysis amino acids, amino sugars, phosphoribitol (a sugar derivative), and other unidentified substances.

Mucoproteins such as those present in blood serum are rich in polysaccharides. The most commonly found sugars in mucoproteins are galactosamine and glucosamine. Also found in mucoproteins are L-fucose and sialic acid (N-acetylneuraminic acid).

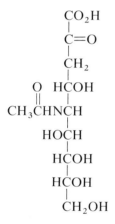

**N-acetylneuraminic acid
(sialic acid)**

references ::

PIGMAN, W., ed., *The Carbohydrates: Chemistry, Biochemistry, Physiology.* New York: Academic Press, Inc., 1957.

STACEY, M., AND S. A. BARKER, *Carbohydrates of Living Tissues.* Princeton, N.J.: D. Van Nostrand Company, Inc., 1961.

STANĚK, J., M. ČERNÝ, AND J. KOCOUREK, *The Monosaccharides.* New York: Academic Press, Inc., 1963.

lipids ::: 5

LIPID IS THE COLLECTIVE TERM USED TO DESCRIBE A GROUP OF SUB-
stances in the cell characterized by their solubility in organic solvents such as ether, benzene, and the like. They are not necessarily
related chemically but are grouped on the basis of their solubility.

In the lipids are included the neutral lipids (fats and oils), the
glycerophosphatides, the sphingolipids, and the isoprenoid lipids.
The latter include a number of substances related by having a
common structural unit: *isoprene.*

Lipids do not form polymeric structures in the same manner that
amino acids form proteins or sugars form polysaccharides. It is true
that rubber is a polymer of isoprene, but rubber is not regarded as
a lipid.

Where lipids enter into the cell structure, they do so by combining
with other molecules, particularly proteins. Subcellular structures
such as membranes, the mitochondria, and others are organizations
of macromolecules but include some small ones such as the lipids.
The unique solubility properties of lipids among those of all other
cell components is reflected in the character of cell membranes,
as will be described later.

The fats and oils belong to the neutral lipids, which are fatty acid esters of glycerol, the fatty acids being generally those with long chains. The term fat is used in a general way, but it should be reserved for the neutral lipids that are solid at ambient temperature; oils are liquid. Both can be represented by the general structure

$$
\begin{array}{c}
\quad\quad\quad O \\
\quad\quad\quad \| \\
CH_2O-C-R \\
| \quad\quad\quad O \\
\quad\quad\quad \| \\
CHO-C-R' \\
| \quad\quad\quad O \\
\quad\quad\quad \| \\
CH_2O-C-R''
\end{array}
$$

The acyl groups $-\overset{O}{\overset{\|}{C}}-R$, $-\overset{O}{\overset{\|}{C}}-R'$, and $-\overset{O}{\overset{\|}{C}}-R''$ can be all the same or can differ from one another. The fully esterified glycerol is called a *triglyceride*.

Triglycerides are hydrolyzed by acids and alkalies into glycerol and fatty acids or alkali salts of fatty acids, respectively. The latter are known as *soaps*. In most organisms there are enzymes that catalyze the hydrolysis of fats and oils.

FATTY ACIDS : The acids from fats and oils are long straight-chain acids; some are unsaturated. In Table 5.1 are listed the names and structures of the most commonly found acids.

The molecule of a long-chain fatty acid can exist in a number of theoretically possible conformations, but the most stable conformation is represented by the zigzag line shown in Figure 5.1. When double bonds are present, the *cis* isomer seems to be preferred in nature.

The most commonly found fatty acids are stearic acid (with 18 carbons) and its unsaturated analogue, oleic acid. It is interesting that double bonds occur frequently in the middle of the molecule. In oleic acid, for example, the double bond is between C_9 and C_{10}.

The melting point of unsaturated fatty acids is lower than the melting point of corresponding saturated acids. By way of an example, oleic acid—with one double bond— is a liquid at ambient temperature, whereas stearic acid, the saturated analogue, is solid.

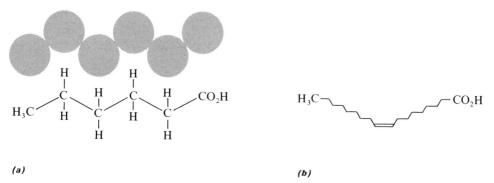

(a)   *(b)*

Figure 5.1 :: Conformation of a saturated fatty acid (hexanoic acid) *(a)* and an unsaturated (C_{18}) *cis* fatty acid *(b)*.

The solubility of fatty acids in water and in organic solvents is dictated by the length of the hydrocarbon chain, often called the *tail*, and the presence of the carboxyl group, called the *head*. The head, which is *hydrophilic* (water-liking), is responsible for the solubility of the acid in water; as the length of the tail increases, solubility in water decreases. Thus acids with up to seven carbons are soluble in water, but those with longer chains are increasingly insoluble. Because the hydrocarbon chain is soluble in lipid solvents, it is called *lipophilic* (lipid-liking).

An interesting consequence of this arrangement—a water-soluble head and a water-insoluble tail—is the formation of spread monolayers when long-chain fatty acids come in contact with water

table 5.1 :: Names and formulas of some fatty acids

FATTY ACID	NO. OF CARBONS	FORMULA	MELTING POINT, °C
Caproic	6	$CH_3(CH_2)_4CO_2H$	− 1.5
Caprylic	8	$CH_3(CH_2)_6CO_2H$	16.5
Capric	10	$CH_3(CH_2)_8CO_2H$	31.3
Lauric	12	$CH_3(CH_2)_{10}CO_2H$	43.6
Myristic	14	$CH_3(CH_2)_{12}CO_2H$	58.0
Palmitic	16	$CH_3(CH_2)_{14}CO_2H$	62.9
Palmitoleic	16	$CH_3(CH_2)_5CH{=}CH(CH_2)_7CO_2H$	−
Stearic	18	$CH_3(CH_2)_{16}CO_2H$	69.9
Oleic	18	$CH_3(CH_2)_7CH{=}CH(CH_2)_7CO_2H$	13
Linoleic	18	$CH_3(CH_2)_4CH{=}CHCH_2CH{=}CH(CH_2)_7CO_2H$	− 5
Linolenic	18	$CH_3CH_2CH{=}CHCH_2CH{=}CHCH_2CH{=}CH(CH_2)_7CO_2H$	− 11
Arachidic	20	$CH_3(CH_2)_{18}CO_2H$	75.2
Arachidonic	20	$CH_3(CH_2)_4(CH{=}CHCH_2)_4(CH_2)_2CO_2H$	−

surfaces. Suppose that a drop of fatty acid is placed very carefully on top of a container filled with clean water; the oil droplet either floats or it spreads, forming a thin film. What determines which event takes place are the interfacial forces (surface tension of water and surface tension of the fatty acid).

Let us consider the second event only. When the fatty acid spreads as a film, it can be shown that the film is one molecule in thickness and that each fatty acid molecule is oriented as shown in Figure 5.2. It is often called a *monomolecular layer*, or simply a monolayer. Other substances with properties similar to fatty acids have a tendency to spread on surfaces, forming monolayers with the polar groups oriented toward the water and the nonpolar groups pointed to the air.

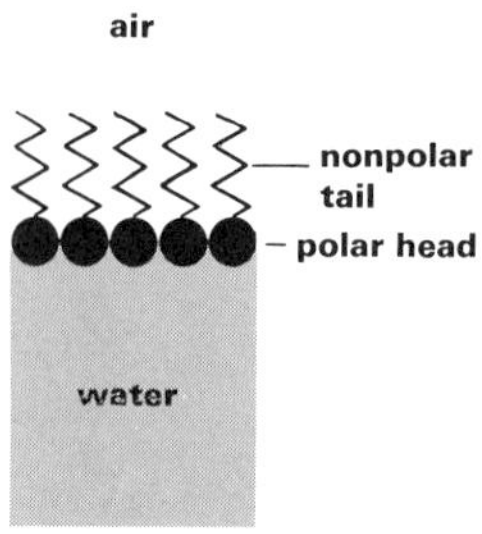

The importance of monolayers to biology is that they are good working models of biological membranes; these are believed to be complex molecular arrangements in which the monolayer is not a simple fatty acid but phospholipid.

figure 5.2 :: Orientation of fatty acid molecules on a liquid surface (water).

TRIGLYCERIDES : Fats and oils are mainly mixed triglycerides, those having more than one type of fatty acid. The fats, being solid at ambient temperature, are made up largely of saturated fatty acids; as the number of double bonds in a triglyceride increase, the melting point decreases. In the oils, for example, there is a predominance of triglycerides with unsaturated fatty acids.

Generally, the properties of the triglyceride are an expression of its fatty acid composition. Two fatty acids are quite frequently found in triglycerides: palmitic acid and oleic acid. Short-chain and very long chain fatty acids are also found but less frequently. The type of acids making up the triglycerides are usually related to the source. In animals, for example, there is a predominance of saturated triglycerides, whereas in plants there is a relative abundance of unsaturated triglycerides.

The fats that are synthesized by the organism serve as supporting material for internal organs in animals; they also accumulate in certain regions of the body and serve as food reserves in addition to their structural role.

glycerophosphatides :: 5.2

The glycerophosphatides are closely related to the triglycerides. They are phosphodiesters of diglycerides and either amino alcohols or inositols, represented by X in the following formula:

$$\begin{array}{c} \overset{\alpha}{CH_2}-O-\overset{\overset{\displaystyle O}{\|}}{C}-R \\ | \\ R'-\overset{\overset{\displaystyle O}{\|}}{C}-O-\underset{\beta}{CH} \\ | \\ CH_2-O-\overset{\overset{\displaystyle OH}{|}}{\underset{\underset{\displaystyle O}{\|}}{P}}-OX \end{array}$$

The acyl groups, represented by $-\overset{\overset{\displaystyle O}{\|}}{C}-R$ and $-\overset{\overset{\displaystyle O}{\|}}{C}-R'$, as in the triglycerides, are either the same or different from one another. The β carbon in glycerophosphatides is an asymmetric carbon and gives rise to two possible optical isomers. All naturally occurring glycerophosphatides have been related in their configuration to L-glycerophosphate:

$$\begin{array}{c} CH_2OH \\ | \\ HO-C-H \\ | \\ CH_2OPO_3H_2 \end{array}$$

The second substituent in the diphosphoester is either an amino alcohol derivative or an inositol. The amino alcohol derivatives found include 2-aminoethanol, choline, and serine. The inositols are related to the carbohydrates and exist in many isomeric forms.

The names lecithins, cephalins, plasmalogens, and inositides are applied to glycerophosphatides in relation to their composition, as will be discussed next.

LECITHINS : The amino alcohol derivative present in *lecithin* is the quaternary ammonium base choline (shown in boldface type):

$$\begin{array}{c} CH_2-O-\overset{\overset{\displaystyle O}{\|}}{C}-R \\ | \\ R'-\overset{\overset{\displaystyle O}{\|}}{C}-O-CH \\ | \\ CH_2-O-\overset{\overset{\displaystyle O^-}{|}}{\underset{\underset{\displaystyle O}{\|}}{P}}-O-\textbf{CH}_2\textbf{CH}_2\overset{+}{\textbf{N}}\textbf{(CH}_3\textbf{)}_3 \end{array}$$

lecithin

The nitrogen in choline carries a formal positive charge and the phosphate group a negative charge so that in solution lecithins are zwitterions at most pHs. The fatty acids in lecithins are the variable components. Frequently the fatty acid in the α position is a saturated fatty acid, and the one in the β position is an unsaturated one. As in the fats and oils the most commonly found fatty acids are those with 16 and 18 carbons.

Lecithins occur widely in plants and animals. Egg yolk is an excellent source of lecithin. In pure form it is a waxy white substance but darkens rapidly when exposed to air.

CEPHALINS : Two classes of *cephalins* are distinguished: ethanolamine cephalins and serine cephalins. They differ from lecithins chemically in the nature of the nitrogen-bearing compound:

$$HOCH_2\underset{\underset{\displaystyle COO^-}{|}}{C}HNH_3^+ \qquad\qquad HOCH_2CH_2NH_2$$

serine   **ethanolamine**

It is readily noted that the three nitrogen-bearing substances are closely related chemically and, as suspected, their formation in organisms proceeds along similar biosynthetic pathways. Lecithins and cephalins are quite similar in many of their properties.

INOSITIDES : *Inositol* is a cyclic hexahydroxy alcohol forming part of the inositides in place of the nitrogen-bearing compounds listed before:

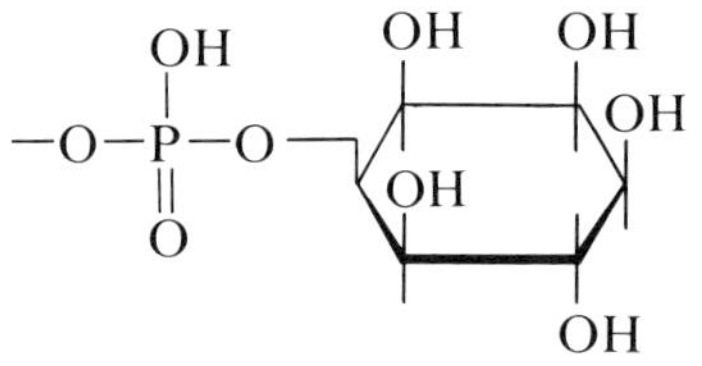

There are nine possible isomers of the inositol in the structure above. The inositides or inositol phosphatides, as they are also known, constitute a substantial portion of the lipid fraction of some tissues.

PLASMALOGENS : Some animal tissues, such as brain and heart, contain glycerophosphatides that yield long-chain aldehydes on hydrolysis. The long-chain aldehyde results from the cleavage of an α,β-unsaturated ether. The structure of a *plasmalogen* is shown here:

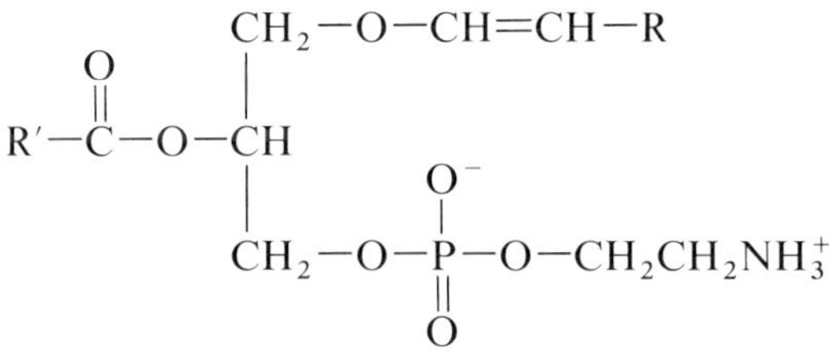

$$CH_2-O-CH=CH-R$$
$$R'-\overset{\overset{O}{\|}}{C}-O-\overset{\displaystyle |}{CH}$$
$$CH_2-O-\overset{\overset{O^-}{|}}{\underset{\underset{O}{\|}}{P}}-O-CH_2CH_2NH_3^+$$

The unsaturated ether is in the α carbon of the glycerol portion, varying in chain length from 12 to 18 carbons. The nitrogen base need not be ethanolamine, as shown in the structure above; plasmalogens with choline have also been found.

sphingolipids :: 5.3

Most *sphingolipids* are also phosphodiesters, but unlike glycerophosphatides the first substituent is not a diglyceride but sphingosine:

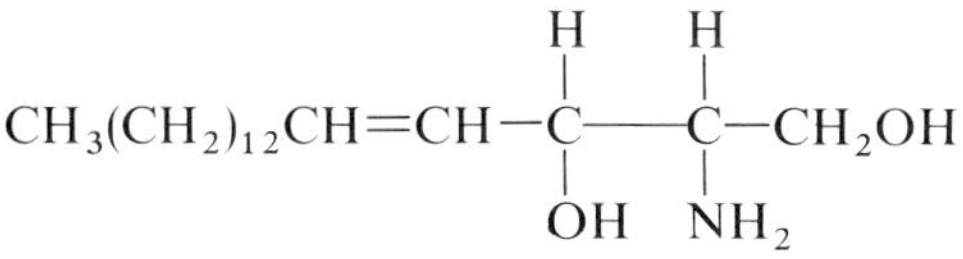

$$CH_3(CH_2)_{12}CH=CH-\overset{\overset{H}{|}}{\underset{\underset{OH}{|}}{C}}-\overset{\overset{H}{|}}{\underset{\underset{NH_2}{|}}{C}}-CH_2OH$$

The second hydroxyl of phosphate is esterified in most instances with choline. Sphingolipids are components of nerve tissue and are abundantly found in brain. The better known sphingolipids will be described briefly.

SPHINGOMYELINS : A *sphingomyelin* can be represented by the structure

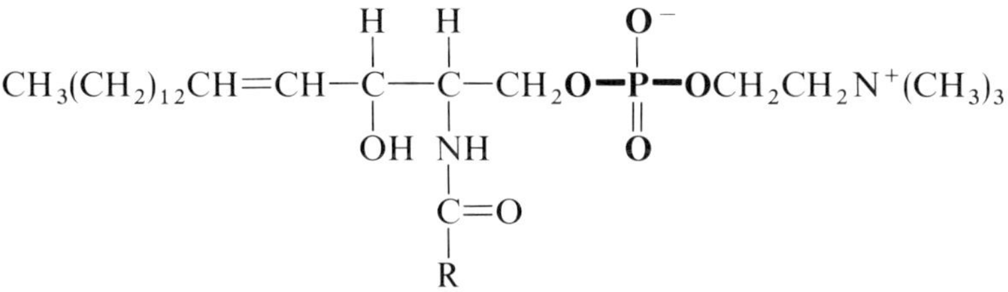

$$CH_3(CH_2)_{12}CH=CH-\overset{\overset{H}{|}}{\underset{\underset{OH}{|}}{C}}-\overset{\overset{H}{|}}{\underset{\underset{NH}{|}}{C}}-CH_2O-\overset{\overset{O^-}{|}}{\underset{\underset{O}{\|}}{P}}-OCH_2CH_2N^+(CH_3)_3$$
$$\underset{\displaystyle R}{\overset{\displaystyle |}{C}=O}$$

The amino group of the sphingosine portion is engaged in amide bond with a long-chain fatty acid. As in the lecithins sphingomyelin exists as a zwitterion over a wide range of pHs.

CEREBROSIDES : In the *cerebrosides* the phosphorylcholine is substituted by a sugar or sugar sulfate; derivatives of the latter are also known as sulfatides (here X represents sphingosine):

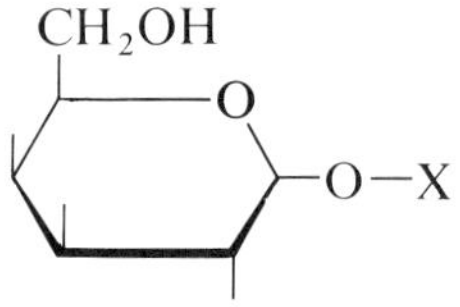

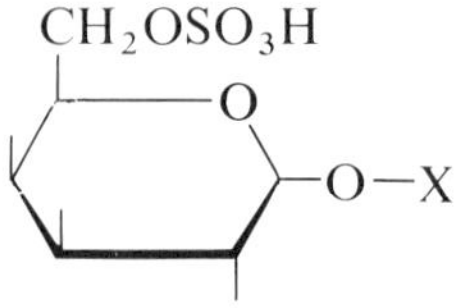

The variable component in cerebrosides is the long-chain fatty acid of the sphingosine moiety and varies according to source. Most of the cerebrosides isolated contain long-chain unsaturated fatty acids.

GANGLIOSIDES : As the name indicates, *gangliosides* are present in ganglionic cells. The structure of gangliosides is not known exactly but several possible structures have been suggested. What is known is that they are rich in carbohydrate, and on hydrolysis they yield sphingosine and fatty acids.

ROLE OF PHOSPHOLIPIDS AND SPHINGOLIPIDS : Phospholipids are highly dispersed in the cell, in contrast to the fats, which are found as deposits of food reserve. As structural cell components the phospholipids are intimately bound to other substances such as protein or carbohydrate. This is manifested in the difficulty with which phospholipids are extracted from cells with solvents such as ether, in contrast to the fats, which are quite easily extracted by ether.

Phospholipids are closely associated with membranes in the cell. It has become almost an axiom in cell biology that where there are membranes one finds phospholipid. There is good evidence for the presence of lipid material in membranes. When it comes to describing the molecular organization of the membranes, we must rely on interpretation of electron micrographs and X-ray diffraction. The most popular model of membranes is that proposed for the myelin sheath covering some nerve fibers. The membrane is visualized as a sandwich of oriented protein molecules holding the phospholipid molecules, which, mentioned previously, have a tendency to form monolayers. The phospholipids with polar and nonpolar groups can orient themselves with their polar heads toward the polar protein layers, leaving the nonpolar tails free to extend perpendicularly to the axis of the protein layers. The model of a membrane is illustrated in Figure 5.3.

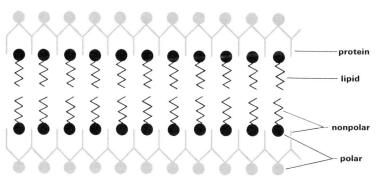

figure 5.3 ::
Schematic representation of a membrane showing the lipid molecules oriented with their polar heads toward the protein layer.

isoprenoid lipids :: 5.4

All the compounds classified under this heading are chemically related to the unsaturated hydrocarbon, isoprene:

$$\underset{\underset{\displaystyle H_2C=C-CH=CH_2}{|}}{CH_3}$$

In the list of isoprenoid lipids are included a large number of biologically important substances: cholesterol, bile acids, several vitamins, sex hormones, carotene, and many more.

Isoprenoid lipids are chemically unrelated to the fats and phosphatides, but they have the same solubility properties. When living material is extracted with a mixture of ether and alcohol, for example, the extract obtained is a mixture of all lipids originally present. The fats and phosphatides can be hydrolyzed with alkali to yield water-soluble substances, whereas the water-insoluble isoprenoid lipids remain unchanged. They can be extracted from the mixture with ether. Because they do not undergo alkali hydrolysis they are often called the *nonsaponifiable fraction*. Saponification is the name given to the alkali hydrolysis of fats.

The chemistry of isoprenoid lipids is too extensive to attempt even a brief discussion here. It is important, however, to review some aspects of the chemistry of steroids.

steroids :: 5.5

Steroids are biogenetically related to the unsaturated aliphatic hydrocarbon squalene, which is an isoprenoid. Chemically, steroids are derivatives of perhydro-1,2-cyclopentanophenanthrane, which is a saturated phenanthrene system with an additional five-membered ring. This structure is commonly called sterane:

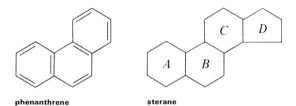

phenanthrene   sterane

A more direct relationship is envisaged between some steroids and other related cyclic hydrocarbons; for example, cholesterol is regarded as a derivative of cholestane:

cholestane   cholesterol

The notation on the rings and the number system is the same for other steroids. Note that on C_{10} and C_{13} methyl groups (C_{18} and C_{19}) substitute hydrogens. This is quite common in most steroids. Other commonly found substituents are hydroxyl groups, mainly at C_3, and side chains at C_{17}.

Isomerism resulting from the type of ring fusion is nearly impossible to represent except by means of models, but it is important to be acquainted with the notation frequently used to symbolize the different isomers. For example, when ring A joins ring B, two possible forms can result: a *trans* form or a *cis* form. Thus the hydrogens in positions 5 and 10 (the two angular hydrogens or substituents) can be on opposite sides (*trans*) or on the same side (*cis*) of a plane. The accepted convention is that, if hydrogen or any substituent is regarded above the plane (above this page, for example), it is represented by a solid line joining it to the carbon and designated β. If it is below the plane of the page, a dashed line is used and designated α. In steroid chemistry two references are often used: 5α-androstane and 5β-androstane:

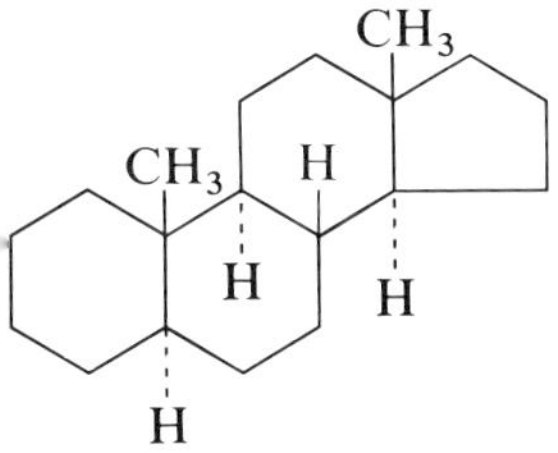

5α-androstane 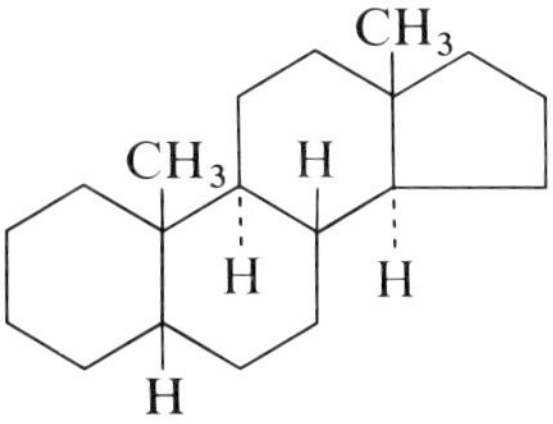   **5β-androstane**

Other substituents are referred to the methyl group: If they are on the same plane they are β, and if they are on opposite sides of the plane they are α:

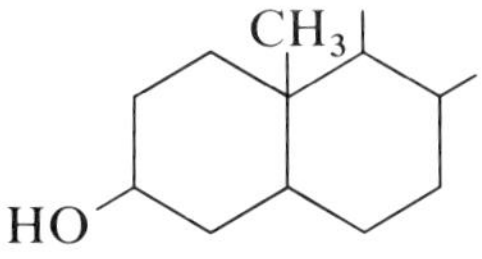

3β-OH 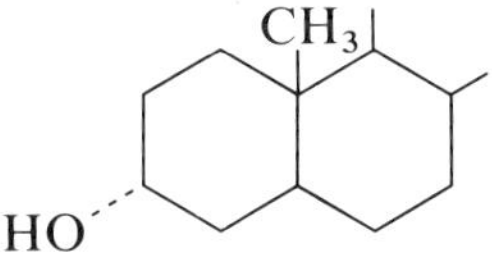   **3α-OH**

In the above examples the —OH group joined to the ring by a solid line is *cis* to the methyl group and both are above the plane of the page; the designation therefore is 3β-OH. In the 3α isomer the OH is joined by a dashed line, indicating that it is oriented *trans* with respect to the methyl group.

STEROLS : *Sterols* are hydroxylated derivatives of the perhydro-1,2-cyclopentanophenanthrene nucleus. They possess a hydroxyl group at C_3, a side chain at C_{17}, and a double bond, mostly at C_5. They occur in plants, animals, and microorganisms; the best known animal sterol is cholesterol. The structure of cholesterol was given previously without considering isomerism. Because there is a double bond at C_5 the isomerism resulting from the fusion of rings *A* and *B* is abolished. The position of the hydroxyl group at C_3, however, is *cis* to the angular methyl group at C_{10}; cholesterol is a 3β-hydroxysteroid, and so are all sterols so far found in nature.

When cholesterol is reduced, it gives rise to two isomeric structures: cholestanol and coprostanol. Both retain the 3β-configuration of the hydroxyl group, but in cholestanol rings *A* and *B* are fused in the *trans* manner and in coprostanol in the *cis* manner:

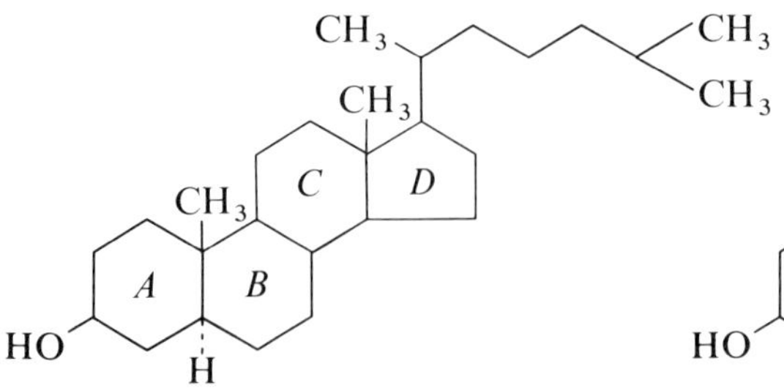

cholestanol

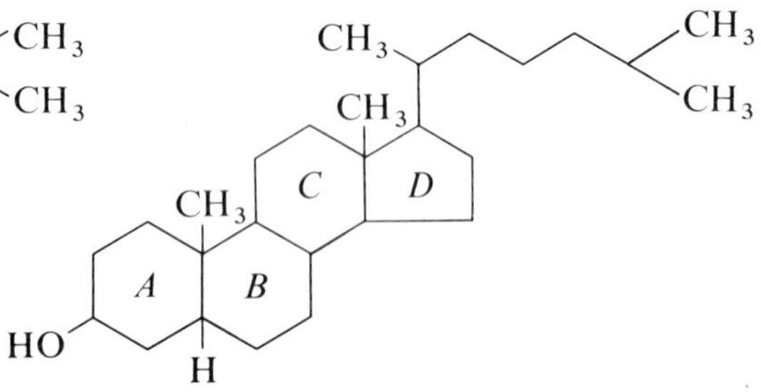

coprostanol

Rings *A* and *B* are fused *cis* or fused *trans*, not only in the products just discussed but in other steroids. Rings *B* and *C* and *C* and *D* are in all cases fused *trans*.

Cholesterol is abundantly present in animal tissues, where in conjunction with phospholipids it forms part of the molecular organization of membranes; it is particularly abundant in the myelin sheath covering some nerve fibers.

Cholesterol is synthesized by the cell from simple molecules (see Chapter 12) and serves as a precursor for the biosynthesis of bile acids, sex hormones, adrenocorticoids, and vitamin D.

Plants do not have cholesterol; instead of cholesterol they have a variety of closely related sterols, the phytosterols. Best known phytosterols are stigmasterol, from soybean oil; β-sitosterol, from wheat germ; and ergosterol, from yeast.

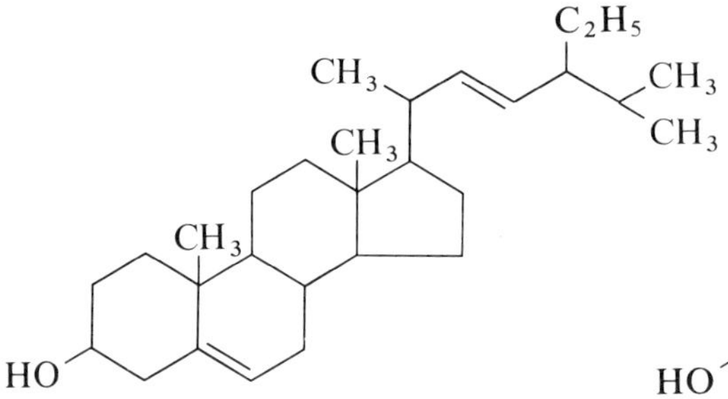

stigmasterol

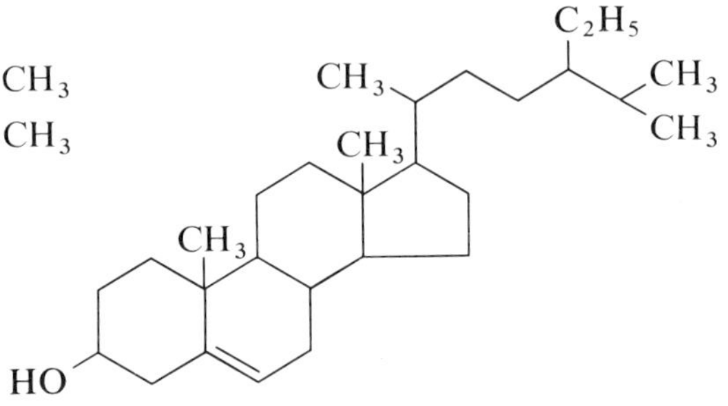

β-sitosterol

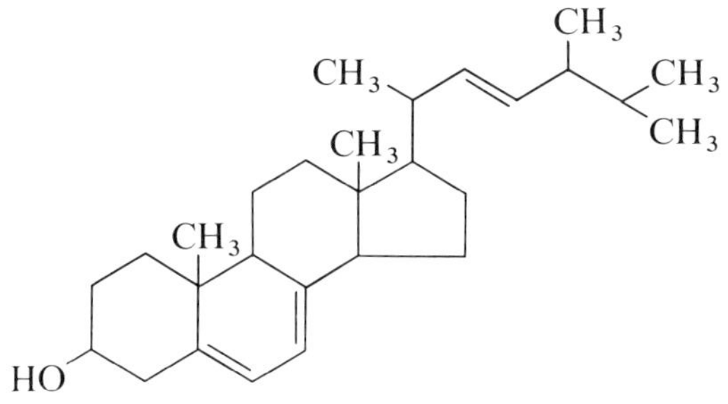

ergosterol

Ergosterol is converted by irradiation with ultraviolet light into calciferol or vitamin D_2:

ergosterol   calciferol (vitamin D₂)

BILE ACIDS : Bile contains among its many components the bile salts, which are amides derived from bile acids and the amino acids glycine and taurine. The *bile acids* possess hydroxyl groups in positions 3, 7, or 12 of the steroid ring system and are α-oriented. The A and B rings are *cis* fused. The side chain at C_{17} is invariably a five-carbon chain:

cholic acid   deoxycholic acid

taurocholic acid   glycocholic acid

The amides, taurocholic and glycocholic acids, are excellent emulsifying agents, as they possess a nonpolar structure and a charged side chain. Their main role in the organism is to emulsify fats during digestion and facilitate their absorption and enzymatic breakdown.

SEX HORMONES : Two chemically different types are distinguished: the *estrogens*, which have some aromatic character, and *progesterone* and *androgens*, which do not. The estrogens and progesterone are commonly known as female sex hormones and the androgens as male sex hormones.

Of the estrogens, estradiol is produced in the ovaries and estrone and estriol formed as a result of enzymatic transformations of estradiol:

estrone   estradiol   estriol

The hydroxyl group at C_3 has phenolic character; it is weakly acidic and can form salts. A consequence of the aromatization of ring *A* is the disappearance of the angular methyl group at C_{10}.

Progesterone, which is also produced in the ovaries, is related more closely to the androgens:

progesterone   testosterone   androsterone

Testosterone is produced in the testes and biochemically transformed to androsterone, which is the product usually found in urine.

CORTICOSTEROIDS : The adrenal cortex of most animals produces a large variety of steroids, but only 7 of the 30 compounds isolated are related to the function of the adrenal cortex. One characteristic of *corticosteroids* is that all have 21 carbon atoms and invariably C_3 is oxidized to a ketone. Another distinguishing feature is the hydroxyl or keto group at C_{11}:

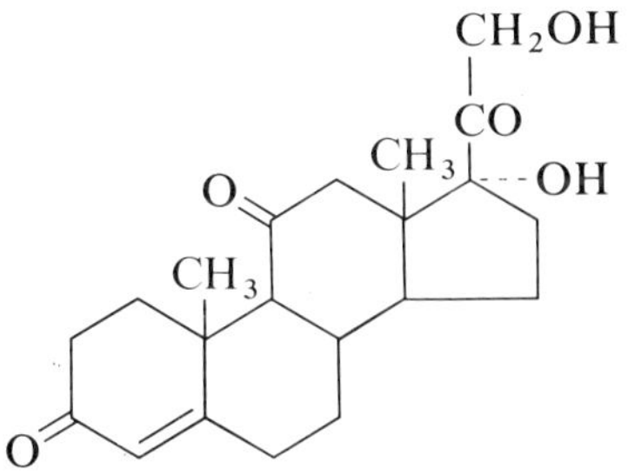

cortisone

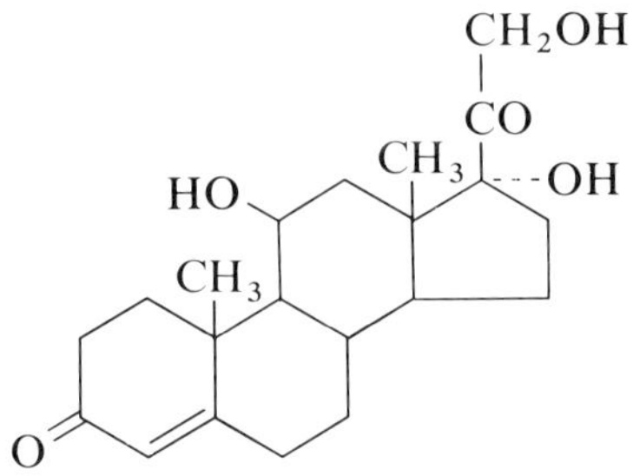

17α-hydroxycorticosterone

The functions of the corticosteroids are quite varied. They stimulate formation and deposition of glycogen, particularly in the liver; they induce the retention of sodium ions, thus maintaining the proper balance of electrolytes in the organism; and they are anti-inflammatory. Not each of the seven corticosteroids possess all these qualities nor do they possess a given quality to the same degree. Through extensive biological investigation it has been possible to assign to a given structure the biological response that it elicits.

references ::

ANSELL, G. B., AND J. N. HAWTHORNE, *Phospholipids: Chemistry, Metabolism and Function.* Amsterdam: Elsevier Publishing Company, 1964.

HANAHAN, D. J., *Lipide Chemistry.* New York: John Wiley & Sons, Inc., 1960.

HILDITCH, T. P., *The Chemical Composition of Natural Fats* (3rd ed.). London: Chapman & Hall, Ltd., 1956.

LOVERN, J. A., *The Chemistry of Lipids of Biochemical Significance.* London: Methuen & Co., Ltd., 1955.

6

NEARLY ALL FUNCTIONS OF THE CELL DEPEND DIRECTLY OR IN-
directly on the action of enzymes. They are the catalysts of the cell,
produced by the cell but capable of catalyzing the same reactions
after they have been isolated and purified.

Approximately 800 enzymes have been identified, some of which
have been isolated in pure form; all are proteins of varying complexity, and except for their catalytic properties enzymes would be
indistinguishable from most globular proteins. The methods
employed to isolate, purify, and analyze enzymes are the same as
those described in Chapter 2 for proteins.

Enzymes are among the most efficient catalysts known; they not
only speed up the rates of chemical reactions manyfold but do so
in a very selective manner. Enzymes, like other catalysts, do not
appear in the end products and are not used up in the reaction;
also when they catalyze a reversible reaction both the forward and
reverse reaction are speeded up, so that equilibrium is reached
faster than in a noncatalyzed reaction; the equilibrium, however,
remains the same.

Enzyme catalysis can be explained in the same way as catalysis in general. In general, a catalyst speeds up the rate of a reaction by reducing the *energy of activation*.

• *Energy of activation.* In a chemical reaction, the equilibrium constant K is a measure of the affinity or reactivity of reactants. For example, in the general reaction

$$A + B \rightleftarrows C + D \qquad \frac{[C][D]}{[A][B]} = K_{eq}$$

K_{eq} would tell us that A and B have a high reactivity or potential energy if K_{eq} is large; at equilibrium, the concentration of A and B is small and the concentration of products C and D is high.

Studies of chemical equilibria allow the prediction of the initial and final states of a reaction; they tell us how far a reaction can go without any details of the intermediate steps. They tell us nothing about the speed of the reaction. For example, from studying chemical equilibria it is possible to predict that glucose in contact with oxygen should oxidize to $CO_2 + H_2O$. The reason is that in the reaction

$$C_6H_{12}O_6 + 6O_2 \rightleftarrows 6CO_2 + 6H_2O$$

K_{eq} is very large and thermodynamically the reaction is possible. It is well known, however, that glucose in contact with oxygen does not oxidize to $CO_2 + H_2O$ until the mixture is heated. At ambient temperature the oxidation of glucose is so slow that the rate cannot be measured by any known procedure.

Other organic reactions reach equilibrium at measurable rates; the classical example is the formation of an ester by mixing an acid and an alcohol. At the other extreme are ionic reactions such as the precipitation of AgCl by mixing $AgNO_3 + NaCl$, which are so fast that they cannot be measured directly.

The existence of very slow reactions is proof that not all molecules of reactants coming into contact react. Because the number of molecules colliding is very large, it must be concluded that *only those molecules with a sufficient amount of energy react*. It has been calculated that only 1 in 10^{15} collisions results in reaction.

According to the collision theory of chemical reactions, the minimum amount of energy required by two colliding particles to react is the *activation energy*. An energy diagram can be drawn (Figure 6.1) to show the energy of activation. A catalyzed reaction is included in the diagram for comparison. Note that the amount of energy E that must be drawn by reactants before reaching point x is less in the catalyzed reaction (E_c) than in the noncatalyzed reaction (E). That is, in the catalyzed reaction the energy barrier is lower than in the noncatalyzed reaction. It can be said of catalyzed reactions that

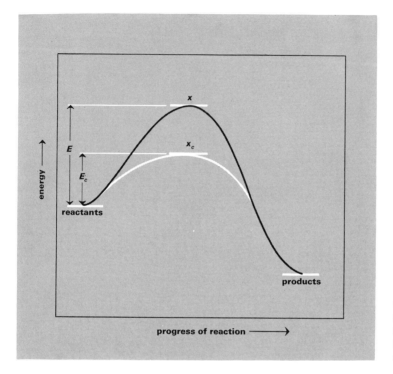

figure 6.1 :: Energy diagram showing the energy of activation for a noncatalyzed and a catalyzed reaction.

they *tunnel* under the energy barrier and of enzyme-catalyzed reactions that they tunnel more effectively. This is shown in Table 6.1, where the energies of activation of several reactions are listed.

The energy of activation can be calculated if the rate of reaction is known at several temperatures. A quantitative relation between temperature and reaction rate is given by the Arrhenius equation:

$$\frac{d \ln k}{dT} = \frac{E}{RT^2} \tag{6.1}$$

REACTION	CATALYST	E
H_2O_2 decomposition	None	18,000
	Colloidal platinum	11,700
	Catalase	5,500
Sucrose inversion	H^+	26,000
	Invertase	11,500
Casein hydrolysis	H^+	20,600
	Trypsin	12,000
Ethyl butyrate hydrolysis	H^+	13,200
	Lipase	4,200

table 6.1 :: Energies of activation of some catalyzed and noncatalyzed reactions[†]

[†] After H. Lineweaver, *J. Am. Chem. Soc.*, **61**: 403 (1939).

in which k is the specific reaction rate, R the gas constant (1.987 cal/mole-°C), T the absolute temperature, and E a constant. E is assumed to represent the energy per mole required to activate molecules so that they can react.

Integrating Equation (6.1),

$$\log k = -\frac{E}{2.303R}\frac{1}{T} + \text{const.} \tag{6.2}$$

or, integrating between limits T_2 and T_1,

$$\log\frac{k_2}{k_1} = \frac{E}{2.303R}\frac{T_2 - T_1}{T_2 T_1} \tag{6.3}$$

E can be evaluated from this equation by measuring reaction rates at two temperatures, or it can be evaluated graphically from Equation (6.2). This is the equation of a straight line of $\log k$ versus $1/T$ with slope $-E/2.303R$, where R is 1.987. The calculated value is in calories (Figure 6.2). ∎

metabolic function of enzymes   :: 6.1

From the point of view of biology, enzymes are of great importance to the life of the cell and thereby to the life of the organism. Life is, by the simplest definition, a manifestation of the numerous inter-locking chemical reactions of the cell, all reactions being deter-mined by the nature and amount of enzymes.

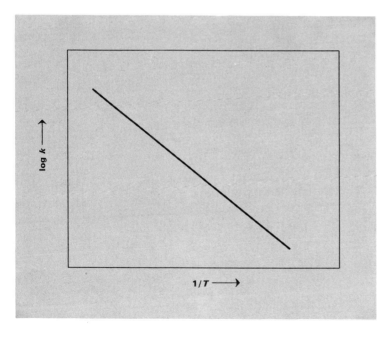

figure 6.2 :: Value of E can be calculated from the slope of the line ($-E/2.303R$).

The orderliness that characterizes the network of chemical reactions in the cell is a consequence of enzyme specificity. According to thermodynamics, an organic substance can be converted to many products of lower free energy, but at the temperature of the cell most conversions would be too sluggish to be of any use. If the reactions were faster, a complex mixture of products would result. By catalyzing one of all thermodynamically possible reactions, one enzyme determines the product that should be formed from a given substance.† Singling out one reaction is what is called *reaction specificity*. But enzymes are also specific toward the substrate, reacting often only with one compound. *Substrate specificity*, as will be seen later, is not always limited to one compound.

It follows that several enzymes are necessary to catalyze all possible reactions of a given substrate. True, not all possible reactions need to occur in the cell, and what is often observed is that substrates react in only few ways, and sometimes only in one way.

To illustrate how a substance reacts in the cell in as many ways as there are enzymes to attack it, let us consider pyruvic acid:

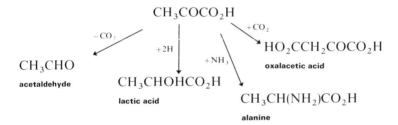

Each of the four reactions is catalyzed by a different enzyme, and for the moment we need not go into the details of the reactions. The above example is only to illustrate that pyruvic acid can be decarboxylated, reduced, aminated, and carboxylated. If all four enzymes were present, all four reactions would occur. What is commonly observed in most cells is that a group of enzymes occurs acting in a concerted fashion.

The situation illustrated above is one in which different products are formed from pyruvic acid; each product could in turn react if specific enzymes were present. For example, acetaldehyde could be reduced to ethanol; oxalacetic acid could be reduced to malic acid; and so on. A sequence of reactions can thus be obtained for pyruvic

† Reactants in enzyme reactions are called *substrates*.

acid. Sequences such as these are usually called *metabolic pathways.*
The sum of all metabolic pathways is the cell's *metabolism.*

nomenclature and classification :: **6.2**

Enzymes are named by using the name of the substrate, the name of
the reaction, or both, but modified by the suffix *ase*: for example,
urease, decarboxylase, and *lactic acid dehydrogenase.* Some
enzymes known for a long time have names unrelated to either
substrate or reaction: *trypsin, pepsin,* and *chymotrypsin.* The
nomenclature is undoubtedly arbitrary and sometimes confusing.
A uniform system for naming enzymes has been recommended but
not yet accepted universally. The system recommended by the
Commission on Enzymes (International Union of Biochemistry)
classifies all enzymes into six major categories (Table 6.2).

specificity :: **6.3**

The specificity of enzymes toward substrates determines what
organic or inorganic substance can be utilized by the cell. This is
observed clearly in the utilization of enantiomeric substances. No
known organism, for example, can utilize D-amino acids for the
biosynthesis of proteins. All the enzymes needed to form a protein
molecule catalyze reactions of the L isomers only. Consequently, in
the living world only substances for which enzymes are known can
be assimilated.

The first step in enzyme catalysis is the formation of an intermediate form or enzyme-substrate complex. Because there is a great

table 6.2 :: Enzyme classification according to the Commission on Enzymes
of the International Union of Biochemistry

---

1. *Oxidoreductases* catalyze the removal of H_2 (dehydrogenases) or addition of O_2 (oxygenases).
They catalyze oxidation of $-CHOH-$, $>CHCH<$, $-CHNH_2$, and others.

2. *Transferases* catalyze group transfers from one substrate to another. Examples of transferred
groups: $-CH_3$, $-CH_2OH$, $-NH_2$.

3. *Hydrolases* catalyze the hydrolitic cleavage of a large variety of bonds: peptide, glycoside, ester.

4. *Lyases* catalyze the nonhydrolytic cleavage of groups from substrates. Examples of cleaved bonds:
$C-C$ in decarboxylations, $C-O$ in removal of water.

5. *Isomerases* catalyze different types of isomerization: *cis-trans*, keto-enol.

6. *Ligases* catalyze formation of bonds, coupled to the cleavage of pyrophosphate bond from a
nucleotide triphosphate.

disparity in molecular size between the enzyme and most substrates, the reaction must be imagined taking place on one small region of the enzyme; this region is called the *active center*. Here the substrate must have a perfect fitting to account for the limited range of substrates reacting with any one enzyme. This situation was aptly compared by E. Fischer to a lock and key relationship. When more than one substrate can combine with a given enzyme, the substrates are structurally very similar.

Of great interest are the various types of stereospecificity encountered. We have already mentioned the specificity of enzymes acting on L-amino acids in the biosynthesis of proteins. Similarly, most enzymes acting on sugars are specific for the D isomers. This type of specificity is usually called *optical specificity*.

It should be noted at this point that the enzymatic synthesis of substances in the cell follows an asymmetric course, which is the reason so many natural products are optically active.

In addition to optical specificity, enzymes possess other types of stereospecificity; some of them will be described.

In geometric *cis-trans* isomers only one member of a pair is attacked by a given enzyme. Fumarase, as an example, attacks fumaric acid and catalyzes the stereospecific addition of water to the double bond but it does not react with the *cis* isomer, maleic acid:

$$
\underset{\textbf{fumaric acid}}{\overset{\displaystyle HCCO_2H}{\underset{\displaystyle HO_2CCH}{\|}}} + H_2O \rightleftharpoons \underset{\textbf{L-malic acid}}{\overset{\displaystyle OH}{\underset{\displaystyle CH_2CO_2H}{\overset{|}{\underset{|}{HCCO_2H}}}}} \qquad \underset{\textbf{maleic acid}}{\overset{\displaystyle HCCO_2H}{\underset{\displaystyle HCCO_2H}{\|}}} + H_2O \longrightarrow \text{no reaction}
$$

The *removal* of water from malic acid, the reverse reaction, yields fumaric acid.

The hydrolysis of diasteromeric disaccharides is another example of stereospecificity. In Chapter 4 two enzymes were described that catalyze the hydrolysis of glycosidic bonds specifically. One, maltase, attacks only α-glycosidic bonds, and the other, emulsin, attacks only β-glycosidic bonds.

A special type of stereospecificity has been observed in enzymatic reactions where the substrate has a carbon atom with a pair of like and a pair of unlike substituents. Glycerol is a representative of this type of compound:

$$
\underset{a}{\overset{b}{\underset{a}{\overset{|}{\underset{c}{C}}}}} \qquad \underset{HOH_2C}{\overset{OH}{\overset{|}{\underset{CH_2OH}{C-H}}}}
$$

In all chemical reactions in solution, the two primary alcohol groups are equally reactive and therefore equivalent; in enzyme reactions they behave as two different groups. For example, esterification with phosphate (actually with adenosine triphosphate), as catalyzed by the enzyme glycerol kinase, results in a product in which only one of the alcohol groups has reacted:

$$\underset{\text{HOH}_2\text{C} \qquad \text{CH}_2\text{OH}}{\overset{\text{OH}}{\underset{}{\overset{|}{\text{C}}}\diagdown\text{H}}} + \text{ATP} \longrightarrow \underset{\text{HOH}_2\text{C} \qquad \text{CH}_2\text{OPO}_3\text{H}_2}{\overset{\text{OH}}{\underset{}{\overset{|}{\text{C}}}\diagdown\text{H}}}$$

reactive group

This type of specificity was explained by A. G. Ogston in 1948 while dealing with a similar situation in which citric acid was the substrate. He explained that if the active center of the enzyme combines with the substrate at three specified points, only one orientation of the substrate on the enzyme is possible. For example, we could assume that glycerol combines with glycerol kinase at three points in the active center. By referring to Figure 6.3, one can observe that glycerol can only fit as shown; turning the substrate to any other position will prevent the specified fit. It is here that the Fischer concept of a lock and key relationship operates quite clearly.

A consequence of the unique fit of glycerol on the enzyme is that the primary alcohol groups of glycerol are bonded to two different places in the active center. Now, it is not unreasonable to assume

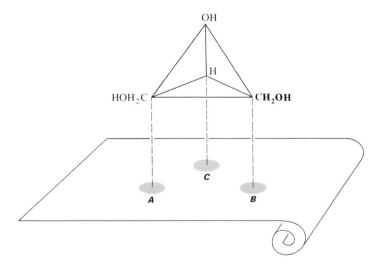

figure 6.3 :: Attachment of glycerol to the active center of the enzyme through points A, B, and C. Only position B contains the catalytic elements. Only the —CH₂OH group in that position reacts. There is no way of bringing the —CH₂OH from position A to B without changing the specified fit of the other groups.

that only one of the two places contains the necessary components to catalyze the reaction. Thus the catalytic activity of glycerol kinase can be seen as located, where it acts on only one of the primary alcohol groups (in boldface type).

The concept proposed by Ogston has been verified experimentally in many cases, and it is now an accepted fact of biochemistry that molecules similar to glycerol, that is, with two equal and two unequal substituents, behave as if they were asymmetrical.

Specificity has not been established satisfactorily for all known enzymes, and present information is somewhat incomplete. One reason for this apparent neglect is that often it is difficult to be sure that one is dealing with a single enzyme. An enzyme believed to be pure can be contaminated by traces of another very active enzyme. If it is tested against several potential substrates, the results would give the impression that the "pure enzyme" acts over a wider range of substrates than it really does.

Occasionally enzymes have been found that catalyze two reactions in sequence. Having failed to identify two enzymes by all known means, the conclusion has been drawn that some enzymes are multifunctional. This is the case with the malic enzyme, which catalyzes two reactions simultaneously:

$$CH_3COCO_2H + CO_2 \rightleftharpoons HO_2CCH_2COCO_2H + 2H\dagger \rightleftharpoons HO_2CCH_2CHOHCO_2H$$

Michaelis-Menten theory :: 6.4

Fischer had already proposed that in an enzymatic reaction there is a close steric relationship between the enzyme and the substrate when in 1913 L. Michaelis and M. L. Menten hypothesized the existence of an *enzyme-substrate complex* as the basis for a theoretical analysis of enzymatic reactions.

Their hypothesis has been verified experimentally; the existence of enzyme-substrate complexes of varying stabilities has been demonstrated by observing rapid changes in the spectral characteristics of the enzyme as it reacts with its substrate.

The Michaelis-Menten theory starts with the premise that an enzyme E reacts with substrate S to form complex ES. No products can be formed except through this route. The complex ES decomposes to yield products P and free enzyme. The overall reaction

† Actually H_2 is not used in the reduction but NADH, a coenzyme of many dehydrogenases.

can be written

$$E + S \rightleftharpoons ES \longrightarrow P + E \qquad (6.4)$$

The reaction $E + S \rightleftharpoons ES$ is assumed to attain equilibrium very rapidly, and the decomposition $ES \longrightarrow P + E$ is considered slow in comparison. Under these conditions the rate at which products are formed should be a function of the concentration of ES. This can be expressed as

$$rate = k[ES] \qquad (6.5)$$

where k is the rate constant.

It should be possible to determine the velocity of an enzyme reaction if the concentration of ES is known, but the concentration of ES is not always a measurable quantity.

The problem can be turned around; if the rate is known, the concentration of ES could be measured, because rate depends on the concentration of ES. Let us apply the mass-action law to the reaction $ES \rightleftharpoons E + S$:

$$\frac{[E][S]}{[ES]} = K_{eq} \qquad (6.6)$$

where K_{eq} represents the dissociation constant of ES. If the concentration of S is increased, the concentration of ES must also increase, to maintain K_{eq}. It should be readily seen that the rate will increase with increasing substrate concentration as long as there is some free enzyme E to react with S. Assume now that substrate is added in a large excess so that all the enzyme is complexed as ES, or, saying it differently, the enzyme is saturated with substrate. Adding more substrate at this point would have no effect on the concentration of ES.

Since rate depends on the concentration of ES (rate $= k[ES]$), it follows that the maximal rate should be attained when the enzyme is saturated. If the assumptions are correct, a plot of reaction velocity versus substrate concentration should give a curve similar to the curve in Figure 6.4.

The maximal velocity is shown by drawing a tangent to the curve; it corresponds to the substrate concentration necessary to saturate the enzyme. If we take a point halfway to the maximal velocity, the substrate concentration corresponding to this velocity is equal to the Michaelis constant, or K_m (expressed in moles per liter).

Referring again to Equation (6.6), when the velocity of the reaction is half the maximal velocity, half the enzyme must be in the form of

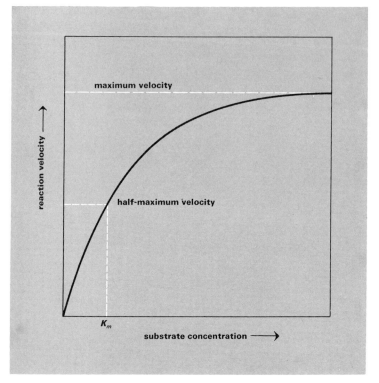

figure 6.4 ::
Relation between substrate concentration and reaction velocity when the concentration of enzyme is constant.

E and half in the form of ES. The two terms, being equal, cancel out and Equation (6.6) becomes

$$[S] = K_{eq} \qquad (6.7)$$

In other words, the substrate concentration at which an enzyme reaches half the maximal velocity is equal to K_{eq}; in this particular case K_{eq} is called K_m (Michaelis constant), and it approximates the dissociation constant of ES.

The K_m of enzymes varies widely. This means that the substrate concentration needed to saturate an enzyme is different for different enzymes. An enzyme with a large K_m value is one that is saturated at high substrate concentrations, and one with a small K_m value is saturated at low substrate concentration. A more rigorous treatment of the Michaelis-Menten theory is given below.

■ The formation of an enzyme-substrate complex and its decomposition can be written as in Equation (6.4):

$$E + S \underset{k_2}{\overset{k_1}{\rightleftharpoons}} ES \overset{k_3}{\longrightarrow} E + P$$

The rate equations for the formation and decomposition of ES are

$$\frac{d[ES]}{dt} = k_1[E][S] - (k_2 + k_3)[ES] \qquad (6.8)$$

and

$$\frac{dP}{dt} = k_3[ES] \qquad (6.9)$$

In the steady state (when the rate at which ES is being formed equals the rate at which it decomposes), the following relationship is valid:

$$k_1[E][S] = (k_2 + k_3)[ES] \qquad (6.10)$$

or

$$\frac{k_2 + k_3}{k_1} = \frac{[E][S]}{[ES]} \qquad (6.11)$$

The Michaelis-Menten theory assumes that the rate of product formation is controlled by the rapid equilibration of E and S with ES; in other words, k_1 and k_2 are greater than k_3, and Equation (6.11) becomes

$$\frac{k_2}{k_1} = \frac{[E][S]}{[ES]} \qquad (6.12)$$

This is simply the dissociation constant of the enzyme-substrate complex

$$K_m = \frac{[E][S]}{[ES]} = K_{eq} \qquad (6.13)$$

As G. E. Briggs and J. B. S. Haldane have pointed out, even if the initial equilibrium is not rapid, the Michaelis-Menten equation is valid; but in this case

$$K_m = \frac{k_2 + k_3}{k_1} = \frac{[E][S]}{[ES]} \qquad (6.14)$$

and K_m is not a true dissociation constant, because E + S and ES are not at equilibrium. Thus in this more complex case $K_m \neq K_{eq}$.

There is no way to evaluate K_m from Equation (6.14), because it is not possible to obtain numerical values for ES or E. This difficulty is circumvented by changing the equation to

$$K_m = \frac{([E] - [ES])[S]}{[ES]} \qquad (6.15)$$

in which the term [E] − [ES] has been substituted for E. The new term represents the concentration of free enzyme, which is the same as total enzyme minus enzyme complexed as ES. Rearranging Equation (6.15) to solve for [ES] we obtain

$$[ES] = \frac{[E][S]}{K_m + [S]} \tag{6.16}$$

where [E] is the total enzyme concentration. Since only a small fraction of the substrate is bound to the enzyme, we assume that [S] is the total substrate concentration.

We have already observed that the breakdown of ES into products and enzyme is at a rate determined by the concentration of ES, or, expressing it mathematically,

$$v = k_3[ES] \tag{6.17}$$

Combining Equations (6.17) and (6.16) we obtain

$$v = \frac{k_3[E][S]}{K_m + [S]} \tag{6.18}$$

We have also noted that maximal velocity is obtained when all the enzyme is in the form of complex ES or when E = ES. We can express this as

$$V = v_{max} = k_3[E] \tag{6.19}$$

Substituting V for $k_3[E]$ in Equation (6.18), the following equation results:

$$v = \frac{V[S]}{K_m + [S]} \tag{6.20}$$

and by rearrangement we obtain

$$K_m = [S]\left(\frac{V}{v} - 1\right) \tag{6.21}$$

Equations (6.20) and (6.21) are both familiar forms of the Michaelis-Menten equation. Plotting v against substrate concentration gives a rectangular hyperbola characteristic of enzyme reactions (Figure 6.4).

K_m has been defined as the substrate concentration needed for the reaction to reach half the maximal velocity. This relationship is obvious when numerical values are substituted in Equation (6.21):

$$K_m = [S]\left(\frac{2}{1} - 1\right) = S \tag{6.22}$$

There are practical disadvantages in measuring maximal velocity; one is that at extreme high concentration of substrate, anomalies are often seen. It is also difficult to decide when maximal velocity is reached. The rate keeps increasing by very small increments as the concentration of substrate is increased.

This difficulty was resolved by H. Lineweaver and D. Burk by changing Equation (6.20) to a linear equation. This is achieved by taking the reciprocal of both terms in Equation (6.20):

$$\frac{1}{v} = \frac{K_m}{V}\frac{1}{S} + \frac{1}{V} \qquad\qquad (6.23)$$

This is the equation of a straight line ($y = mx + b$). A plot of $1/v$ versus $1/S$ gives a straight line with a slope K_m/V, as shown in Figure 6.5. The advantage here is that the plot can be made from relatively few points and the line is extrapolated to infinitely high substrate concentration, or $1/S = 0$. If the line extends to intercept the abscissa, the intercept $1/S$ becomes $-1/K_m$. (In the straight-line equation when $y = 0$, $x = -b/m$.)■

factors influencing enzyme reaction velocity :: 6.5

Section 6.4 dealt with the effect of substrate concentration on the velocity of enzyme-catalyzed reactions. Other factors affecting the velocity are pH, temperature, activators, and inhibitors.

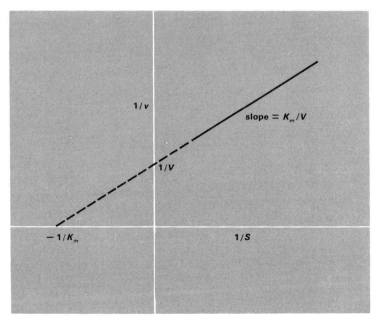

figure 6.5 :: Plot of the reciprocal of substrate concentration ($1/S$) against the reciprocal of the reaction velocity ($1/v$) gives a straight line.

When substrates are used in large excess, the velocity of the reaction is proportional to the concentration of enzyme (Figure 6.6). There should be no difficulty in appreciating this fact in the framework of the Michaelis-Menten theory. When substrate is in excess, the enzyme is saturated and the velocity of the reaction is maximal. If the enzyme concentration is doubled and the substrate is still in excess, the velocity should double, because we now have twice as much saturated enzyme.

Before discussing the effects of pH and temperature on the velocity of enzyme reactions, something should be said about the units of measurement. The *turnover number* is the number of substrate molecules transformed in 1 minute by one enzyme molecule. This presupposes that the molecular weight of the enzyme is known, which often is not the case. The enzyme unit is used in most cases and is defined as the *amount of enzyme needed to transform 1 micromole of substrate in 1 minute.*

EFFECT OF pH : Measurements of enzyme reaction velocity must take into account pH and temperature and in some cases the

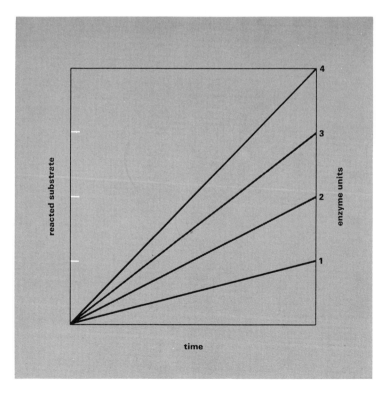

figure 6.6 ::
Relation between enzyme concentration and reaction velocity when the substrate is in excess. Four times more substrate reacts with four units of enzyme than with one unit of enzyme assuming the velocity remains constant in time.

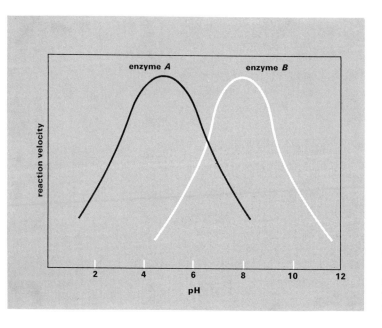

figure 6.7 ::
Relation between
reaction velocity of
two enzyme-catalyzed
reactions and pH.

presence of activators and inhibitors. With all other factors constant, the velocity of enzyme reactions is affected by the pH of the environment. All enzymes reach maximal velocity at some pH range. When velocity is plotted against pH, curves similar to those of Figure 6.7 are obtained.

The effect of pH on the velocity of enzyme reactions is understandable; enzymes are polyelectrolytes that respond to any changes in pH. Like other proteins they possess many dissociable groups, and their degree of dissociation, which could account for catalytic properties, is dependent on pH; so is the net charge of the enzyme. Also many substrates are substances with dissociable groups. Which ionic species of substrate predominates in solution is determined by pH, and one can easily imagine that some species could be more reactive than others. We must also consider that the stability of enzymes toward pH varies greatly. Some enzymes begin to denature and to lose activity at pHs where other enzymes are quite stable.

EFFECT OF TEMPERATURE : Temperature affects enzyme reactions for the same reason it affects any other chemical reaction: At higher temperatures more molecules become activated. It has been known for a long time that the velocity of a chemical reaction doubles or trebles for every 10°C rise.

With enzyme reactions there is a complication: At temperatures over 40°C, enzymes begin to denature, losing their activity. What is gained in velocity by increasing the temperature is lost by the denaturation of the enzyme. At temperatures in the range 20 to 30°C, for example, there is little denaturation and the velocity of the enzyme reaction increases with increasing temperature.

EFFECT OF ACTIVATORS : Many enzymes do not function optimally or do not function at all until a second substance has been added to the reaction mixture. Some of these substances are specific organic molecules or inorganic ions (mainly metal ions). Activation by inorganic ions is quite common, and the rate of an enzyme reaction, when the enzyme needs an activator, becomes dependent on the concentration of the activator. It is incorrect, therefore, to attempt measurements of enzyme reaction rates except where an adequate concentration of activator is present.

EFFECT OF INHIBITORS : In contrast, inhibitors slow down or stop an enzyme reaction. We are not speaking of concentrated acids or strong reagents, which would, on contact with enzymes, bring total destruction. The inhibitors we have in mind are substances that are effective in small amounts and inhibit the reaction without changing the structure of the enzyme to any considerable degree. Two types of inhibitors are recognized.

COMPETITIVE INHIBITORS : A competitive inhibitor is a substance with a structure similar to that of the substrate. For example, malonic acid is an inhibitor of enzymes acting on succinic acid:

$HO_2CCH_2CO_2H$ $HO_2CCH_2CH_2CO_2H$

malonic acid   **succinic acid**

The inhibitor combines with the active center of the enzyme to form an enzyme-inhibitor complex EI. Since the rate of the reaction depends on the concentration of ES alone, it becomes possible to calculate the extent of inhibition by applying the same arguments to the formation of EI as were applied to the formation of ES.

This type of inhibition can be reversed by increasing the substrate concentration. In other words, the substrate can displace the inhibitor from the active center. In Figure 6.8 is shown a Lineweaver-Burk plot of an enzyme-catalyzed reaction with and without a competitive inhibitor.

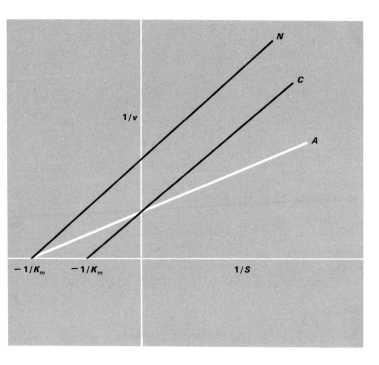

figure 6.8 ::
Reciprocal plots of v
and S. With no inhibitor
(A); with a competitive
inhibitor (C); and with a
noncompetitive inhibitor
(N). Note that A and N
have the same K_m but a
different V_{max} (intercept).
A and C have the same
V_{max} but different K_m.

NONCOMPETITIVE INHIBITORS : These are substances that bind firmly to the enzyme and are not displaced by the addition of substrate. Generally they are quite reactive, and they attack functional groups of enzymes under very mild conditions. The greater their affinity for the enzyme, the greater the extent of inhibition.

A classical example of noncompetitive inhibition is represented by the reaction of the —SH group of enzymes with a variety of compounds. The —SH group shows great nucleophilic reactivity, and it can enter into many substitution reactions. For example, it reacts with halogenated acids such as ICH_2CO_2H : it reacts with organometallic compounds to form mercaptides.

In all these reactions the product is not an easily dissociated EI complex. The inhibition cannot be reversed by increasing the substrate concentration, as was the case with competitive inhibitors. The graphic analysis in Figure 6.8 clearly shows the difference between competitive and noncompetitive inhibition.

nature of the active center :: 6.6

The term active center has been used frequently without explaining its exact nature. It has only been said that the active center is a small region of the enzyme where substrates react by selective attachment followed by breaking and making of bonds.

Complexing between enzyme and substrate is possible by inter-actions resulting in hydrogen bonds, electrostatic attraction, or hydrophobic bonds between substrate and, in all probability, amino acid side chains of the active center.

Starting with the premise that amino acid side chains make up the active center, it becomes necessary to ask *which type* of side chains and how they are arranged. To answer these points it would seem necessary to have knowledge of the tertiary structure of the enzyme, but the tertiary structure of most enzymes will not be known for some time, so indirect approaches must be made.

It can be guessed that the amino acids of the active center need not be neighboring amino acids in the polypeptide chain. A situa-tion can be visualized in which amino acids distantly located from one another could be brought into close proximity by the foldings of the polypeptide backbone, as illustrated by the situation in Figure 6.9.

An arrangement such as this explains in a way why denaturation of an enzyme is accompanied by loss of activity. Denaturation is, as explained in Chapter 2, a process resulting in the disorganization of the tertiary structure.

If it is not possible to arrive at the precise structure of the active center, it is still feasible to find methods that permit detection of the active groups in the center. Some of these methods will be described.

IDENTIFICATION OF ACTIVE GROUPS : The chemical nature of the active groups in the center can be deduced from the behavior of

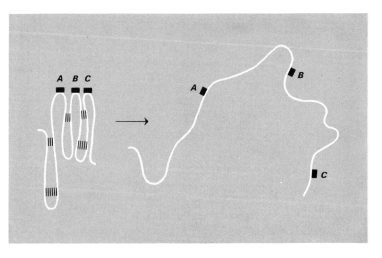

figure 6.9 :: Active center built from three amino acid residues (*A*, *B*, and *C*) located at distant points in the polypeptide chain but brought into close proximity by the foldings of the chain. On the right, the three amino acids become separated upon denaturation.

enzymes toward specific chemical agents and from enzyme
kinetics.

Considering here only chemical agents, recall that reagents which
react readily with the —SH of proteins tend to be inhibitors of a
number of enzymes. It becomes probable, although not certain, that
the —SH group is part of the active center of those enzymes
inhibited by reagents that attack the —SH group specifically.

The analysis can be carried still further; for example, by titrating
the —SH groups of an enzyme it is possible to predict the number
of active centers. —SH reacts readily with p-chloromercuri-
benzoate, and the number of reacting groups can be measured by
titration of the enzyme with this reagent.

The —SH group seems to be a common component of the active
center of many enzymes. Other commonly detected groups are the
—OH of tyrosine and serine, the imidazolyl group of histidine,
some free —NH$_2$ groups (lysine), and free carboxyl groups
(glutamic and aspartic acids). They can be detected by the effect
of specific reagents on enzyme activity. The specific reagents most
frequently used and the groups attacked are shown in Table 6.3.

table 6.3 :: Compounds commonly used to detect specific groups on the
active center

COMPOUND FORMULA AND TRIVIAL NAME		MAIN REACTIVE GROUPS ON ENZYME
CH$_3$CO—O—CH$_3$CO	Acetic anhydride	Lys(—NH$_2$), Ser(OH), Tyr(OH)
ICH$_2$CO$_2$H	Iodoacetic acid	Cys(SH), His(—NH)
Cl·Hg—⬡—CO$_2$H	p-Chloromercuribenzoate	Cys(SH)
O$_2$N—⬡(NO$_2$)—F	2,4-Dinitrofluorobenzene	Lys(—NH$_2$), Tyr-OH, His(—NH)
O$_2$N—⬡—O$_2$C$_2$H$_3$	p-Nitrophenylacetate	Ser(OH) on active center of hydrolases
F—P(OCH(CH$_3$)$_2$)$_2$ with O	Diisopropylfluorophosphate	Ser(OH) on active center of hydrolases

It is not always possible to deduce the nature of the active center from the inhibition of enzyme activity by specific reagents. First, inhibition as a consequence of structural changes in the enzyme has to be ruled out. Also, not all groups in an enzyme are equally reactive. Different reactivities of similar groups toward the same reagent are well illustrated by the reaction of diisopropyl fluorophosphate (DFP) with the hydrolases:

$$\underset{O}{\overset{\displaystyle OCH(CH_3)_2}{F-P}}\overset{}{\underset{OCH(CH_3)_2}{}}$$

DFP, one of the commonly known nerve gases, esterifies the —OH group of serine but *only* when serine is in the active center of particular enzymes. Other serine side chains do not react. Since the hydrolases are inhibited by DFP, it can be assumed that the active center of those hydrolases contains a serine side chain. Furthermore, the number of active centers in a hydrolase can be determined by measuring the number of DFP molecules reacting with the enzyme.

The active groups just discussed are the side chains of amino acids, forming part of the enzyme molecule. But many enzymes are conjugated proteins in which the prosthetic group is a small organic molecule. In those enzymes the prosthetic group is a component part of the active center, as we shall see later.

Many prosthetic groups are readily detected on enzymes by observing their absorption spectra in solution. In some instances it is even possible to observe structural changes during catalysis as manifested by a change in the absorption spectrum.

theories of enzyme reaction mechanisms :: 6.7

The complexing between enzyme and substrate has been verified by experiment; we even have some information on the nature of the side chains in the active center. But not much is known about the exact mechanism by which enzymes speed up reactions more efficiently than do any other known catalysts.

One can comprehend readily that a substrate tied up to an enzyme loses freedom and might react more readily with functional groups on the enzyme than if it were in solution. On the enzyme, the bonds of the substrate are brought into contact with the reactive site with no energy consumption. As a matter of fact, calculations show that the complexing step is accompanied by a small decrease in free energy; in other words, this is a favorable step. Also by binding the substrate into a more or less fixed position, the enzyme-substrate complex formed is an unstable intermediate and very reactive.

When we speak of reaction mechanisms we are speaking of a description of the path followed by the enzyme-substrate complex as it is transformed into products. Such descriptions have been possible in a few instances. An enzyme that has been studied intensively is chymotrypsin, and the proposed mechanism will be discussed next as a model of enzyme-catalyzed reactions.

CHYMOTRYPSIN-CATALYZED HYDROLYSIS : Chymotrypsin is a hydrolase that catalyzes the hydrolysis of derivatives of carboxylic acids, particularly amides of some amino acids. The molecular weight of chymotrypsin is 24,800, and it has one serine in the active center per molecule of enzyme, as shown by titration with DFP.

From kinetic data obtained at various pHs, the deduction has been made that the active center can be protonated with an apparent pK of 7; this corresponds to the pK of a histidine side chain. Thus we know that the active center has a serine group and a histidine group. With this basic information, M. L. Bender proposed a mechanism similar to a base-catalyzed hydrolysis:

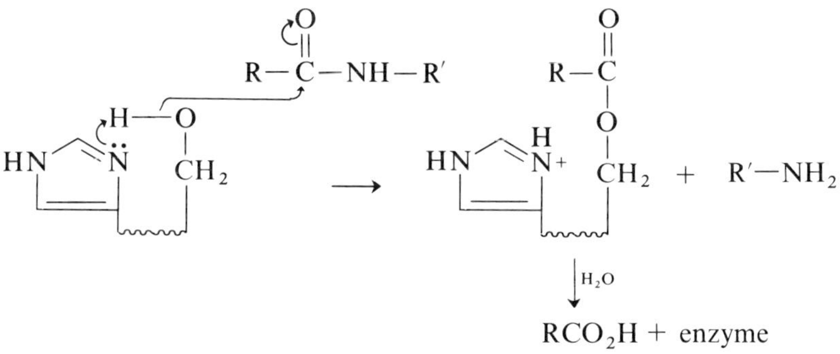

The imidazolyl of histidine is a basic group that removes the proton from the serine $-OH$ as the serine attacks the carbonyl of the amide. The leaving amine is then protonated by an acid group in the center. This completes the first stage of the reaction, in which the enzyme establishes a covalent bond with the substrate while causing another bond to break. In a second step, the ester just formed is attacked by water releasing the second product.

KOSHLAND THEORY : An amplified view of the template theory of Fischer is that the active center has two components: one responsible for substrate specificity and a second responsible for the catalysis proper. Furthermore, in the view of the template theory, only substrates with a given set of dimensions and shape can fit into the specificity region; catalysis follows as an inevitable sequence because the fitting brings bonds to be broken into place with the catalytic site.

D. E. Koshland, Jr., has listed several instances of substances that bind to enzymes without suffering change and substances that could not possibly fit on the active center and still react catalytically. In addition to those observations, there are others of a kinetic nature that cannot be explained satisfactorily by the template theory.

Another explanation was needed, and Koshland has provided us with a hypothesis for the structure of the active center. He has still kept many features of the template theory, but his concept of the active center is new. The active center, according to Koshland, is not a fixed region that is either fitted or not fitted by a substrate. Instead, it is imagined as a flexible region that can be modified by the incoming substrate. The modification is induced by conformation changes in the enzyme. Simply stated, the substrate makes the fitting possible by "molding" the active center; this idea has been depicted in Figure 6.10.

The induced fit by the intended substrate causes the catalytic components of the active center to align themselves with some of

figure 6.10 :: Conception of a flexible active center. The substrate induces alignment of catalytic components *A* and *B*. (*After D. E. Koshland, Jr.*)

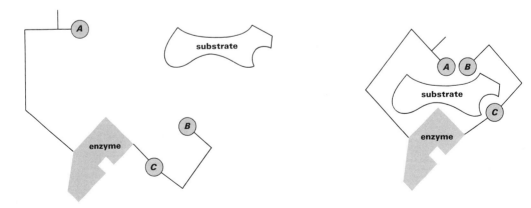

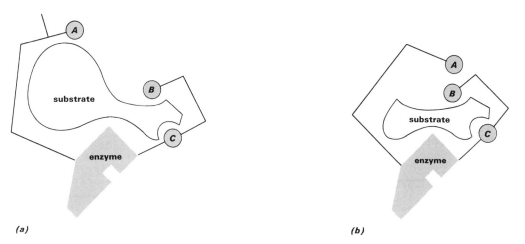

(a)   (b)

figure 6.11 :: Substrate that is too large (*a*) or one that is too small (*b*)
bind on the enzyme but fail to induce alignment of the catalytic components
A and *B*. (*After D. E. Koshland, Jr.*)

the substrate's bonds which are to be broken. This picture can be
elaborated further by considering a substance other than the
intended substrate but structurally not too different. Substances
such as this could also induce its fit in the active center and complex
with the enzyme. But it will not react if the substance is either too
large or too small to cause the alignment of its bonds with the
catalytic components of the active center (Figure 6.11).

The Koshland theory has found experimental support; it explains
enzyme inhibition and resolves in part some of the difficulties
arising in the template theory.

An important consequence of the theory of flexible active centers
is that slight changes in the conformation of the enzyme can bring
about changes on the active center. This phenomenon is best noted
in what is known as *allosterism*. It means that a protein which
ordinarily combines with some small molecule loses this binding
property by combining first with another molecule through a
different place in the protein molecule. The first time such a
phenomenon was observed was with hemoglobin in the 1920s.
Proteins possessing this characteristic are called *allosteric proteins*.

The effect is explained as follows. An allosteric protein can bind a
ligand on a place in the molecule that has a given arrangement. But
the same protein has a second place in its molecule that can fit
another ligand. The latter could be quite different from the first.
In accordance with Koshland's view, the second ligand could

induce its fit and cause conformational changes in the protein molecule. This conformational change can propagate to the first center in the molecule. This would change its geometry and lose its affinity for the first ligand. The process is illustrated in Figure 6.12.

The concept of allosteric enzymes offers an explanation of an often-observed phenomenon in the cell: *feedback inhibition*. Let us consider a sequence of reactions leading from starting material A to a final product Z:

$$A \xrightarrow{E_1} B \xrightarrow{E_2} C \dashrightarrow Z$$

Each step is catalyzed by a different enzyme. When the concentration of product Z reaches a given point, it begins to inhibit enzyme E_1, which catalyzes the first step in the sequence. The structure of Z is totally different from the structure of A, so that no competitive inhibition is possible. However, Z reacts with enzyme E_1 in some way and prevents further production of Z by blocking the first step in the sequence ($A \rightarrow B$). This process of feedback inhibition can be explained satisfactorily if the assumption is made that enzyme E_1 is an allosteric enzyme with a specified binding place for product Z. In accordance with the ideas of Koshland, the complexing between E_1 and Z could give rise to conformational changes in the enzyme, changes that propagate to the active center of the enzyme. If the change is intense enough, the active center could understandably lose its specificity for the intended substrate A, as shown in Figure 6.12.

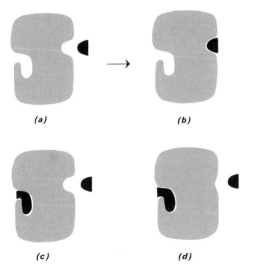

(a)

(b)

(c)

(d)

figure 6.12 :: Schematic representation of an allosteric enzyme (*a*) binding a substrate in place (*b*). The binding of a second ligand in another place on the enzyme (*c*) distorts the active center for the substrate, which fails to bind (*d*).

The name *coenzyme* is applied to a nonprotein organic molecule acting together with the protein (apoenzyme) in the catalytic system. If the nonprotein organic molecule is readily dissociated from the apoenzyme, it is generally considered a coenzyme. If it is firmly bound to the apoenzyme, the name *prosthetic group* is used.

The distinction between coenzyme and prosthetic group is not always possible. The ease of dissociation is hardly precise unless a specified dissociation constant is agreed upon. Other ways of distinguishing between coenzyme and prosthetic group have been adopted, but for the purposes of this book we shall consider coenzyme and prosthetic group as being the same.

Coenzymes in combination with their respective apoenzymes act as carriers of chemical groups and, in this way, they catalyze group transfers. This can be represented by a general reaction:

$$EC + Ax \rightleftarrows ECx + A$$

$$ECx + B \rightleftarrows EC + Bx$$

in which the group x of substrate Ax is transferred to B in a reaction mediated by the enzyme-coenzyme complex EC. As we shall see in Chapter 7, x can be any of a number of atoms or group of atoms: hydrogen, methyl groups, amino groups, and many others.

One coenzyme is often associated with a wide array of enzymes catalyzing reactions of widely different substrates. For example, oxidation of glucose, xanthine, amino acids, succinic acid, and some other compounds is catalyzed by enzymes all of which have a flavine derivative as coenzyme.

A list of the most important coenzymes and their structures is given in Table 6.4. It should be noted that vitamins are either coenzymes or some part of a more complex coenzyme molecule. This observation explains why vitamins play such a vital role in the functioning of the cell.

The name *activator* used earlier in this chapter is usually reserved for inorganic anions and cations that are essential for enzyme activity. Metals are particularly important as activators, and of these the most common are magnesium, manganese, zinc, iron, cobalt, and molybdenum.

table 6.4 :: Important coenzymes

STRUCTURE AND NAME	VITAMIN	FUNCTION

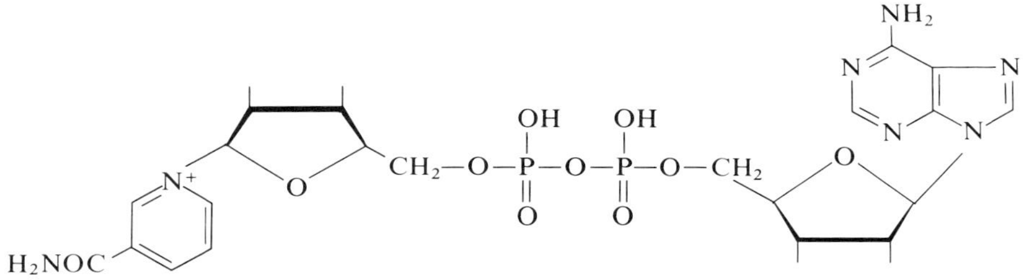

nicotinamide adenine dinucleotide (NAD$^+$)

Nicotinamide — Hydrogen transfer

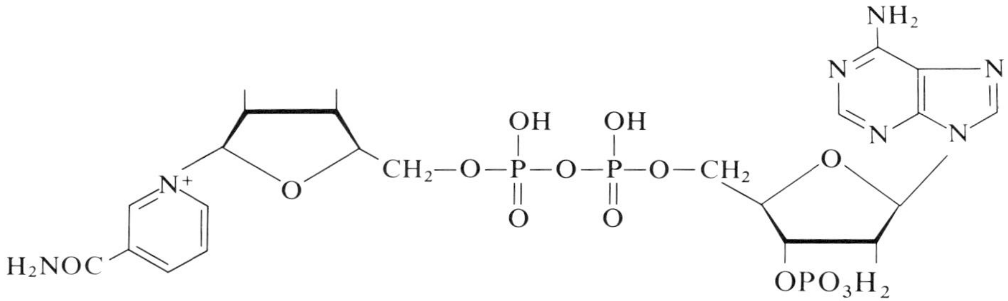

nicotinamide adenine dinucleotide phosphate (NADP$^+$)

Hydrogen transfer

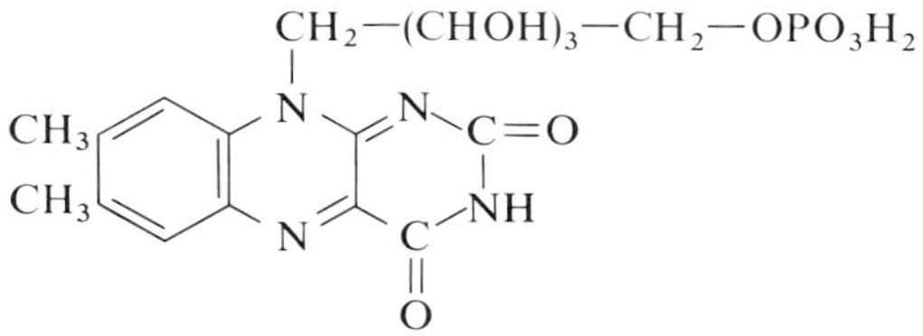

$CH_2-(CHOH)_3-CH_2-OPO_3H_2$

flavin mononucleotide (FMN)

Riboflavin — Hydrogen transfer

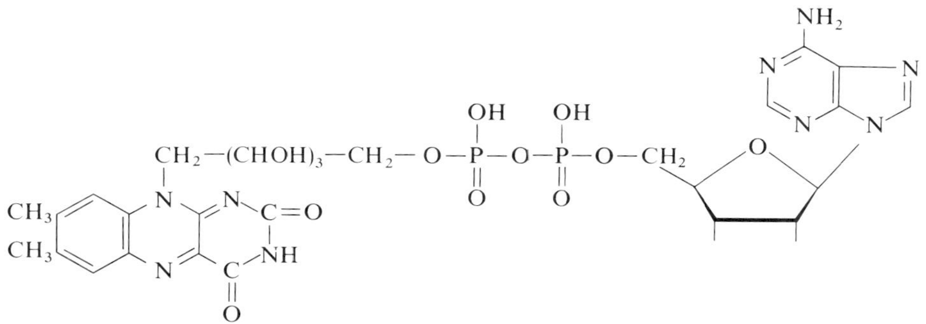

Hydrogen transfer

Hydrogen and acyl group transfer

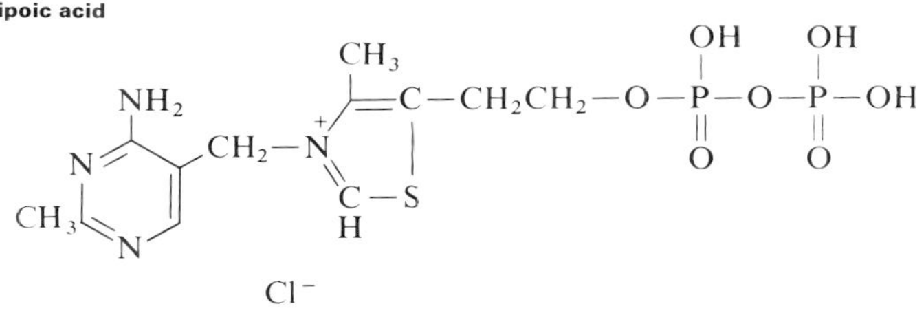

Decarboxylation

Thiamin

Pyridoxine

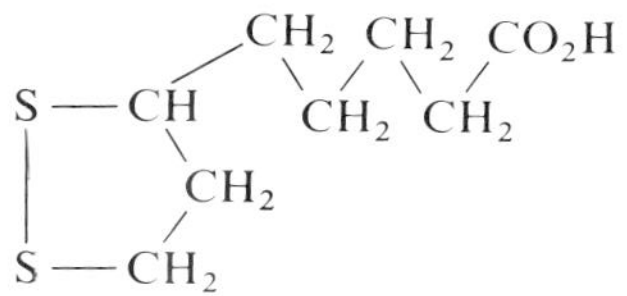

Decarboxylation: others

NH$_2$

CH$_2$—(CHOH)$_3$—CH$_2$—O—P—O—P—O—CH$_2$

flavin adenine dinucleotide (FAD)

CH$_3$

CH$_3$

lipoic acid

CH$_2$ CH$_2$ CO$_2$H

CH$_2$ CH$_2$

CH$_2$

S—CH   CH$_2$

S—CH$_2$

thiamin pyrophosphate

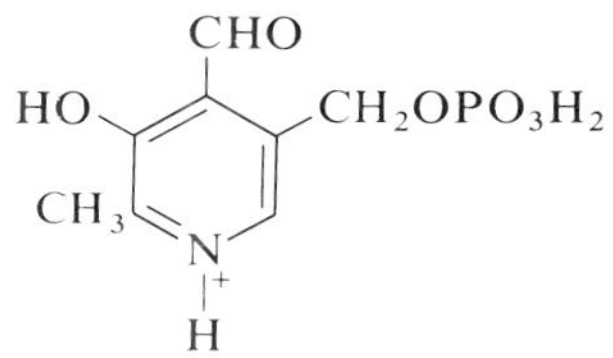

NH$_2$

CH$_2$—N

CH$_3$

C—CH$_2$CH$_2$—O—P—O—P—OH

OH   OH

Cl$^-$

pyridoxal phosphate

CHO   CH$_2$OPO$_3$H$_2$

HO

CH$_3$ N$^+$

H

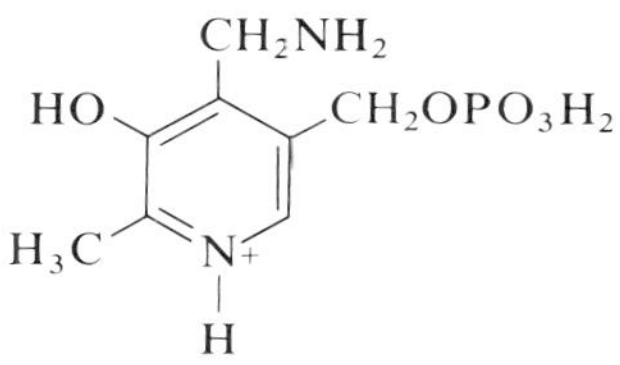

pyridoxamine phosphate

CH$_2$NH$_2$ CH$_2$OPO$_3$H$_2$

HO

H$_3$C   N$^+$

H

119

table 6.4 :: (continued)

STRUCTURE AND NAME	VITAMIN	FUNCTION
biotin	Biotin	Carboxylation
coenzyme A (HS—CoA)	Pantothenic acid	Acyl group transfer
tetrahydrofolic acid	Folic acid	Formyl group transfer

biotin:

$$\text{O=C} \begin{matrix} \text{HN} & \text{NH} \\ | & | \\ \text{HC} & \text{CH} \\ | & | \\ \text{H}_2\text{C} & \text{S} \end{matrix} \text{CH—(CH}_2)_4\text{CO}_2\text{H}$$

coenzyme A (HS—CoA):

$$\text{OPO}_3\text{H}_2$$
$$\text{CH}_2\text{—O—P—O—P—O—CH}_2\text{CCHOHCNHCH}_2\text{CH}_2\text{CNHCH}_2\text{CH}_2\text{SH}$$

tetrahydrofolic acid:

$$\text{C—NH—CH—CO}_2\text{H}$$

references ::

BOYER, P. D., H. LARDY, AND K. MYRBACK, eds., *The Enzymes*, Vols. I–VIII. New York: Academic Press, Inc., 1959–1963.

DIXON, M., AND E. C. WEBB, *Enzymes* (2nd ed.). New York: Academic Press, Inc., 1964.

HUTCHINSON, D. W., *Nucleotides and Coenzymes*. New York: John Wiley & Sons, Inc., 1965.

NEILANDS, J. B., AND P. K. SUMPF, *Outlines of Enzyme Chemistry* (2nd ed.). New York: John Wiley & Sons, Inc., 1958.

WAGNER, A. F., AND K. FOLKERS, *Vitamins and Coenzymes*. New York: Wiley-Interscience Publishers, 1964.

enzyme   :::
reactions   :::

7

ENZYME REACTIONS HAVE THEIR COUNTERPARTS IN ORDINARY organic reactions, and like organic reactions in general they fall under few categories according to the description of their mechanisms. Thus substitutions, additions, rearrangements, and eliminations are readily recognized among enzyme reactions. Although these categories indicate in broad terms the process that a substrate is undergoing, it tells us little about the mechanism of the reaction.

Despite the large number of known enzymes, the number of reactions is relatively small. This is so because for any given reaction there are dozens of enzymes each specific for a given substrate. But the reaction often can be described for all substrates in identical terms. For example, oxidation by loss of hydrogen is catalyzed by many enzymes, all functioning with the same carrier coenzyme NAD^+. Although the apoenzyme specifies which substrate is attacked, the NAD^+ accepts the hydrogen by the same mechanism from all the different substrates attacked.

Although it is possible to classify all enzyme reactions under the broad categories of organic reactions, other classifications are more appropriate, because quite often the exact mechanism of the enzyme reaction is not known. In the classification of enzymes given in Table 6.2, the transferases, hydrolases, and ligases belong mainly to substitution reactions and the lyases to elimination reactions. The oxidoreductases fall under substitution, addition, and elimination and the isomerases under rearrangement.

This section will deal with prototypes of enzyme reactions of wide scope, which are conveniently classified as oxidation-reduction, isomerization, hydrolysis, phosphorylation, acetylation, methylation, decarboxylation, and dehydration.

oxidation-reduction ::   7.1

One of the most common types of reaction in the living cell is the oxidation of substrates. By definition, oxidation occurs when a substance loses electrons and reduction when it gains electrons. Oxidation can occur in several ways, but in the cell the most common way is for the substrate to lose hydrogen, which is the same as saying that it loses a proton and an electron. This type of reaction is catalyzed by the dehydrogenases.

Other types of oxidation involve addition of oxygen to the substrate and withdrawal of electrons without protons. Examples of all three types are

$$CH_3CHOHCO_2H \longrightarrow 2H + CH_3COCO_2H$$

$$R-SO_2H + \tfrac{1}{2}O_2 \longrightarrow R-SO_3H$$

$$2FeCl_2 + Cl_2 \longrightarrow 2FeCl_3$$

$$(Fe^{2+} - e^- \longrightarrow Fe^{3+})$$

DEHYDROGENATION : Loss of hydrogen is catalyzed by a large group of dehydrogenases functioning in partnership with NAD^+ and less frequently with $NADP^+$—also by a group of enzymes known as flavoproteins, because they have a flavin prosthetic group (F). The NAD^+, $NADP^+$ enzymes, and the flavoproteins attack a large number of substrates, some of which are listed in Table 7.1.

There is a distinction between NAD^+ (or $NADP^+$) catalysis and flavoprotein catalysis: NAD^+ carries hydrogen from substrate AH_2 to substrate B with no immediate need for oxygen; flavoproteins, on the other hand, carry hydrogen from substrate

table 7.1 :: A few of the substrates attacked by dehydrogenases†

NAME	FORMULA	COFACTOR
Ethanol	CH_3CH_2OH	NAD^+
Lactic acid	$CH_3\overset{\displaystyle OH}{\underset{\displaystyle H}{C}}CO_2H$	NAD^+
Malic acid	$HO_2C\overset{\displaystyle OH}{\underset{\displaystyle H}{C}}CH_2CO_2H$	NAD^+
Isocitric acid	$HO_2C\overset{\displaystyle OH}{\underset{\displaystyle CO_2H}{C}}HCHCH_2CO_2H$	NAD^+ ($NADP^+$)
Glycerol	$HOH_2C\overset{\displaystyle OH}{\underset{\displaystyle H}{C}}CH_2OH$	NAD^+
Hydroxybutyric acid	$H_3C\overset{\displaystyle OH}{\underset{\displaystyle H}{C}}HCH_2CO_2H$	NAD^+
Glucose-6-phosphate	(cyclic structure) $C-C-C-C-CCH_2OPO_3H_2$ with O bridge, HO, OH H OH, H, H OH H H	$NADP^+$
Glutamic acid	$HO_2C(CH_2)_2\overset{\displaystyle HNH}{C}HCO_2H$	NAD^+ ($NADP^+$)
D-Amino acids	$R\overset{\displaystyle HNH}{C}HCO_2H$	FAD
Aldehydes (as hydrates)	$R-\overset{\displaystyle OH}{\underset{\displaystyle H}{C}}-OH$	FAD
Succinic acid	$HO_2C\overset{}{\underset{\displaystyle H}{C}}H\overset{}{\underset{\displaystyle H}{C}}HCO_2H$	FAD
Dihydrolipoic acid	$HS-$ ... R ... $HS-$	FAD

† The boldface H atoms are transferred.

AH$_2$ to oxygen directly as shown schematically by means of curved arrows:

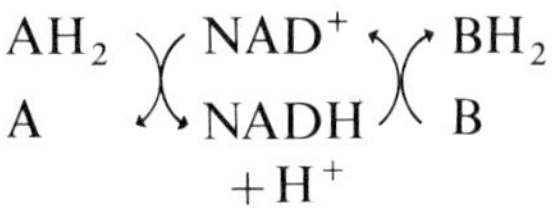

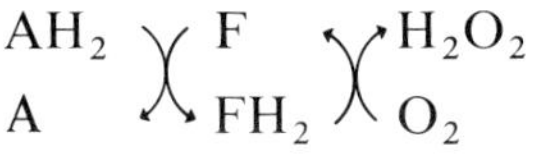

$$AH_2 \diagdown NAD^+ \diagdown BH_2$$
$$A \diagup NADH \diagup B$$
$$+H^+$$

$$AH_2 \diagdown F \diagdown H_2O_2$$
$$A \diagup FH_2 \diagup O_2$$

Curved arrows are used to represent the flow of hydrogen. They will be used in other cases to represent the flow of chemical groups and electrons.

The reduction of NAD$^+$ (or NADP$^+$) occurs in the pyridine ring of *niacinamide* (niacin is the name of the vitamin nicotinic acid; see the structure in Table 6.4):

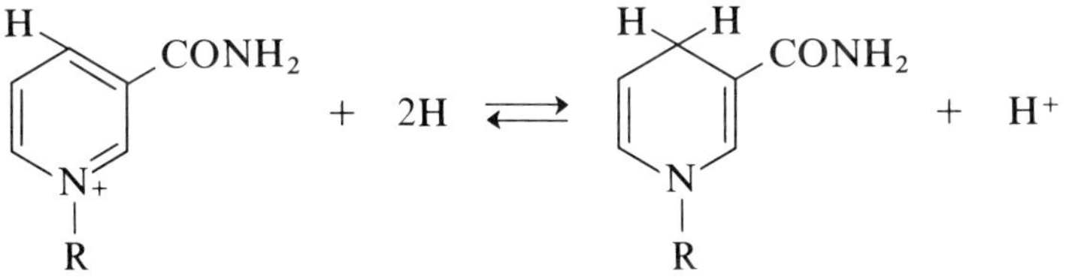

It has become customary to represent the oxidized form as NAD$^+$ and the reduced form as NADH + H$^+$.

The reduction of the pyridine ring is by the addition of a hydride ion (a hydrogen atom with an extra electron, H:) coming from the substrate; the other hydrogen, having lost its electron, is released to the medium as a proton. The reaction is shown here:

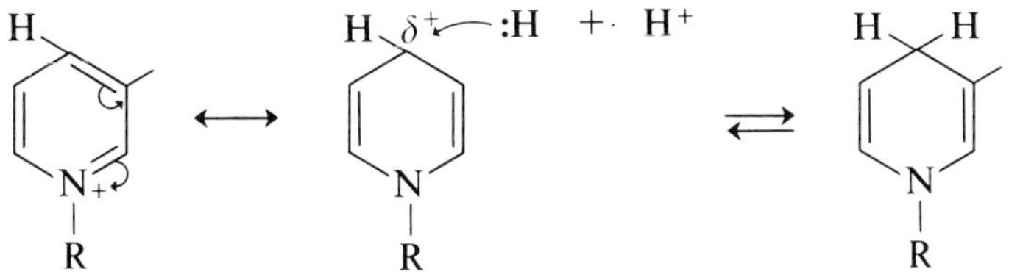

The reduction of the pyridine ring is accompanied by a loss of cyclic conjugation or aromatic character. The change is manifested in a change in the absorption spectrum, as shown in Figure 7.1.

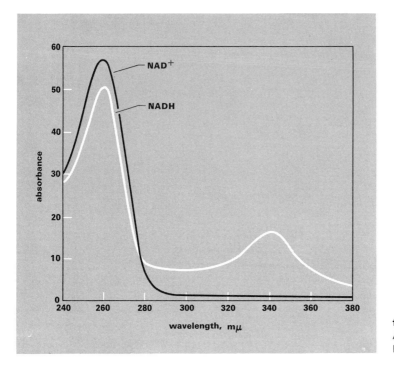

figure 7.1 :: Absorption spectra of NAD$^+$ and NADH.

In the flavoprotein dehydrogenases the flavin is reduced:

The reduction is accompanied by a loss of yellow color. The characteristic yellow of flavin enzymes is due to the system of conjugated double bonds seen in the oxidized form and lost upon reduction, as shown above.

As already noted, most dehydrogenases use NAD$^+$ or a flavin as the hydrogen carrier, but these are not the only known hydrogen carriers. Others, perhaps too specialized to be presented in a general discussion, will appear from time to time.

OXYGEN ADDITION : The names oxygenases and hydroxylases are applied to enzymes oxidizing substrates by the addition of oxygen. The oxygenases catalyze mainly cleavage of aromatic rings by addition of molecular oxygen, and the hydroxylases (as the name clearly indicates) catalyze specific hydroxylations of aromatic substances:

LOSS OF ELECTRONS : Still another—and very important—type of oxidation in the cell involves the withdrawal of electrons from a substrate without loss of protons. Put another way, the oxidation results from a change of valence.

Enzymes catalyzing this type of reaction are those with an iron-porphyrin prosthetic group: Cytochrome oxidase, for example, is an enzyme complex that catalyzes the transfer of electrons from cytochrome c to oxygen:

$$2Fe^{2+} + :\ddot{O}: \longrightarrow 2Fe^{3+} + (:\ddot{O}:)^{2-}$$

The resulting oxygen dianion combines with protons from the medium to form water. The involvement of protons in the reaction here is not the same as in the dehydrogenases.

A more detailed discussion of electron-transfer reactions is presented in Chapter 8.

isomerization :: 7.2

Isomerization is the same as rearrangement, a general type of reaction in which the change occurs only in the position of the atoms in the molecule. Enzymes have been described catalyzing the following types of rearrangements:

ENOLIZATION : The enolization of ketoses and aldoses is a reaction leading to their mutual interconversion in the cell. Fructose, for example, is readily converted to glucose or glucose to fructose. Enolizations of other substances in the cell proceed by identical mechanisms but, as expected, are catalyzed by different enzymes.

Since fructose and glucose exist in their hemiacetal ring structures, it is a prerequisite for the ring to open before enolization occurs. It is not known whether this step is enzymatic or not. But once the ring is open, the enzyme catalyzes the formation of an enediol anion:

$$
\begin{array}{c}
\text{H} \\
\text{H}-\overset{|}{\text{C}}-\text{OH} \\
\overset{|}{\text{C}}\!\!\stackrel{\frown}{=}\!\text{O} \\
\overset{|}{\text{R}}
\end{array}
\quad\rightleftharpoons\quad
\begin{array}{c}
\text{H}-\text{C}-\text{OH} \\
\|\\
\text{C}-\text{O}^- + \text{H}^+ \\
\overset{|}{\text{R}}
\end{array}
$$

The intermediate enediol anion can give rise to glucose:

$$
\begin{array}{c}
\text{H}-\text{C}-\text{OH} \\
\|\\
\text{C}-\text{O}^- \\
\overset{|}{\text{R}}
\end{array}
\rightleftharpoons
\begin{array}{c}
\text{HC}\!\!\stackrel{\frown}{-}\!\text{O}^{\backprime} \\
\overset{\|}{\text{C}}-\text{OH} \\
\overset{|}{\text{R}}
\end{array}
\longleftrightarrow
\begin{array}{c}
\text{H}-\text{C}=\text{O} \\
\overset{|}{{}^-\text{C}}-\text{OH} + \text{H}^+ \\
\overset{|}{\text{R}}
\end{array}
\rightleftharpoons
\begin{array}{c}
\text{H}-\text{C}=\text{O} \\
\text{H}-\overset{|}{\text{C}}-\text{OH} \\
\overset{|}{\text{R}}
\end{array}
$$

Although this mechanism illustrates the conversion of a ketose to an aldose, in enzyme reactions the substrates are usually the phosphate esters; thus the enzyme glucose phosphate isomerase catalyzes the interconversion of glucose-6-phosphate and fructose-6-phosphate.

INTRAMOLECULAR TRANSFER : The migration of a functional group of the substrate from one position to another in the molecule is well illustrated by the isomerization of some phosphoesters. An example of this reaction is the conversion of 3-phosphoglycerate to 2-phosphoglycerate[†]:

$$
\begin{array}{c}
\text{CO}_2\text{H} \\
\text{H}-\overset{|}{\text{C}}-\text{OH} \\
\overset{|}{\text{CH}_2\text{OPO}_3\text{H}_2}
\end{array}
\quad\rightleftharpoons\quad
\begin{array}{c}
\text{CO}_2\text{H} \\
\text{H}-\overset{|}{\text{C}}-\text{OPO}_3\text{H}_2 \\
\overset{|}{\text{CH}_2\text{OH}}
\end{array}
$$

The reaction in this particular instance is catalyzed by phosphoglycerate phosphomutase. To explain this rearrangement it was necessary to invoke the formation of an intermediate: either 2,3-diphosphoglycerate acting as cofactor or a phosphorylated enzyme intermediate. Although there is no sufficient evidence for a phosphorylated enzyme intermediate, it still remains a distinct possibility. The necessity for a diphosphoglycerate as a cofactor

† It is accepted biochemical terminology to designate acids as their salts because, at the pH of the cell, they are ionized. Thus lactic acid becomes lactate, citric acid citrate, etc., even when written in the undissociated form.

leads to a possible mechanism for its role as illustrated here:

$$
\begin{array}{ccc}
\begin{array}{c} CO_2H \\ | \\ H-C-OH \\ | \\ CH_2OPO_3H_2 \end{array} & \longrightarrow & \begin{array}{c} CO_2H \\ | \\ H-C-OPO_3H_2 \\ | \\ CH_2OPO_3H_2 \end{array} \\
+ & & + \\
\begin{array}{c} CO_2H \\ | \\ H-C-OPO_3H_2 \\ | \\ CH_2OPO_3H_2 \end{array} & \longrightarrow & \begin{array}{c} CO_2H \\ | \\ H-C-OPO_3H_2 \\ | \\ CH_2OH \end{array}
\end{array}
$$

Thus the cofactor becomes the product and the original substrate molecule regenerates the cofactor.

EPIMERIZATION : Changes in configuration of stereoisomers are known for some sugar derivatives and amino acids. The name *racemase* is reserved for enzymes catalyzing the change of configuration of substrates with a single asymmetric center. The name *epimerase* is used for enzymes catalyzing the change of configuration of substrates with several asymmetric centers.

A prototype of racemization is the change of L-alanine to D-alanine catalyzed by alanine racemase. The enzyme has pyridoxal phosphate as a prosthetic group, which is responsible for the reaction. In Section 7.7 the mechanism of pyridoxal action is given in detail. Here it is sufficient to say that when alanine reacts with the pyridoxal of the enzyme the bonds about the α carbon of alanine are labilized; thus the hydrogen can be eliminated as a proton:

$$
\begin{array}{ccc}
\begin{array}{c} CO_2H \\ | \\ Pyr^+=N-CH \\ | \\ CH_3 \end{array} & \overset{-H^+}{\rightleftharpoons} & \begin{array}{c} CO_2H \\ | \\ Pyr^+=N-C \\ | \\ CH_3 \end{array} \quad \longleftrightarrow \quad \begin{array}{c} CO_2H \\ | \\ Pyr-N=C \\ | \\ CH_3 \end{array}
\end{array}
$$

The temporary abolition of the center of asymmetry results from the rearrangement shown above, and this is attended by racemization.

Epimerization of sugar derivatives (sugar nucleotides) is not well understood. For example, uridine diphosphate (UDP)-galactose† is converted to UDP-glucose† by the action of an epimerase:

† The complete structures are presented in Section 10.4.

The conversion, which resembles a Walden inversion, has also been explained as resulting from abolition of the asymmetry at C_4 by oxidation or dehydration. The reintroduction of the —OH group can lead to change in configuration.

cis-trans INTERCONVERSION : Geometric isomers are interconverted enzymatically in some instances. These reactions are not too common, but one of great importance for its role in vision is illustrated here: the conversion of Δ^{11}-*cis* retinene to all-*trans* retinene:

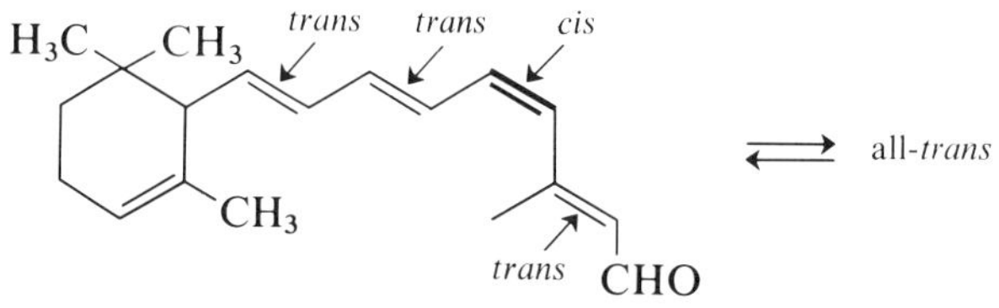

hydrolysis :: 7.3

Next to oxidation-reduction, hydrolysis is the most common enzymatic reaction known. Substrates undergoing hydrolysis include not only the macromolecules—proteins, nucleic acids, and polysaccharides—but such widely diverse substances as arginine, sucrose, fats, glutamine, and many more.

The hydrolysis of macromolecules, when it occurs outside the cell, is catalyzed by the digestive enzymes. Organisms normally do not assimilate macromolecules; they first cleave them into their component units, and in the case of proteins the amino acids are reassembled into definite protein structures according to a pattern prescribed by the genes.

Bonds attacked by the hydrolases include the peptide, glycosidic, phosphoester, acyl ester, anhydride, amide, and others. Representatives of each group are listed in Table 7.2.

phosphorylation :: 7.4

ATP and other nucleoside triphosphates occupy a unique position in the cell. ATP, especially, serves as a reservoir of chemical-bond energy that can be converted into other forms of energy. Most synthetic reactions in the cell are driven by ATP (see the structure in Chapter 2).

table 7.2 :: Representative enzyme reactions catalyzing hydrolysis

BOND SPLIT	TYPE OF ENZYME	PRODUCT
R R | | —HNCH**CONH**CHCO— ↑	Endopeptidase	Polypeptides
R R | | H₂NCH**CONH**CHCO— ↑	Aminopeptidase	An amino acid + polypeptide
R R | | —HNCH**CONH**CHCO₂H ↑	Carboxypeptidase	An amino acid + polypeptide
—O O _O_↑/ _O—	Glycosidases	Oligo- and mono- saccharides
OH | HO—P—O—R || ↑ O	Phosphatases	Phosphate + R
OH ↓ | R—O—P—O—R′ || ↑ O	Nucleases	Ribo- and deoxyribo- nucleotide
O || R—C—O—R ↑	Esterases	Acids and alcohols
O || R—C—S—CoA ↑	Thiolesterases	Acids + HS-CoA
O || R—C—NH₂ ↑	Amidases	Acids + NH₃

In the organism ATP is formed by the phosphorylation of ADP (adenosine diphosphate):

$$
\text{Adenosine} - \text{O} - \overset{\overset{\displaystyle \text{OH}}{|}}{\underset{\underset{\displaystyle \text{O}}{\|}}{\text{P}}} - \text{O} - \overset{\overset{\displaystyle \text{OH}}{|}}{\underset{\underset{\displaystyle \text{O}}{\|}}{\text{P}}} - \text{OH} + H_3PO_4
$$

ADP

$$\updownarrow$$

$$
\text{Adenosine} - \text{O} - \overset{\overset{\displaystyle \text{OH}}{|}}{\underset{\underset{\displaystyle \text{O}}{\|}}{\text{P}}} - \text{O} - \overset{\overset{\displaystyle \text{OH}}{|}}{\underset{\underset{\displaystyle \text{O}}{\|}}{\text{P}}} - \text{O} - \overset{\overset{\displaystyle \text{OH}}{|}}{\underset{\underset{\displaystyle \text{O}}{\|}}{\text{P}}} - \text{OH} + H_2O
$$

ATP

The formation of ATP from ADP + H_3PO_4 requires energy (endergonic reaction), whereas its hydrolysis is attended by a large decrease in free energy (exergonic). The free energy of hydrolysis of ATP, for example, is about 7 kcal/mole, which is unusually high for a phosphoester. Because of its high free energy of hydrolysis, ATP and similar compounds are called *energy-rich compounds*.

Phosphorylation of substrates is an important reaction in the organism; ATP is the main phosphorylating agent functioning with specific enzymes called *kinases*. Some substrates, which normally undergo phosphorylation in the cell, are listed in Table 7.3.

▪ *Chemical equilibrium and free energy.* In Chapter 6 we have seen that the equilibrium constant (K_{eq}) is a measure of the extent to which substances react. Put another way, it is a measure of chemical affinity. Here we shall see how K_{eq} is related to the change in free energy and how it can be used to calculate the free energy of a reaction.

Absolute values of free energy are not generally measured, but in thermodynamics one does measure the change in free energy in passing from an initial state to a final state. When a reactant A passes to product B, there is a change in free energy represented by ΔF (the term ΔG is also widely used, but we shall continue using ΔF).

When the free-energy content of the product B is less than the free-energy content of reactant A, ΔF is negative ($-\Delta F$); the reaction is exergonic and ΔF is available to do work or to be released as heat or both. But if the free-energy content of product B is greater than the free-energy content of reactant A, ΔF is positive ($+\Delta F$); the reaction is endergonic and it absorbs energy to proceed.

The equilibrium constant K_{eq} is related to the change in free energy by one of the most useful equations in chemistry:

$$\Delta F^0 = -RT \ln K_{eq}$$

table 7.3 :: Examples of phosphorylation by ATP

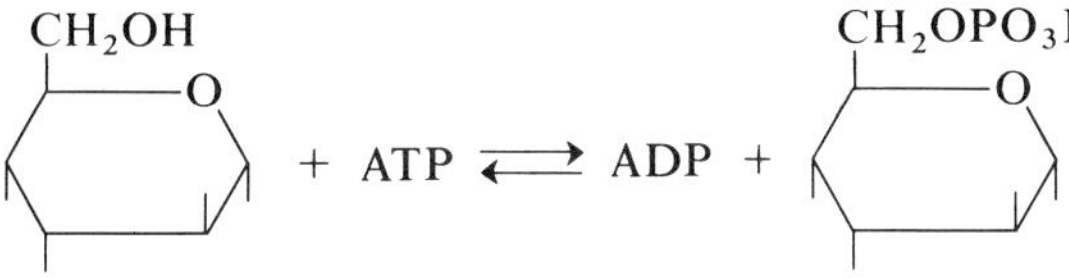

$$\text{(glucose ring with } CH_2OH) + ATP \rightleftarrows ADP + \text{(ring with } CH_2OPO_3H_2)$$

glucose

$$\begin{matrix} CH_2OH \\ | \\ HCOH \\ | \\ CH_2OH \end{matrix} + ATP \rightleftarrows ADP + \begin{matrix} CH_2OPO_3H_2 \\ | \\ HCOH \\ | \\ CH_2OH \end{matrix}$$

glycerol

$$(CH_3)_3N^+CH_2CH_2OH + ATP \rightleftarrows ADP + (CH_3)_3N^+CH_2CH_2OPO_3H_2$$

choline

$$\begin{matrix} CH_3 \\ | \\ CO \\ | \\ CO_2H \end{matrix} + ATP \rightleftarrows ADP + \begin{matrix} CH_2 \\ \| \\ C-OPO_3H_2 \\ | \\ CO_2H \end{matrix}$$

pyruvate

$$\begin{matrix} CH_3 \\ | \\ CO_2H \end{matrix} + ATP \rightleftarrows ADP + \begin{matrix} CH_3 \\ | \\ C-OPO_3H_2 \\ \| \\ O \end{matrix}$$

acetate

$$HO_2CCH_2-\overset{\overset{\displaystyle CH_3}{|}}{N}\underset{\underset{\displaystyle NH}{\overset{\|}{C}}}{}NH_2 + ATP \rightleftarrows ADP + HO_2CCH_2-\overset{\overset{\displaystyle CH_3}{|}}{N}\underset{\underset{\displaystyle NH}{\overset{\|}{C}}}{}NH-PO_3H_2$$

creatine

$$H_2O_3POCH_2\text{(ribose ring)}B + ATP \rightleftarrows ADP + H_3O_6P_2OCH_2\text{(ribose ring)}B$$

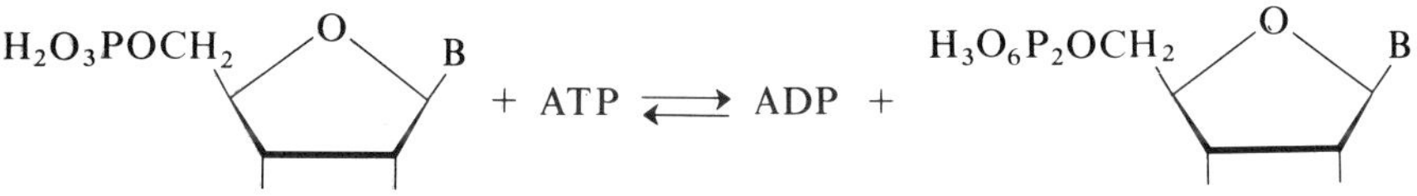

a nucleotide

in which R is the gas constant (1.987 cal/mole-°C),† T the absolute temperature, and K_{eq} the equilibrium constant. ΔF^0 (not to be confused with ΔF) refers
to a reaction in which the reactants in their *standard states*, 1 mole/liter for
solutions, are converted into products in their standard states (1 mole/liter).

Let us consider how K_{eq} will determine whether a reaction is exergonic or
endergonic. First, let us assume a situation in which equilibrium is attained
when both reactants and products are at unit concentration (activity rather
than concentration is used for exact calculations). Then in this hypothetical
reaction

$$A \rightleftarrows B \quad K_{eq} = \frac{B}{A} = \frac{1}{1} = 1 \quad \text{and} \quad \Delta F^0 = -RT \ln 1 = 0$$

But now let us consider a reaction in which equilibrium is attained at
27°C when the concentration of B is 10 times the concentration of A:

$$\frac{B}{A} = K_{eq} = \frac{10}{1} \qquad \begin{aligned} \Delta F^0 &= -RT \ln K_{eq} \\ &= -2 \times 300 \times 2.3 \log 10 \\ &= -1{,}380 \log 10 = -1{,}380 \text{ cal} \end{aligned}$$

Because K_{eq} is relatively large, the reactants at unit concentration tend to
react to give products at unit concentration. The reaction is exergonic.

Now let us consider a third possibility, in which equilibrium is attained
when the concentration of B is 10 times less than the concentration of A:

$$\frac{B}{A} = K_{eq} = \frac{1}{10} \qquad \begin{aligned} \Delta F^0 &= -RT \ln K \\ &= -2 \times 300 \times 2.3 \log 0.1 \\ &= -1{,}380 \log 0.1 = +1{,}380 \text{ cal} \end{aligned}$$

Because K_{eq} is relatively small, reactants at unit concentration have no
tendency to react to give products at unit concentration unless 1,380 cal are
absorbed. The reaction is endergonic.

So far we have only discussed situations in which both reactants and
products are at unit concentrations (standard states). This is a situation not
likely to be found in living systems, where concentrations of reactants are
totally different. In this case a more general equation can be used:

$$\Delta F = \Delta F^0 + RT \ln \frac{[B]}{[A]}$$

where the brackets represent concentrations. In the last example ΔF^0 was
positive; this means that at unit concentration A cannot go to B at unit
concentration spontaneously.

---

† For subsequent calculations this figure is rounded to 2.

But it is still possible to convert A to B by increasing the concentration of A. Let us assume that the concentration of A has been increased where it is 20 times the concentration of B:

$$\Delta F = \Delta F^0 + RT \ln \frac{[B]}{[A]}$$
$$= 1{,}380 + 2 \times 300 \times 2.3 \log \tfrac{1}{20}$$
$$= 1{,}380 + 1{,}380(-1.301)$$
$$= 1{,}380 - 1{,}795 = -415 \text{ cal}$$

ΔF under these conditions is negative, meaning that the reaction can take place spontaneously. Generally by increasing substantially the concentration of reactants, it is possible for a reaction to proceed notwithstanding its positive ΔF^0. By simple inspection of equilibrium constants it is possible to distinguish between exergonic and endergonic reactions.

When a substance such as ATP hydrolyses, the free energy of reaction is 7 kcal. This is, of course, lost as heat and no useful work is done. Organisms have developed systems to convert the potential energy in ATP into other forms of energy. For example, the energy stored in ATP can be utilized to drive endergonic reactions; we speak in this case of coupled reactions. This can be illustrated by two hypothetical reactions having a common intermediate:

$$A \rightleftarrows B \qquad K_{eq} = 0.01 \qquad\qquad\qquad (7.1)$$

$$B \rightleftarrows C \qquad K_{eq} = 1{,}000 \qquad\qquad\qquad (7.2)$$

B is common to the two reactions; it is a product of the first and the reactant of the second reaction. By simple inspection of the values of K_{eq} we can state that Equation (7.1) is endergonic and Equation (7.2) exergonic. Because they share an intermediate, the energy of the second reaction can be utilized to drive the first. A simple calculation will show how:

$$\Delta F^0 = -RT \ln 0.01 = -1{,}380 \log 0.01$$
$$= 2{,}760 \text{ cal} \qquad\qquad (7.3)$$

$$\Delta F^0 = -RT \ln 1{,}000 = -1{,}380 \log 1{,}000$$
$$= -4{,}140 \text{ cal} \qquad\qquad (7.4)$$

The free energy of Equation (7.4) is more than adequate to drive Equation (7.3). The overall process goes spontaneously with a change of free energy of $-1{,}380$ cal $(2{,}760 - 4{,}140)$.

High-energy compounds. The most important coupling mechanism in living systems is through the formation of ATP and other energy-rich compounds listed in Table 7.4.

The term *energy-rich* has been adopted arbitrarily to designate substances with free energies of hydrolysis of over 5 kcal. The bonds hydrolyzed are represented by the sign $\sim$, as shown in the formulas of Table 7.4, and are called energy-rich (or high-energy) bonds. The term energy-rich bond is not to be confused with *bond energy*, a term used in physical chemistry to describe the energy necessary to break a bond. It takes energy to break chemical bonds (80.5 kcal/mole to break a C—C bond).

The biochemical meaning of energy-rich bond is synonymous with chemical potential. The free energy of hydrolysis listed in Table 7.4 represents the changes of free energy when chemical groups such as the terminal phosphate of ATP is transferred to water. All values listed can be compared because they are based on a common acceptor, water. The change in free energy when the terminal phosphate group of ATP is transferred to another acceptor will depend also on the nature of the acceptor molecule. For these reasons the term *group-transfer potential* has been suggested to describe the chemical potential of compounds such as ATP in displacement or "transfer" reactions.

What gives energy-rich compounds their high group-transfer potential is a matter that has received considerable attention, but only a brief discussion is possible here. Let us first compare the stability of ATP with the stability of the component molecules such as phosphate.

table 7.4 Energy-rich compounds and free energies of hydrolysis

TYPE AND EXAMPLE	REACTION	$-\Delta F^0$, KCAL/MOLE
Pyrophosphate	$\mathbf{P} \sim \mathbf{P} \rightleftarrows P_i + P_i$†	6
Nucleoside diphosphates (ADP)	adenosine-$\mathbf{P} \sim \mathbf{P} \rightleftarrows$ adenosine-$\mathbf{P} + P_i$	6
Nucleoside triphosphates (ATP)	adenosine-$\mathbf{P} \sim \mathbf{P} \sim \mathbf{P} \rightleftarrows$ adenosine-$\mathbf{P} \sim \mathbf{P} + P_i$	7
Enolphosphates (phosphoenolpyruvate)	$CH_2{=}C{-}O{\sim}\mathbf{P} \rightleftarrows P_i + CH_3{-}C{=}O$ with CO_2H groups	12
Guanidinium (creatine phosphate)	creatine phosphate structure $\rightleftarrows P_i + $ creatine structure	8
Thioesters (acetyl-CoA)	$CH_3\overset{O}{\overset{\|}{C}}{\sim}SCoA \rightleftarrows CH_3\overset{O}{\overset{\|}{C}}OH + HSCo$	8

† P_i represents an inorganic phosphate, PP_i an inorganic pyrophosphate. For the sake of convenience in some structures, $-PO_3H_2$ is abbreviated to $\mathbf{P}-$, pyrophosphate to $\mathbf{P} \sim \mathbf{P}-$, and triphosphate to $\mathbf{P} \sim \mathbf{P} \sim \mathbf{P}-$.

Free phosphate gains stability through resonance. When more than one structure can be assigned to a compound none truly represents the compound. The compound is represented by a hybrid of all the structures; for example, phosphate can be represented by many structures, some of which are shown here†:

$$HO-\overset{\overset{O^-}{|}}{\underset{\underset{O_-}{|}}{P}}=O \longleftrightarrow HO-\overset{\overset{O}{\|}}{\underset{\underset{O_-}{|}}{P}}-O^- \longleftrightarrow HO-\overset{\overset{O^-}{|}}{\underset{\underset{O}{\|}}{P}}-O^- \quad etc.$$

The oxygens in the phosphate are equivalent because electrons between atoms are delocalized. The more resonance structures are possible for a compound, the more stable it is.

When phosphate is in combination as in pyrophosphate, the number of possible resonance structures is severely restricted, since the bridge oxygen cannot participate and stability decreases:

$$HO-\overset{\overset{O}{\|}}{\underset{\underset{O_-}{|}}{P}}-O-\overset{\overset{O^-}{|}}{\underset{\underset{O}{\|}}{P}}-O^- \longleftrightarrow HO-\overset{\overset{O}{\|}}{\underset{\underset{O_-}{|}}{P}}-O-\overset{\overset{O}{\|}}{\underset{\underset{O_-}{|}}{P}}-O^- \quad etc.$$

resonance structures

The same argument is used for the restriction of resonance in ATP and all other energy-rich compounds. But resonance restriction is not the only factor that imparts instability and high chemical potential to these compounds. To go into other factors is beyond the scope of this book. ▪

acetylation :: **7.5**

Acetylations in the organism have been known for a long time, but the mechanism of the process has been described only recently.

Biological acetylations are made possible by a number of specific enzymes functioning with coenzyme A (structure in Table 6.4). Although the structure of coenzyme A is complex, all reactions can be described by dealing only with the —SH group of the coenzyme. In a simplified way coenzyme A can be written HSCoA.

The function of coenzyme A is that of a true carrier; it is acetylated by complex reactions that will appear in other sections of this book. The acetyl derivative, $CH_3COSCoA$, is an excellent acetylating agent functioning together with specific enzymes.

† The sign ↔ is used to indicate resonating structures; it should never be confused with the sign ⇌ used to represent reversible reactions.

The acetylation of a substrate R is usually accompanied by the release of coenzyme A, which can again be acetylated:

$$CH_3COSCoA \diagdown R$$
$$HSCoA \diagup \diagdown RCOCH_3$$

The reactivity of acetyl-CoA is attributed to its thioester nature. Thioesters unlike oxygen esters are unstable and reactive. The acetyl group in thioesters has a strong ketonic character, making them good acetylating agents:

$$CH_3 \overset{\delta^+}{-} \overset{\delta^-}{C} - S - CoA$$
$$\underset{\underset{\delta^-}{O}}{\|}$$

The carbonyl carbon becomes a good center for nucleophilic attack by such nucleophiles as amines, alcohols, and others.

Activation of the CH_3- of acetyl-CoA results in the dissociation of a hydrogen, producing an anion:

$$H \overset{\frown}{-} CH_2 - \underset{\underset{O}{\|}}{C} - S - CoA \rightleftharpoons \bar{C}H_2 - \underset{\underset{O}{\|}}{C} - S - CoA + H^+$$

The anion enters into condensation reactions with a number of substrates, leading to synthetic reactions such as elongation of the chain of fatty acids and formation of citrate.

The free energy of hydrolysis of acetyl-CoA is very large; for this reason it is also called an energy-rich compound.

Acetyl-CoA is not the only active thioester known in biological systems. Succinyl-CoA and malonyl-CoA are also formed enzymatically and both participate in biosynthetic reactions.

methylation :: **7.6**

Enzymatic methylations are made possible by sulfonium S-adenosyl methionine, a product of an enzyme reaction between methionine and ATP:

$$\begin{array}{c} NH_2 \\ | \\ HCCH_2CH_2-S \\ | \qquad | \\ CO_2H \qquad CH_3 \end{array} + \text{adenosine} -P \sim P \sim P \longrightarrow$$

methionine   **ATP**

$$\downarrow$$

$$\begin{array}{c} NH_2 \\ | \\ HCCH_2CH_2-\overset{+}{S}-\text{adenosine} + P_i + PP_i \\ | \qquad | \\ CO_2H \qquad CH_3 \end{array}$$

S-adenosylmethionine

S-adenosylmethionine is often called *active methyl* and is known to react with several substrates under the influence of specific enzymes (Table 7.5, page 140).

The methylation of a suitable substrate yields, in addition to the methylated product, the demethylated S-adenosylmethionine called S-adenosylhomocysteine (AHC). The latter serves as a methyl-group acceptor from other compounds, and in this regard it may be considered a carrier coenzyme transferring methyl groups from a substrate A to substrate B:

$$H_3CA \diagdown \diagup AHC \qquad \diagdown \diagup BCH_3$$
$$CH_3$$
$$A \diagup \diagdown AHC \qquad \diagup \diagdown B$$

The situation is not quite as simple as it seems, because suitable methylated substrates that react with AHC are not very common. Also, methyl groups are synthesized in the cell by a complex sequence of reactions involving the intervention of several enzymes and cofactors.

decarboxylation :: **7.7**

Decarboxylation entails the cleavage of C—C bonds, releasing carbon dioxide. Some substrates can decarboxylate nonenzymatically, as is the case with oxalacetate, but most do it by the action of specific enzymes. The keto acids, which are the main source of the carbon dioxide produced in the cell, are decarboxylated mainly by enzymes with thiamine pyrophosphate. On the other hand, amino acids are decarboxylated by enzymes with pyridoxal phosphate.

Because the thiamine enzymes and the pyridoxal enzymes function according to general mechanisms, the present discussion will not be limited to decarboxylation but will include other reactions catalyzed by the same proposed mechanisms.

table 7.5 :: Common substrates methylated enzymatically by S-adenosyl-methionine (S-AM)

nicotinamide → N-methyl nicotinamide

serotonin
(5-hydroxytryptamine) → N-methyl serotonin

guanidoacetate + S-AM → creatine

$$CH_2OOCR$$
$$CHOOCR$$
$$CH_2-O-P-O-CH_2CH_2NH_2 \quad + S\text{-}AM \longrightarrow R^{\dagger}-CH_2CH_2NHCH_3$$

phosphatidyl ethanolamine → monomethyl phosphatidyl ethanolamine

$$R-CH_2CH_2NHCH_3 + S\text{-}AM \longrightarrow R-CH_2CH_2NH^+(CH_3)_2$$

dimethyl phosphatidyl ethanolamine

$$R-CH_2CH_2N(CH_3)_2 + S\text{-}AM \longrightarrow R-CH_2CH_2N^+(CH_3)_3$$

choline

† R represents the boldface portion of the formula.

THIAMINE ENZYMES : In Table 6.2 the structure of thiamine pyrophosphate was given. It is a prosthetic group for several enzymes, among which are some α-keto acid decarboxylases. The reactive portion of the thiamine molecule resides in the thiazole ring.

Thiamine catalysis has been explained by assuming the formation of a stable anion attached to the apoenzyme (only the thiazole ring of thiamine is shown):

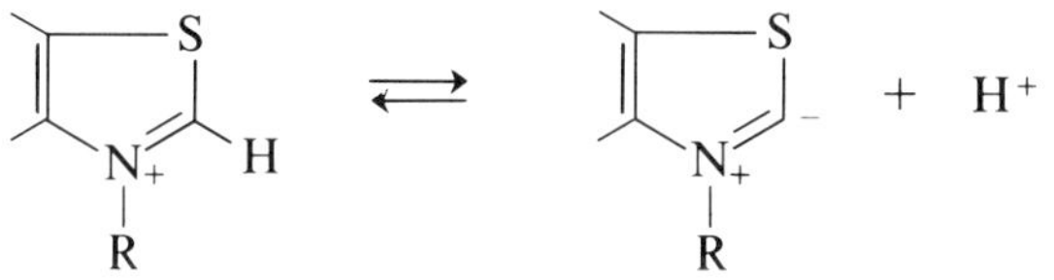

Evidence for the ionization of the thiazole ring has been obtained by showing that in heavy water (D_2O) there is exchange of D for H.

To illustrate a possible mechanism of decarboxylation, let us consider the decarboxylation of pyruvate:

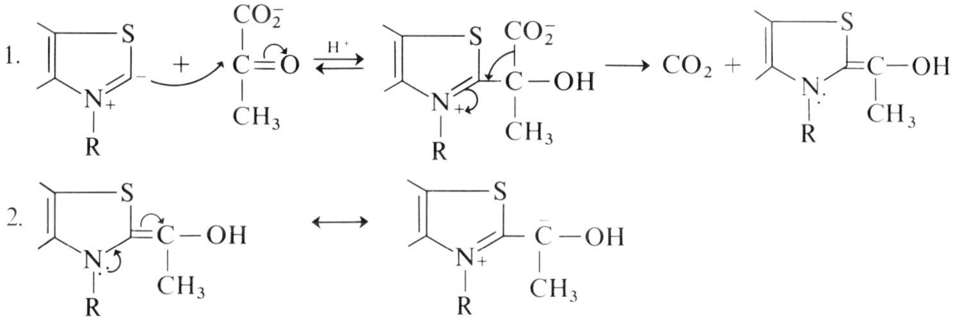

Intermediate (2) is called *active acetaldehyde* and is formed from pyruvate by the action of pyruvate decarboxylase. It can undergo several reactions, one of which is shown here:

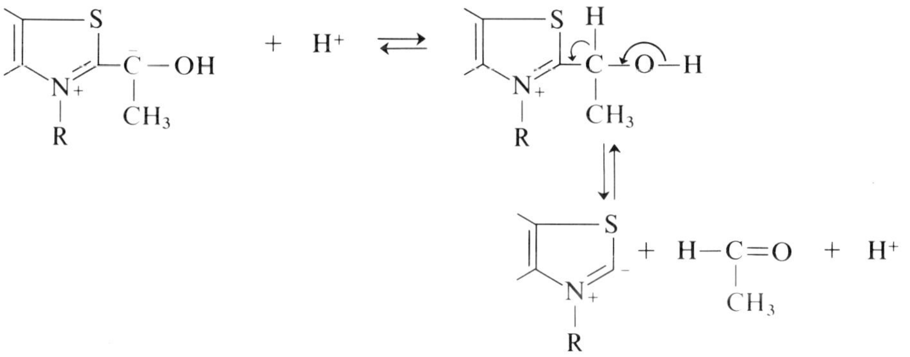

Another C—C bond cleavage is catalyzed by the enzyme trans-ketolase by a mechanism similar to that described for decarboxylation. The reaction involves the cleavage of a ketol group from suitable substrates and condensation to an aldehyde:

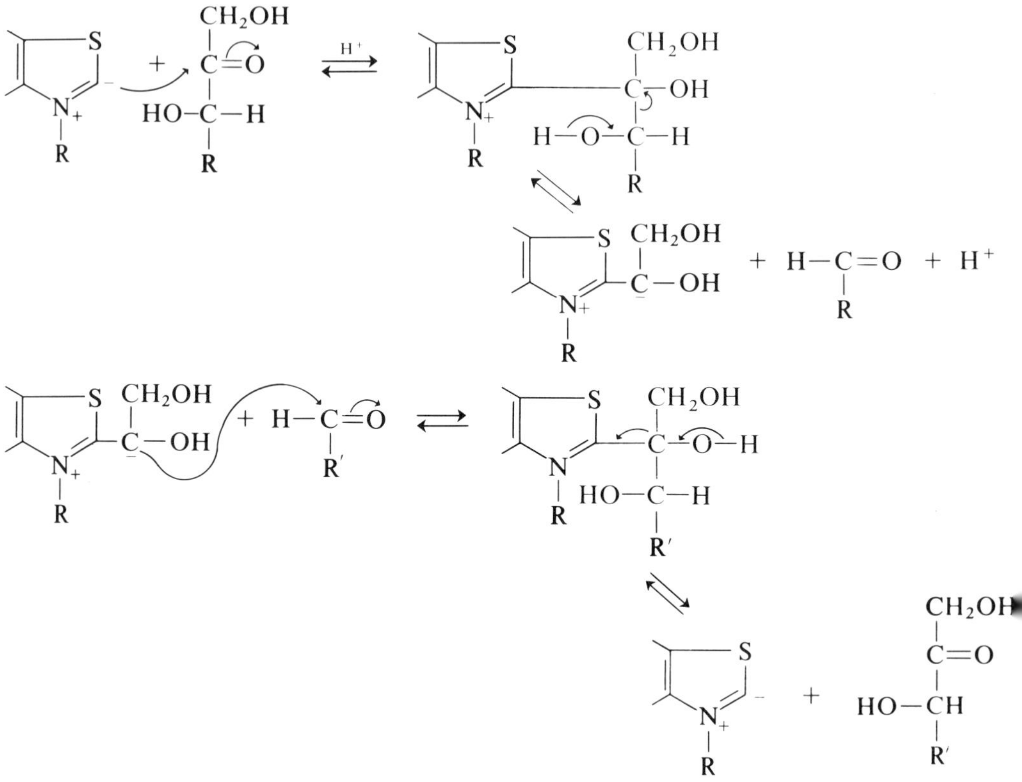

Several enzymes having thiamine pyrophosphate as prosthetic group react specifically and in a manner dictated by the nature of the apoenzyme or protein portion. The same situation is observed with pyridoxal enzymes, as will be shown next.

PYRIDOXAL ENZYMES : Nearly all pyridoxal enzymes catalyze reactions of amino acids: racemization, decarboxylation, transamination, elimination of substituents, and others. All the reactions can be described by the same mechanism and, as is the case with other enzymes sharing the same prosthetic group, the apoenzyme determines which reaction will be catalyzed.

Pyridoxal phosphate is attached to the apoenzyme tightly; the aldehyde group of pyridoxal reacts with amino acids, forming a Schiff base:

$$\underset{\substack{\text{CH}_2\text{OPO}_3\text{H}_2}}{\overset{\text{CH}_3\quad\text{OH}}{\text{HN}}}\text{—CHO} \;+\; \underset{\text{R}}{\overset{\text{CO}_2\text{H}}{\text{H}_2\text{N}-\text{C}-\text{H}}} \;\rightleftharpoons\; \underset{\substack{\text{CH}_2\text{OPO}_3\text{H}_2}}{\overset{\text{CH}_3\quad\text{OH}}{\text{HN}}}\text{—CH}=\text{N}-\underset{\text{R}}{\overset{\text{CO}_2\text{H}}{\text{C}}}\text{—H}$$

The formation of a Schiff base between the enzyme's pyridoxal and substrate has been demonstrated spectrophotometrically.

As already mentioned for racemization, there is a shifting of electrons leading to labilization of all bonds around the α-carbon atom of the amino acid. For example, in racemization and trans-amination the α hydrogen dissociates:

$$\underset{\substack{\text{CH}_2\text{OPO}_3\text{H}_2}}{\overset{\text{CH}_3\quad\text{OH}}{\text{H}^+\text{N}}}\text{CH}=\text{N}-\underset{\text{R}}{\overset{\text{CO}_2\text{H}}{\text{C}}}\text{—H} \;\rightleftharpoons\; \underset{\substack{\text{CH}_2\text{OPO}_3\text{H}_2}}{\overset{\text{CH}_3\quad\text{OH}}{\text{HN}}}=\text{CH}-\text{N}=\underset{\text{R}}{\overset{\text{CO}_2\text{H}}{\text{C}}} \;+\; \text{H}^+$$

The temporary abolition of the center of asymmetry is responsible for the change in configuration in the racemase reaction.

Decarboxylation can be explained by a similar mechanism: weakening of the α C-carboxyl bond attended by the cleavage of CO_2:

$$\underset{\substack{\text{CH}_2\text{OPO}_3\text{H}_2}}{\overset{\text{CH}_3\quad\text{OH}}{\text{H}^+\text{N}}}\text{CH}=\text{N}-\underset{\text{R}}{\overset{\text{CO}_2\text{H}}{\text{C}}}\text{—H} \;\rightleftharpoons\; \underset{\substack{\text{CH}_2\text{OPO}_3\text{H}_2}}{\overset{\text{CH}_3\quad\text{OH}}{\text{HN}}}\text{CH}-\text{N}=\underset{\text{R}}{\text{CH}} \;+\; \text{CO}_2$$

$$\underset{\substack{\text{CH}_2\text{OPO}_3\text{H}_2}}{\overset{\text{CH}_3\quad\text{OH}}{\text{H}^+\text{N}}}\text{—CH}=\text{N}-\underset{\text{R}}{\text{CH}} + \text{H}_2\text{O} \;\rightleftharpoons\; \underset{\substack{\text{CH}_2\text{OPO}_3\text{H}_2}}{\overset{\text{CH}_3\quad\text{OH}}{\text{H}^+\text{N}}}\text{—CHO} + \underset{\text{R}}{\overset{\text{H}}{\text{H}_2\text{N}-\text{C}-\text{H}}}$$

The basis for the electron shift is the strong pull by the N of the pyridoxal, an effect transmitted to the α carbon by the system of conjugated double bonds.

Transamination is a well-known reaction between amino acids and keto acids. In general,

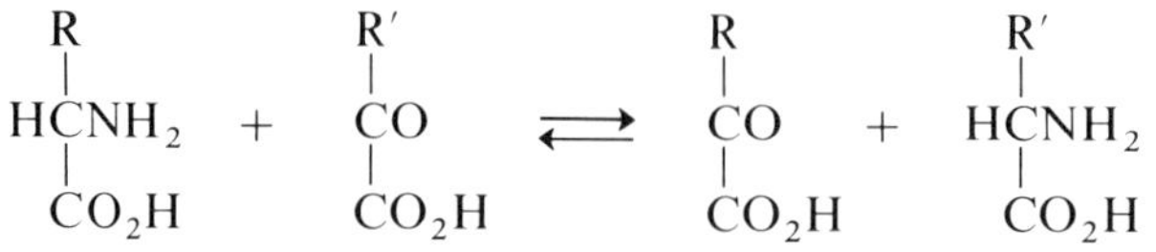

$$
\underset{\substack{|\\CO_2H}}{\overset{\substack{R\\|}}{HCNH_2}} + \underset{\substack{|\\CO_2H}}{\overset{\substack{R'\\|}}{CO}} \rightleftharpoons \underset{\substack{|\\CO_2H}}{\overset{\substack{R\\|}}{CO}} + \underset{\substack{|\\CO_2H}}{\overset{\substack{R'\\|}}{HCNH_2}}
$$

Note that the net effect is the amination of the keto acid to yield an amino acid while the amino acid becomes a keto acid. This reaction, of great importance biologically, is catalyzed by a pyridoxal enzyme and the mechanism is similar to racemization. The α hydrogen is eliminated as shown before, and the product reacts as follows:

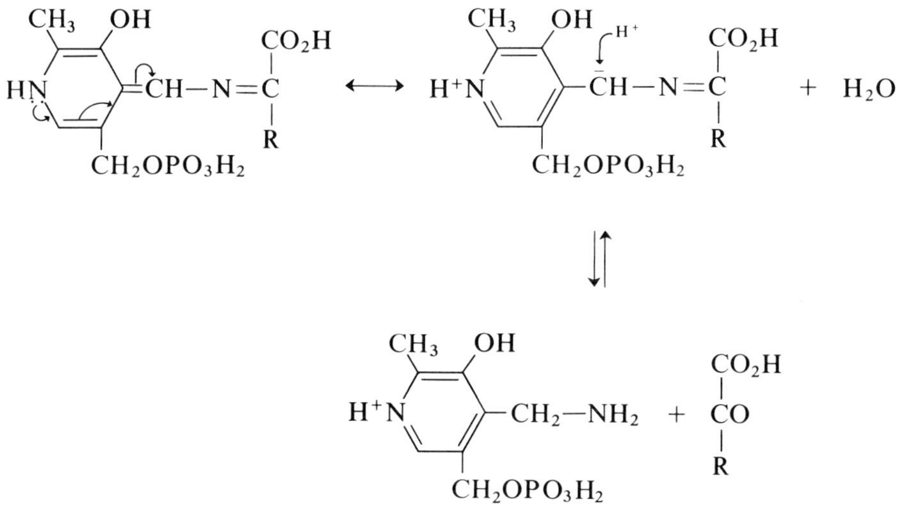

The intermediate adds a proton and hydrolyzes to yield a keto acid, while the prosthetic group is changed to pyridoxamine. In the presence of a second keto acid, the pyridoxamine enzyme reacts, forming a Schiff base, thus reversing the process and aminating the keto acid.

Transaminases are widely distributed; they attack a large number of amino acids, but the keto acids serving as substrates are more limited. In Table 7.6 are listed the better known transaminases, functioning with α-ketoglutarate as the amino-group acceptor.

dehydration :: **7.8**

Dehydration involves an elimination reaction leading to double-bond formation. The reversal—the addition of water to a double bond—is an example of an addition reaction. Enzymatic loss of water is stereospecific and so is the reverse reaction. We have already considered in Chapter 6 the stereospecific loss of water from L-malic acid to form fumaric acid and the reverse reaction.

The enzymes catalyzing loss of water (dehydrases) and those catalyzing addition of water (hydrases) cannot be grouped under one category on the basis of their coenzyme. Some are pyridoxal enzymes; others require Fe^{2+}, Mg^{2+}, or Mn^{2+} and —SH compounds. No unified mechanism for hydration-dehydration is known. In Table 7.7 are listed some known reactions in this category.

table 7.6 :: Widely distributed transamination reactions with α-ketoglutaric acid

AMINO ACID	PRODUCTS
$CH_3CH(NH_2)CO_2H$ alanine	CH_3COCO_2H + Glu pyruvate
$HO_2CCH_2CH(NH_2)CO_2H$ aspartate	$HO_2CCH_2COCO_2H$ + Glu oxalacetate
$(CH_3)_2CHCH_2CH(NH_2)CO_2H$ leucine	$(CH_3)_2CHCH_2COCO_2H$ + Glu α-ketoisocaproate
$CH_3CH_2CH(CH_3)CH(NH_2)CO_2H$ isoleucine	$CH_3CH_2CH(CH_3)COCO_2H$ + Glu α-keto-β-methyl valerate
$(CH_3)_2CHCH(NH_2)CO_2H$ valine	$(CH_3)_2CHCOCO_2H$ + Glu α-ketoisovalerate
⬡—$CH_2CH(NH_2)CO_2H$ phenylalanine	⬡—CH_2COCO_2H + Glu phenylpyruvate
HO—⬡—$CH_2CH(NH_2)CO_2H$ tyrosine	HO—⬡—CH_2COCO_2H + Glu p-hydroxyphenylpyruvate

table 7.7 :: Some enzymatic dehydrations

$$
\begin{array}{c}
CO_2H \\
| \\
CH_2 \\
| \\
HOCH \\
| \\
CO_2H
\end{array}
\xrightarrow{-H_2O}
\begin{array}{c}
HCCO_2H \\
\| \\
HO_2CCH
\end{array}
$$

ʟ-malate   **fumarate**

$$
\begin{array}{c}
OH \\
| \\
HO_2CCH_2CCH_2CO_2H \\
| \\
CO_2H
\end{array}
\xrightarrow{-H_2O}
\begin{array}{c}
HO_2CCH=CCH_2CO_2H \\
| \\
CO_2H
\end{array}
$$

citrate   *cis*-**aconitate**

$$
\begin{array}{c}
CH_2OH \\
| \\
CHOPO_3H_2 \\
| \\
CO_2H
\end{array}
\xrightarrow{-H_2O}
\begin{array}{c}
CH_2 \\
\| \\
COPO_3H_2 \\
| \\
CO_2H
\end{array}
$$

2-phosphoglycerate   **phosphoenolpyruvate**

$$
\begin{array}{c}
O \\
\| \\
R-CH_2CHCH_2CSCoA \\
| \\
OH
\end{array}
\xrightarrow{-H_2O}
\begin{array}{c}
O \\
\| \\
R-CH_2CH=CH-C-SCoA
\end{array}
$$

hydroxyacyl-CoA   **enoyl-CoA**

$$
\begin{array}{c}
CH_2OH \\
| \\
CHNH_2 \\
| \\
CO_2H
\end{array}
\xrightarrow{-H_2O}
\begin{array}{c}
CH_2 \\
\| \\
C-NH_2 \\
| \\
CO_2H
\end{array}
\longrightarrow
\begin{array}{c}
CH_3 \\
| \\
CO \quad + NH_3 \\
| \\
CO_2H
\end{array}
$$

serine   **amino acrylate**†   **pyruvate**

† Probable intermediate.

references ::

BRESLOW, R., *Organic Reaction Mechanisms.* New York: W. A. Benjamin, Inc., 1965.

INGRAHAM, L. L., *Biochemical Mechanisms.* New York: John Wiley & Sons, Inc., 1962.

KOSOWER, E. M., *Molecular Biochemistry.* New York: McGraw-Hill, Inc., 1962.

MARTIN, R. B., *Introduction to Biophysical Chemistry.* New York: McGraw-Hill, Inc., 1964.

THE ENERGY NEEDS OF AN ORGANISM ARE SATISFIED DIRECTLY BY the energy-rich compounds discussed in Chapter 7. They are the agents used to couple exergonic to endergonic reactions. ATP, the most generally used compound, drives the synthesis of cell constituents such as proteins, nucleic acids, polysaccharides, steroids, and many others. It also serves as a source of energy in the performance of physical activities.

As ATP is utilized in the course of cellular activity, ADP is produced and phosphorylated into ATP again. The reaction $ADP + P_i \rightleftarrows ATP + H_2O$ in the cell uses about 10 to 12 kcal/mole, to be supplied in some way. Organisms have developed several means to utilize energy in various forms to phosphorylate ADP.

Plants and photosynthetic bacteria make use of solar energy; light energy flows through the photosynthetic machinery of the chloroplast and is converted into the chemical-bond energy of ATP. Some of the simple forms of life utilize energy from the oxidation of elements (H_2, Fe, S, etc.) or simple compounds (NO_2^-, NH_3, etc.). This is usually observed among the autotrophic bacteria.

But the majority of organisms utilize the energy released during the oxidation of organic substances ingested as part of their diet. The oxidation of glucose to CO_2 and H_2O, for example, is accompanied by a decrease in free energy of over 600 kcal/mole. A substantial portion of this energy is trapped in the formation of ATP, as we shall see by mechanisms to be discussed later in this chapter.

oxidation-reduction :: **8.1**

▪ Oxidation is defined as the withdrawal of electrons and reduction as the addition of electrons. Because electrons are not free in solution, every oxidation must have a corresponding reduction.

When a substance such as malate is oxidized, it loses two hydrogens, that is, two electrons and two protons, but a second substance must be reduced at the same time. In the enzymatic oxidation of malate NAD^+ is the electron acceptor.

Generally the oxidation of a substance by another entails transfer of electrons. The electron acceptor must have a greater affinity for electrons than the electron donor. This affinity for electrons is a measurable physical quantity called the *oxidation-reduction* or *redox potential*. Therefore it is possible to predict, if one knows the redox potentials, the tendency of a substance to oxidize another.

Because the redox potential is a relative quantity, it must be referred to some standard. The accepted standard is the hydrogen electrode shown in Figure 8.1. It is a half-cell in which the reaction

$$\tfrac{1}{2}H_2 \rightleftarrows H^+ + e^-$$

takes place.

The solution of H^+ is at a concentration of 1 g-ion per 1,000 g of solvent and hydrogen gas at 1 atmosphere pressure (atm). Nothing can be measured until a second half-cell is connected to the hydrogen electrode. For example, in Figure 8.1 a mixture of Fe^{2+} and Fe^{3+} salts in equal concentration makes up the other half-cell. Here a reaction also takes place:

$$Fe^{2+} \rightleftarrows Fe^{3+} + e^-$$

Immersed in both half-cells are platinum electrodes; if connected, a current flows from the hydrogen half-cell to the iron salts cell. The electromotive force or potential is measured in a voltmeter at 0.74 volt. The redox potential of the system Fe^{3+}/Fe^{2+} is $+0.74$ volt. The plus sign indicates that it is positive with respect to the standard hydrogen electrode.

Any redox system can thus be compared with any other redox system. The symbol E_0 is used for standard potentials, that is, the potentials measured

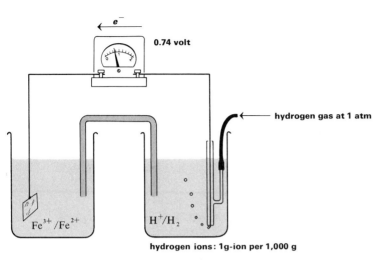

figure 8.1 ::
Standard hydrogen electrode connected to a half-cell made up of ferric and ferrous salts on an equal ratio. Electrons flow from the hydrogen half-cell toward the iron salts cell. The following reaction takes place:
$Fe^{3+} + e^- = Fe^{2+}$
$\frac{1}{2}H_2 - e^- = H^+$

against the hydrogen electrode when the ratio of oxidized to reduced forms is 1.

The redox potential, like ΔF, is related to concentration by an equation similar to that in the chemical-equilibrium part of Section 7.4:

$$E = E_0 + \frac{RT}{n\mathscr{F}} \ln \frac{[\text{oxidized}]}{[\text{reduced}]}$$

where E is the redox potential measured in volts, E_0 the standard potential, R the gas constant (8.135 joules/°C), T the absolute temperature, n the number of electron equivalents, and $\mathscr{F}$ a conversion factor ($\mathscr{F}$ = faraday = 96,500 coulombs).

Suppose we wish to know the redox potential of the system Fe^{3+}/Fe^{2+} when the ions are present in concentrations of 0.01 and 0.001 M, respectively, at 25°C:

$$E = 0.74 + \frac{8.3 \times 298}{1 \times 96,000} \times 2.3 \log \frac{0.01}{0.001} = 0.806 \text{ volt}$$

Measurements are normally made at 30°C ($T = 303$); thus we can simplify the equation:

$$\frac{8.3 \times 303}{1 \times 96,500} \times 2.3 = 0.06$$

and

$$E = E_0 + 0.06 \log \frac{[\text{Ox}]}{[\text{Red}]}$$

where one electron is transferred as in the example given. When two electrons are transferred it becomes

$$E = E_0 + 0.03 \log \frac{[\text{Ox}]}{[\text{Red}]}$$

All values E_0 are related to the standard hydrogen electrode at unit activity (1 M, pH 0). But in biological systems we deal with nearly neutral solutions. A correction is made for changes in pH. At pH 7, the hydrogen electrode has a potential difference of 0.42 volt when measured against the standard hydrogen electrode. The symbol E_0' is used to designate standard redox potentials measured at pH 7 or other specified pH. In Table 8.1 are listed some important redox systems and their redox potentials.

Oxidation-reduction and free energy. The transfer of electrons entails a change in free energy. In the cell depicted in Figure 8.1 a current flows through the wire. This is available to do work and corresponds to the change in free energy. The change of free energy when two redox systems are brought together at pH 7 can be computed from the equation†

$$\Delta F^{0\prime} = -n\mathscr{F} \, \Delta E_0'$$

The value of $-n\mathscr{F} \, \Delta E_0'$ is in volt-coulombs or joules and converted to calories by dividing by 4.18 (1 cal = 4.18 joules). For one-electron transfer:

$$\frac{96,500}{4.18} = 23,063 \text{ cal/volt equivalent}$$

Suppose that two redox systems with E_0' values of -0.050 and -0.0150 volt are brought together. The free-energy change is

$$\Delta E_0' = -0.050 - (-0.150) = 0.100 \text{ volt}$$

$$\Delta F^0 = -23,063 \times 0.100 = -2,306 \text{ cal} = -2.3 \text{ kcal}$$

† Just as the values ΔE_0 must be corrected for changes in pH, so ΔF^0 must be redefined with reference to this new standard state; in other words, ΔF^0 applies to the conversions of 1 M substrates to 1 M products at pH 7.

SYSTEM	POTENTIAL, VOLTS
$NAD^+/NADH + H^+$	-0.32
Riboflavin/riboflavin-H_2	-0.20
Pyruvate/lactate	-0.19
Oxalacetate/malate	-0.166
Cytochrome b (Fe^{3+}/Fe^{2+})	-0.04
Fumarate/succinate	0.03
Cytochrome c (Fe^{3+}/Fe^{2+})	0.26
Cytochrome a (Fe^{3+}/Fe^{2+})	0.29
$\frac{1}{2}O_2/H_2O$	0.81

† Oxidized/reduced at pH 7.

table 8.1 :: Redox potentials of some important biological systems†

Here the transfer of one electron from one redox system to another of lower potential is attended by a decrease in free energy equivalent to 2.3 kcal. The process is obviously exergonic. ▪

mitochondrion ::

The mitochondrion is a cell particle intimately associated with the generation of ATP. As shown in the electron micrograph in Figure 1.6, the mitochondrial structure has well-defined features to which biochemical functions have been assigned. A cell has several hundred mitochondria that function as energy converters. The mitochondrion has been called a "power plant" and a "biochemical machine." The latter name is quite appropriate, because in the mitochondrion are present all the enzymes and cofactors needed to oxidize some organic substances and utilize the energy of oxidation to esterify ADP.

As this chapter progresses, it should become evident that in the cell enzymes are not randomly distributed—they are associated with the various components of the cell in a manner such that there is true separation (compartmentation) of the catalytic events.

SIZE, SHAPE, AND STRUCTURE : In the main a mitochondrion is a rod-shaped body about $3\,\mu$ in length and 0.5 to $1.0\,\mu$ in width. Sometimes several mitochondria join end to end but seldom fuse side to side. Spherically shaped mitochondria are also known; they tend to fuse into elongated strands.

In Figure 8.2 are shown schematically the continuous membranes of the mitochondrion. The outer membrane is smooth and forms a sac; within this sac is the inner membrane, with its infoldings or

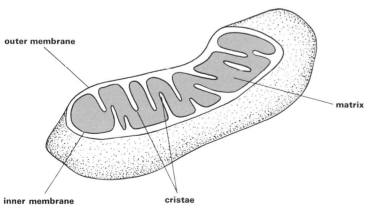

figure 8.2 ::
Mitochondrion, showing the arrangement of the cristae.

outer membrane

matrix

inner membrane   cristae

cristae. The inner portion or matrix is made up mainly of protein and lipid and has the consistency of a semifluid.

The introduction of techniques to disassemble the mitochondria has made it possible to understand better the function of each structural component. For example, the matrix is believed to contain enzymes catalyzing the oxidation of pyruvate, fatty acids, and some amino acids. While these substances are oxidized, NAD^+ (or $NADP^+$) and FAD (or FMN) are correspondingly reduced.

The mitochondrial membranes hold tightly multienzyme systems and carriers—the *respiratory assemblies*—which are responsible for oxidizing the reduced coenzymes and for coupling the energy of oxidation to phosphorylation of ADP.

First we shall deal with the oxidation of substrates such as pyruvate and fatty acids that takes place in the mitochondrial matrix and then proceed to discuss the mechanism by which the energy released by oxidation is coupled to the phosphorylation of ADP.

oxidation of pyruvate: citrate cycle :: 8.3

Pyruvate is the product of reactions undergone by several compounds, but mainly it is the product of glucose degradation. Pyruvate penetrates the mitochondrion where it is oxidized to completion. The oxidation of pyruvate entails a series of reactions operating in a cyclical fashion and known collectively as the Krebs or citrate cycle and shown schematically in Figure 8.3. Each reaction will be discussed in turn.

FORMATION OF ACETYL-CoA : The citrate cycle proper begins with acetyl-CoA (acetylated coenzyme A), which is the end product of reactions undergone by pyruvate when pyruvate is oxidized and decarboxylated by the action of the multienzyme system known as pyruvate dehydrogenase complex.

Each of the enzymes and cofactors of the complex has been clearly defined, and each catalytic step in the conversion of pyruvate to acetyl-CoA is discussed here:

First, pyruvate reacts with a decarboxylase, a thiamine pyrophosphate (TPP) enzyme, to form active acetaldehyde by a mechanism discussed in Chapter 7:

$$
\begin{array}{l}
CH_3 \\
| \\
C{=}O + \text{TPP-enzyme} \rightleftharpoons CH_3\overset{\text{O}}{\overset{||}{C}}\text{-TPP-enzyme} + CO_2 \\
| \\
CO_2^-
\end{array}
$$

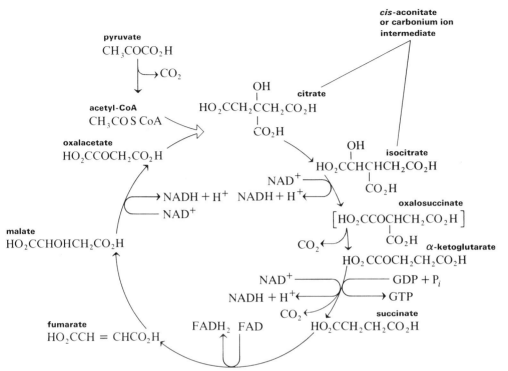

figure 8.3 :: Citrate, or Krebs, cycle. The reactions attended by the reduction of coenzymes are shown. Other details of the cycle are discussed in the text.

In the next step, active acetaldehyde reacts with α-lipoic acid, a coenzyme functioning as an acetyl carrier in the presence of pyruvate dehydrogenase:

$$CH_3\overset{O}{\overset{\|}{C}}-TPP\text{-}E + \overset{S-\diagdown^R}{\underset{S-\diagup}{|}} \underset{H^+}{\rightleftharpoons} CH_3\overset{O}{\overset{\|}{C}}-S-\overset{R}{\underset{HS-\diagup}{\diagdown}} + TPP\text{-}E$$

The resulting acetyl lipoate reacts with coenzyme A, a reaction catalyzed by a specific transferase to yield acetyl-CoA and dihydrolipoate:

$$CH_3\overset{O}{\overset{\|}{C}}-S-\overset{R}{\underset{HS-\diagup}{\diagdown}} + HSCoA \rightleftharpoons CH_3\overset{O}{\overset{\|}{C}}-S-CoA + \overset{HS-\diagdown^R}{\underset{HS-\diagup}{}}$$

Finally, the catalytic cycle is completed by the oxidation of reduced lipoate by NAD^+; this reaction is catalyzed by the enzyme lipoamide dehydrogenase:

$$\text{HS}\overset{R}{\underset{HS}{\diagup}} + \text{NAD}^+ \rightleftharpoons \text{NADH} + \text{H}^+ + \overset{R}{\underset{S}{\diagup}}\begin{smallmatrix}S\end{smallmatrix}$$

The overall conversion of pyruvate to acetyl CoA can be represented by the equation

$$\text{pyruvate} + \text{HSCoA} + \text{NAD}^+ \xrightarrow[\text{TPP, Mg}^{2+}]{\text{lipoate}} \text{acetyl-CoA} + \text{NADH} + \text{H}^+ + \text{CO}_2$$

FORMATION OF CITRATE : The condensation of acetyl-CoA with oxalacetate is catalyzed by the citrate-condensing enzyme. As already discussed, the carbonyl group in acetyl-CoA has a strong ketonic character while the methyl group reacts as a nucleophile:

$$\text{H}^+\ \text{CH}_2\overset{\overset{O}{\|}}{\text{C}}-\text{S}-\text{CoA}$$
$$+$$
$$\overset{\overset{O}{\|}}{\text{C}}\text{CH}_2\text{CO}_2\text{H}$$
$$|$$
$$\text{CO}_2\text{H}$$

$$\xrightleftharpoons[-\text{H}_2\text{O}\ -\text{H}^+]{+\text{H}^+,\ +\text{H}_2\text{O}}$$

$$\text{HO}_2\text{CCH}_2\overset{\overset{\text{OH}}{|}}{\text{C}}\text{CH}_2\text{CO}_2\text{H} + \text{HSCoA}$$
$$|$$
$$\text{CO}_2\text{H}$$

The hydrolysis of the thioester accompanying the formation of citrate is attended by a large decrease in free energy, forcing the reaction to the right: that is, it favors citrate formation.

FORMATION OF ISOCITRATE : The enzyme aconitase speeds up the formation of cis-aconitate and isocitrate and an equilibrium is established between the three tricarboxylic acids:

$$\text{HO}_2\text{CCH}_2\overset{\overset{\text{OH}}{|}}{\text{C}}\text{CH}_2\text{CO}_2\text{H} \xrightleftharpoons[\text{Fe}^{2+}]{-\text{H}_2\text{O}} \text{HO}_2\text{CCH}=\overset{}{\text{C}}\text{CH}_2\text{CO}_2\text{H} \xrightleftharpoons[\text{Fe}^{2+}]{+\text{H}_2\text{O}}$$
$$|\qquad\qquad\qquad\qquad\qquad\qquad |$$
$$\text{CO}_2\text{H}\qquad\qquad\qquad\qquad\qquad \text{CO}_2\text{H}$$

citrate   *cis*-**aconitate**

$$\text{HO}_2\text{CCHCHCH}_2\text{CO}_2\text{H}$$
$$|\qquad\qquad\overset{\text{OH}}{}$$
$$\text{CO}_2\text{H}$$

isocitrate

In the formation of *cis*-aconitate, the course of the reaction is asymmetric. The two identical substituents in citrate, $-CH_2CO_2H$, are not equivalent. As shown in Chapter 6, enzymes can catalyze reactions of only one of the two identical groups. In this case only one of the $-CH_2CO_2H$ groups react as above.

FORMATION OF α-KETOGLUTARATE : The oxidation of isocitrate is accompanied by a decarboxylation to yield α-ketoglutarate:

$$\underset{\underset{CO_2H}{|}}{\overset{\overset{OH}{|}}{HO_2CCHCHCH_2CO_2H}} + NAD^+ \xrightarrow[\text{or Mn}^{2+}]{\text{Mg}^{2+}} NADH + H^+ +$$

$$\overset{\overset{O}{\|}}{HO_2CCCH_2CH_2CO_2H} + CO_2$$

Isocitric dehydrogenase, the intervening enzyme from the mitochondrion, functions with NAD^+, but there is in the cell's cytoplasm another isocitric dehydrogenase that functions with $NADP^+$. Because NADPH is not a substrate for mitochondrial oxidases that are specific for NAD^+, an exchange of hydrogens with NAD^+ regenerates the oxidized form. This occurs by a transhydrogenation reaction:

$$NADPH + H^+ + NAD^+ \rightleftharpoons NADH + H^+ + NADP^+$$

FORMATION OF SUCCINATE : The decarboxylation of α-ketoglutarate and simultaneous oxidation of the product is a process similar to that described for pyruvate. It requires a thiamine enzyme, CoA, α-lipoic acid, NAD, and Mg^{2+}. As expected, the product is not succinate but succinyl-CoA. This substance is cleaved in the mitochondrion by one of several possible mechanisms. One is shown here:

$$\overset{\overset{O}{\|}}{HO_2CCCH_2CH_2CO_2H} \longrightarrow \longrightarrow \longrightarrow \overset{\overset{O}{\|}}{CoASCCH_2CH_2CO_2H}$$

α-ketoglutarate   **succinyl-CoA**

$$\text{succinyl-CoA} + P_i + GDP \rightleftharpoons GTP + \text{succinate} + HSCoA$$

and

$$GTP + ADP \rightleftharpoons ATP + GDP$$

The phosphorolytic cleavage of succinyl-CoA is very complex. What is of interest at the moment is that an energy-rich compound, guanosine triphosphate, is formed at the expense of the energy released by the cleavage of succinyl-CoA, another energy-rich compound.

OXIDATION OF SUCCINATE : Succinate is the only intermediate in the citrate cycle that is oxidized by an enzyme containing flavine adenine dinucleotide (FAD)–succinic dehydrogenase:

$$HO_2CCH_2CH_2CO_2H + FAD \rightleftharpoons FADH_2 + HO_2CCH=CHCO_2H$$

The enzyme is intimately bound as part of the respiratory assembly, which will be discussed later.

FORMATION OF MALATE : The sterospecific addition of water across the double bond of fumarate yields L-malate:

$$HO_2CCH=CHCO_2H + H_2O \rightleftharpoons HO_2C\overset{OH}{\underset{H}{C}}CH_2CO_2H$$

fumarate   L-**malate**

FORMATION OF OXALACETATE : The cycle is completed when malate is oxidized by the action of NAD^+-linked malic dehydrogenase:

$$HO_2C\overset{OH}{\underset{H}{C}}CH_2CO_2H + NAD^+ \rightleftharpoons NADH + H^+ + HO_2C\overset{O}{C}CH_2CO_2H$$

The oxalacetate produced in the last reaction of the cycle can condense with a new molecule of acetyl-CoA to form citrate and thus begin the cycle again.

The overall reaction for the oxidation of acetate as acetyl-CoA may be written

$$CH_3COSCoA + 3H_2O = 2CO_2 + 8[H] + HSCoA$$

in which no oxygen is shown to participate. What the above expression shows is that during the citrate cycle, 8[H] are produced (or 10[H], starting from pyruvate). The 8[H], as shown in the diagram of Figure 8.3, reduce three molecules of NAD^+ and one molecule of FAD. The reduced coenzymes do not remain reduced but are immediately oxidized by oxygen in a process mediated by the respiratory assembly of the mitochondrion.

oxidation of fatty acids :: **8.4**

The oxidation of pyruvate by the enzyme complex pyruvate dehydrogenase yields, as already seen, acetyl-CoA, which is directed into the citrate cycle. Another important source of acetyl-CoA is the fatty acids that are split from dietary triglycerides. They are oxidized by the action of mitochondrial enzymes functioning in sequence to yield acetyl-CoA.

  The degradation of a fatty acid involves several steps, as illustrated in Figure 8.4. Each step will be discussed in turn.

ACTIVATION : A fatty acid is converted to its acyl-CoA derivative by the action of an activating enzyme according to the reaction

$$RCOOH + ATP + HSCoA \rightleftharpoons R\overset{\overset{\displaystyle O}{\displaystyle \|}}{C}SCoA + AMP + PP_i$$

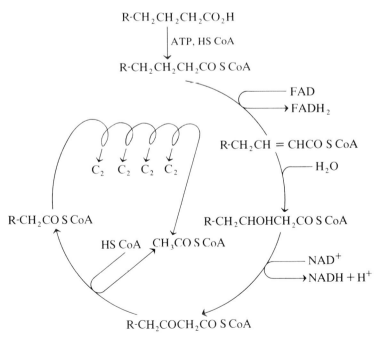

figure 8.4 ::
Mitochondrial oxidation of fatty acids. The process is repetitive and is schematically viewed as a spiral.

The enzymes catalyzing these reactions act according to their specificities upon short-, medium-, and long-chain fatty acids. Note that to activate a molecule of fatty acid, a molecule of ATP must be consumed. Other reactions in which ATP cleaves into adenosine monophosphate (AMP) and pyrophosphate are also known.

FIRST OXIDATION : The resulting acyl-CoA undergoes oxidation, as illustrated here by showing the last four carbons of the acyl-CoA :

$$RCH_2CH_2CH_2\overset{\overset{\textstyle O}{\|}}{C}SCoA + FAD \rightleftharpoons FADH_2 + RCH_2CH{=}CH\overset{\overset{\textstyle O}{\|}}{C}SCoA$$

Here also enzyme specificity is broad ; that is, there are few enzymes catalyzing the dehydrogenation in accordance to length of the carbon chain. The product is an α,β-unsaturated acyl-CoA.

HYDRATION : The α,β-unsaturated acyl-CoA adds water to the double bond sterospecifically :

$$RCH_2CH{=}CH\overset{\overset{\textstyle O}{\|}}{C}SCoA + H_2O \rightleftharpoons RCH_2\underset{\underset{\textstyle H}{|}}{\overset{\overset{\textstyle OH}{|}}{C}}CH_2\overset{\overset{\textstyle O}{\|}}{C}SCoA$$

The reaction is catalyzed by the enzyme crotonase (enoyl hydratase) and the product is L(+)-β-hydroxyacyl-CoA.

SECOND OXIDATION : L(+)-β-hydroxyacyl-CoA undergoes dehydrogenation by the action of a dehydrogenase functioning with NAD$^+$:

$$RCH_2\underset{\underset{\textstyle H}{|}}{\overset{\overset{\textstyle OH}{|}}{C}}CH_2\overset{\overset{\textstyle O}{\|}}{C}SCoA + NAD^+ \rightleftharpoons NADH + H^+ + RCH_2\overset{\overset{\textstyle O}{\|}}{C}CH_2\overset{\overset{\textstyle O}{\|}}{C}SCoA$$

CLEAVAGE : Finally, the β-ketoacyl-CoA formed cleaves by reacting with another molecule of coenzyme A, a reaction catalyzed by the enzyme β-ketothiolase :

$$RCH_2\overset{\overset{\textstyle O}{\|}}{C}CH_2\overset{\overset{\textstyle O}{\|}}{C}SCoA + HSCoA \rightleftharpoons RCH_2\overset{\overset{\textstyle O}{\|}}{C}SCoA + CH_3\overset{\overset{\textstyle O}{\|}}{C}SCoA$$

In sum, the original fatty acid after several reactions loses the two terminal carbon atoms as acetyl-CoA. The other product is an activated fatty acid with two less carbons than the original. As shown in Figure 8.4, the process is repeated again with the shortened fatty acyl-CoA until all the carbons of the fatty acid are split off as acetyl-CoA.

An acid with 16 carbons, for example, will yield 8 molecules of acetyl-CoA, while 7 FAD and 7 NAD^+ molecules are reduced. When the 8 acetyl-CoA units are funneled into the citrate cycle, 24 (8×3) molecules of NAD^+ and 8 (8×1) of FAD are reduced. The total oxidation of a 16-carbon fatty acid is attended by the reduction of 31 NAD^+ molecules and 15 FAD molecules; this represents a vast quantity of chemical potential.

respiratory assembly :: **8.5**

The oxidation of pyruvate through the citrate cycle and the oxidation of fatty acids are the two most important reactions resulting in the reduction of coenzymes. As already mentioned, reduced coenzymes do not remain reduced but are immediately oxidized by oxygen in a process mediated by the respiratory assembly. This not only regenerates the oxidized forms of coenzymes but in the process—which is attended by a large decrease in free energy—ADP is phosphorylated to ATP. In other words, the energy released by the oxidation of reduced coenzymes is partially "trapped" in the form of chemical potential represented by ATP.

The respiratory assemblies or chains are held within the mito-chondrial membranes. They consist of molecular organizations capable of functioning as catalytic units. They can be cleaved from the membranes by chemical agents and studied in an isolated form. By this type of experimentation, it has been possible to reconstruct a respiratory assembly, which is visualized as a chain of enzymes and carriers as shown in Figure 8.5.

An assembly such as this accepts hydrogens from the reduced coenzymes (NADH and flavoproteins shown as FP_1, FP_2, etc.). The reduced coenzymes react with a bound form of NAD^+. The coenzymes thus return to their oxidized state while bound NAD^+ is reduced to $NADH + H^+$. In its reduced form, the bound NAD reacts with a flavoprotein that accepts both hydrogens.

Up to this point the process has been one of hydrogen transfer from substrate to FP by mechanisms discussed in Chapter 7. It is now important to consider the way in which hydrogen is transferred from the flavoprotein to oxygen.

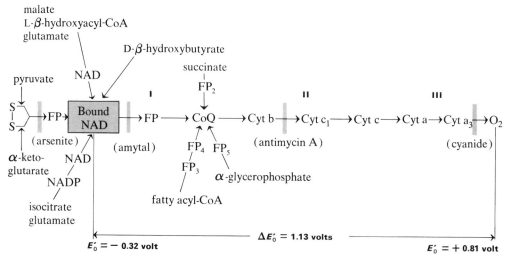

figure 8.5 :: Respiratory chain. Esterification of ADP occurs at sites indicated by Roman numerals. Points of inhibition by specific substances are indicated. (*After A. L. Lehninger.*)

The transfer is no longer a transfer of hydrogen but a transfer of electrons, with the protons being released into the medium. Electrons are transferred from the flavoprotein to oxygen via the cytochromes, which as we shall see in a moment are iron-containing proteins. Their iron is successively reduced and oxidized as shown here:

$$FPH_2 \diagdown CoQ \diagup 2Fe^{2+} \diagdown Cyt\ b \diagup 2Fe^{3+} \diagdown Cyt\ c_1 \diagup 2Fe^{2+} \diagdown Cyt\ c \diagup 2Fe^{3+} \diagdown Cyt\ a \diagup 2Fe^{2+} \diagdown Cyt\ a_3 \diagup :\ddot{O}:$$

It is almost certain that between the flavoprotein and cytochrome b is interposed another carrier (as shown in the scheme above): coenzyme Q.

COENZYME Q : The name *coenzyme Q* is used to describe a group of compounds with quinone structures found in nature:

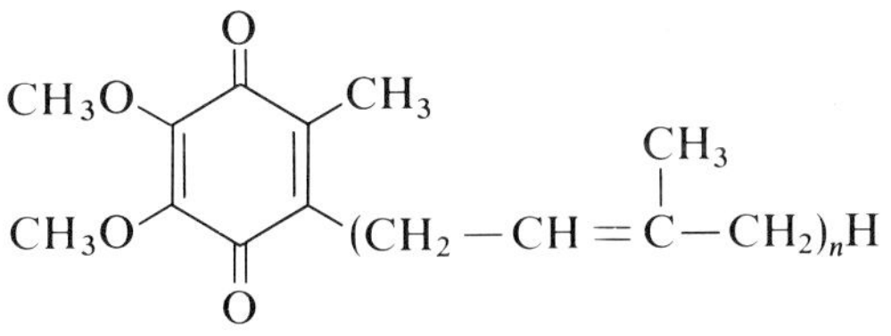

(The term in parentheses is the isoprenoil unit.)

In the mitochondria are present quinones, known as ubiquinones, in which the length of the side chain varies with the source of the mitochondria. The length of the side chain is usually indicated by a subscript; for example, Q_{10} means that the side chain is made up of 10 isoprenoid units.

The reduction of coenzyme Q by hydrogen (or reduced flavo-protein) entails the transfer of both protons and electrons:

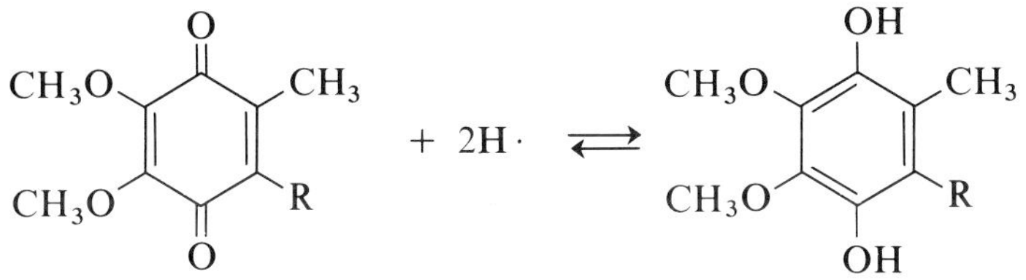

to yield the corresponding hydroquinone. The oxidation of cyto-chrome b by $CoQH_2$ entails transfer of electrons only; the protons are released to the solvent.

THE CYTOCHROMES : The cytochromes are conjugated proteins containing a ferroporfirin pigment. They were originally known as *myohematins*, a name coined by C. A. McMunn in 1886 to describe pigments obtained from animal tissues and with characteristic visible absorption spectra.

McMunn's discovery did not receive the recognition it deserved until 1925, when D. Keilin confirmed their existence by spectro-scopic means. Keilin made an extensive study of the myohematins and changed their name to *cytochromes*, after finding that they are distributed not only in animal tissues but also in plants, yeast, and bacteria.

Keilin identified three cytochromes on the basis of their absorp-tion spectra and named them cytochromes a, b, and c. Since then many more cytochromes have been identified (about 30), and their designations are made according to which of the original 3 they resemble; thus $a_1, a_2, a_3, c_1, c_2, c_3$, etc.

The cytochromes of the respiratory assembly from animal mitochondria have been shown in Figure 8.5 to correspond to Cyt b, Cyt c_1, Cyt c, Cyt a, and Cyt a_3.

Cytochrome c has been obtained in pure form and its structure investigated. It is a protein of molecular weight 13,000 and contains one iron per molecule. The porphyrin group is firmly attached to the protein through thioether linkages:

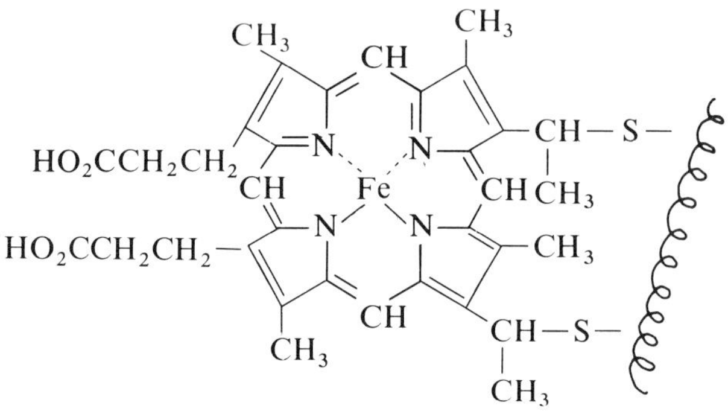

Cytochrome b has been very difficult to study and to date there remains much argument regarding its properties and function. However, it is certain that cytochrome b is part of the respiratory assembly.

Cytochrome a and cytochrome a_3 are not easily separated from one another. They differ in properties, particularly in regard to their behavior toward inhibition. Cytochrome a fails to combine with reagents known to form complexes with iron, such as carbon monoxide and cyanide, but cytochrome a_3 combines with both agents. Moreover, reduced cytochrome a is not autoxidizable (oxidized by molecular oxygen), but reduced cytochrome a_3 is autoxidizable.

Cytochrome a_3 is the terminal electron carrier in the chain, as shown in Figure 8.5. It reacts in its reduced state with oxygen by transferring one electron:

$$2Fe^{2+} + \ddot{\text{:}}\overset{..}{O}\text{:} \longrightarrow 2Fe^{3+} + \ddot{\text{:}}\overset{..}{O}\text{:}^{2-}$$

Cyt a, reduced   **Cyt a, oxidized**

The resulting oxygen ion reacts with the protons released by $CoQH_2$:

$$O^{2-} + 2H^+ = H_2O$$

This reaction completes the journey of the two hydrogens originally present in the substrates that were oxidized within the mitochondrion.

INHIBITION BY SPECIFIC INHIBITORS : Much has been learned about cell respiration by using substances that specifically inhibit a given component of the respiratory assembly. Several such inhibitors and the sites of inhibition are shown in Figure 8.5. Something has already been said about the combination of CO and CN⁻ with cytochrome a_3. It should be added that cytochrome a_3, by combining with cyanide, for example, cannot function as an electron carrier. Because cytochrome a_3 is the terminal acceptor of electrons before oxygen takes them up, it follows that the entire respiratory chain is inhibited. The high toxicity of cyanide is readily explained on this basis.

Other inhibitors attack other members of the respiratory chain; the sites of action can be deduced by determining which members of the chain remain functional after the inhibitor has been added. For example, in the presence of antimycin A_1, the transfer of electrons is blocked at the cytochrome b stage. In this case, NAD, FP, and cytochrome b are found to be fully reduced, while cytochromes c, a, and a_3 are found to be oxidized. This places the site of action of antimycin A at the cytochrome b stage.

oxidative phosphorylation :: **8.6**

The overall oxidation of 1 mole of reduced NAD^+ in the mitochondria is accompanied by a decrease in free energy equivalent to 52 kcal.† A substantial portion of the free energy of oxidation goes into the phosphorylation of ADP to form ATP. The process, known as oxidative phosphorylation, is very complex and not understood in all its details.

A few comments can be made regarding oxidative phosphorylation. One is that experimentally it is possible to measure ATP formation in mitochondria when NADH is oxidized. The measurements show that for every molecule of NADH oxidized three molecules of ATP are formed:

$$NADH + H^+ + \tfrac{1}{2}O_2 + 3ADP + 3P_i \longrightarrow NAD^+ + 3ATP + H_2O$$

The free energy of oxidation of NADH, 52 kcal/mole, is more than adequate to account for the 3 moles of ATP formed if we use the

† $\Delta E_0' = 1.13$ volts $-\Delta F^0 = 1.13 \times 23,063 \times 2 = 52,122$ or   52.1 kcal

approximate value of 10 kcal/mole for the esterification of ADP.

The sites in the respiratory assembly at which the phosphorylations take place have been shown with roman numerals in Figure 8.5. The precise mechanism of the energy coupling is not yet known. Most theories postulate the existence of mediators or common intermediates in electron transport and ATP formation. For example,

$$AH_2 + B + X \rightleftarrows A \sim X + BH_2$$
$$A \sim X + P_i \rightleftarrows P_i \sim X + A$$

$$\overline{AH_2 + B + P_i + ADP \rightleftarrows A + BH_2 + ATP}$$

where X represents the common intermediate, AH_2 the reduced carrier, and B the oxidized carrier.

The oxidation of substrates in the mitochondria is intimately coupled to oxidative phosphorylation. Just as one measures ATP formation during the oxidation of NADH, the oxygen consumed can also be measured. The ratio ATP formed to oxygen consumed (P/O ratio) is indicative of the efficiency by which coupling takes place. A P/O ratio of 3 is commonly found.

There are a number of substances that inhibit phosphorylation but not oxygen consumption. These agents are commonly known as *uncouplers* of oxidative phosphorylation; among them are dinitrophenol, oligomycin, antimycin A, dicoumarol, and others. All have been used extensively as a means to study oxidative phosphorylation.

In the presence of an uncoupler, the oxidation of NADH continues but no ATP is formed. The free energy of oxidation of NADH appears as heat in this case.

energy yields :: 8.7

If the oxidation of 1 mole of NADH results in the formation of 3 moles of ATP, the yield of ATP from the oxidation of pyruvate or a fatty acid can be calculated readily.

The oxidation of 1 mole of pyruvate by the mitochondrial machinery is attended by the reduction of 4 moles of NAD^+ and 1 mole of FAD. The yield of ATP is computed in Table 8.2 on the basis of 3 ATP per mole of oxygen or P/O = 3. A similar computation is shown in Table 8.3 for the oxidation of palmitic acid.

STEP(S)	NO. OF ATP MOLECULES FORMED	table 8.2 :: ATP yield during the oxidation of pyruvate

1a. $CH_3COCO_2H + NAD^+ + HSCoA \rightarrow$
$CH_3COSCoA + CO_2 + NADH + H^+$ 0

b. $NADH + H^+ + \frac{1}{2}O_2 \rightarrow NAD^+ + H_2O$ 3

2a.
$$\overset{\displaystyle OH}{\underset{\displaystyle CO_2H}{HO_2C\overset{|}{C}HCHCH_2CO_2H}} + NAD^+ \rightarrow$$

$CO_2 + HO_2CCOCH_2CH_2CO_2H + NADH + H^+$ 0

b. $NADH + H^+ + \frac{1}{2}O_2 \rightarrow NAD^+ + H_2O$ 3

3a. $HO_2CCOCH_2CH_2CO_2H + NAD^+ + HSCoA \rightarrow$
$HO_2CCH_2CH_2COSCoA + CO_2 + NADH^+$
$+ H^+$ 0

b. $NADH + H^+ + \frac{1}{2}O_2 \rightarrow NAD^+ + H_2O$ 3

c. $HO_2CCH_2CH_2COSCoA + GDP + P_i \rightarrow$
$HO_2CCH_2CH_2CO_2H + GTP + HSCoA$ 1

4a. $HO_2CCH_2CH_2CO_2H + FAD \rightarrow$
$HO_2CCH{=}CHCO_2H + FADH_2$ 0

b. $FADH_2 + \frac{1}{2}O_2 \rightarrow FAD + H_2O$ 2

5a. $HO_2CCHOHCH_2CO_2H + NAD^+ \rightarrow$
$HO_2CCOCH_2CO_2H + NADH + H^+$ 0

b. $NADH + H^+ + \frac{1}{2}O_2 \rightarrow NAD^+ + H_2O$ <u>3</u>

  Total   15

STEP(S)	NO. OF ATP MOLECULES FORMED	table 8.3 :: ATP yield during the oxidation of palmitate

1a. $C_{16}H_{31}CO_2H + ATP + 8HSCoA$
$+ 7NAD^+ + 7FAD \rightarrow 8CH_3COSCoA$
$+ AMP + PP_i + 7NADH + 7H^+ + 7FADH_2$

b. $7NADH + 7H^+ + 3\frac{1}{2}O_2 \rightarrow 7H_2O$ 21

c. $7FADH_2 + 3\frac{1}{2}O_2 \rightarrow 7H_2O + 7FAD$ 14

2. Citrate cycle :
    $8CH_3COSCoA + 16O_2 \rightarrow$
    $16CO_2 + 8H_2O + 8HSCoA$ <u>96</u>

  Total   131

  One high-energy phosphate bond is used up
    in the activation of palmitate   <u>− 1</u>

  Net yield   130

It should be noted that in the conversion of α-ketoglutarate to succinate ATP is produced indirectly by reactions already discussed. In this case, the phosphorylation of ADP is not due to the flow of electrons on the respiratory assembly. It is a phosphorylation that occurs at the level of the substrate. Other phosphorylations of this type will be discussed in other parts of the book.

The reduction of NAD^+ is not a process that takes place exclusively in the mitochondria. There are, in fact, many reactions catalyzed extramitochondrially that result in the production of NADH. Reoxidation of the coenzyme takes place in an indirect way because the mitochondrial membrane is impermeable to NADH but not to NAD^+. A known mechanism is the reaction of NADH with dihydroxyacetone phosphate:

$$NADH + H^+ + \begin{array}{c} CH_2OH \\ | \\ CO \\ | \\ CH_2OPO_3H_2 \end{array} \rightleftarrows \begin{array}{c} CH_2OH \\ | \\ CHOH \\ | \\ CH_2OPO_3H_2 \end{array} + NAD^+$$

dihydroxyacetone   **glycerophosphate**
phosphate

The glycerophosphate formed penetrates the mitochondrion, where it is oxidized to dihydroxyacetone phosphate, so the latter compound serves as a shuttle for hydrogens from cytoplasm to mitochondrion and in the process regenerates NAD^+.

references ::

KLOTZ, I. M., *Some Principles of Energetics in Biochemical Reactions.* New York: Academic Press, Inc., 1957.

KREBS, H. A., AND H. L. KORNBERG, *Energy Transformations in Living Matter.* Berlin: Springer-Verlag, 1957.

LEHNINGER, A. L., *The Mitochondrion.* New York: W. A. Benjamin, Inc., 1964.

LEHNINGER, A. L., *Bioenergetics.* New York: W. A. Benjamin, Inc., 1965.

RACKER, E., *Mechanisms in Bioenergetics.* New York: Academic Press, Inc., 1965.

CHAPTER 8 DEALT MAINLY WITH THE WAYS BY WHICH MOST LIVING cells produce ATP by utilizing the energy released in the mitochondria during the oxidation of pyruvate and acetyl-CoA.

In this chapter we shall consider the main sources of pyruvate and acetyl-CoA. These two substances are produced in the cell from a variety of compounds originating in the foodstuffs ingested by an organism. The transformation of a large variety of organic compounds into pyruvate and acetyl-Coa is made possible in the cell by sequences of enzymatic reactions that will be discussed here.

metabolic pathways :: 9.1

Acetyl-CoA can be regarded as fuel for the mitochondrial production of ATP. Acetyl-CoA is not a readily available organic substance, however, and organisms must produce it from substances on which they feed.

Two immediate precursors of acetyl-CoA have already been mentioned: pyruvate and fatty acids. The fatty acids are produced from dietary fats by hydrolysis, then assimilated by the cell, where they undergo complete oxidation in the mitochondrion, as discussed in Chapter 8. Pyruvate, on the other hand, is not so easily formed, nor is it present in any significant amount in common foodstuffs. It is usually formed in the cell from other substances of dietary origin by a series of enzymatic reactions interlocked into networks or metabolic pathways.

Pyruvate is an immediate precursor of acetyl-CoA, so any substance that can be converted into pyruvate is a potential source of acetyl-CoA. Several amino acids after deamination undergo reactions to yield pyruvate; other amino acids are known to yield acetyl-CoA directly without forming pyruvate first.

In all these sequences of enzymatic reactions we are dealing with degradative or catabolic reactions. It should be noted, however, that intermediates in the degradative sequences are also starting materials for the biosynthesis of other compounds. Biosynthesis of cell constituents or anabolism, and degradation or catabolism, are intimately bound through common enzymes and common reactions. One process is not necessarily the reverse of the other, even if some enzymes are shared by the two processes.

In this chapter we shall deal only with catabolic pathways and only with those representing the flow of carbon from carbohydrates and proteins into acetyl-Coa.

A word of caution is needed at this point. A metabolic pathway explains how a given organism can convert a substance into a desired end product; it represents a flow diagram to show how the carbons of, say, an amino acid flow into acetyl-CoA or into some other substance. It does not take into account the factors controlling the flow, factors that operate in the intact organism, such as hormones and enzyme inhibitors.

Metabolic pathways are usually deduced from the nature of the enzymes present in a cell under conditions far removed from its natural state. The cells are usually destroyed and extracted to determine which enzymes are present.

There is another reason why metabolic pathways do not reflect the real situation in the living cell. The accepted pathways are often composite flow diagrams deduced from the nature of enzymes present in different cells of different organisms. They would closely resemble the real situation only if we could prove their universality; this would be difficult to do. Nevertheless, some of the reactions to be discussed in this chapter probably are of such wide scope that we may discuss them in a universal sense.

Biochemical uniformity in the living world is an accepted concept. There is uniformity in the way cells utilize a large variety of compounds from food by converting them into some common end product such as acetyl-CoA and in the way ATP is generated.

First we shall deal with the production of pyruvate from carbohydrates and proteins and then with the production of acetyl-CoA from sources other than fatty acids and pyruvate.

conversion of glucose to pyruvate: glycolysis :: **9.2**

Glucose is one of nature's most abundant foodstuffs. It is the product of hydrolysis of glucans such as starch, glycogen, cellulose, and others. It is also present in the free state or in combination with other molecules such as in sucrose and lactose, both of which are abundant in nature.

The biodegradation of glucose or glycolysis was recognized early as the fundamental process of alcoholic fermentation and of anaerobic muscle contraction. These two apparently dissimilar events were investigated almost simultaneously, and the results revealed that the two processes were almost identical (Figure 9.1).

In both instances glucose is broken into two trioses, which undergo additional changes to yield pyruvate. All the reactions involved in the conversion of glucose to pyruvate were found to be the same in skeletal muscle and brewer's yeast. The difference is in the end product. In muscle, pyruvate is reduced to lactate, while in yeast pyruvate is decarboxylated to acetaldehyde, which is then reduced to ethanol. The two processes can be represented by

$$C_6H_{12}O_6 \longrightarrow 2CH_3CHOHCO_2H \quad \text{(in muscle)}$$

$$C_6H_{12}O_6 \longrightarrow 2C_2H_5OH + 2CO_2 \quad \text{(in yeast)}$$

An outstanding feature of this process is that oxygen is not necessary. As glucose breaks down, ATP is generated by coupling an oxidation reaction to the phosphorylation of ADP. The oxidation step is a dehydrogenation mediated by NAD^+; the entire sequence would come to a halt if the resulting NADH could not be oxidized. In the absence of oxygen NADH is oxidized by pyruvate in muscle or by acetaldehyde in yeast.

If there is any single feature that characterizes glycolysis it is the regeneration of NAD^+ by a reaction of NADH with one of the

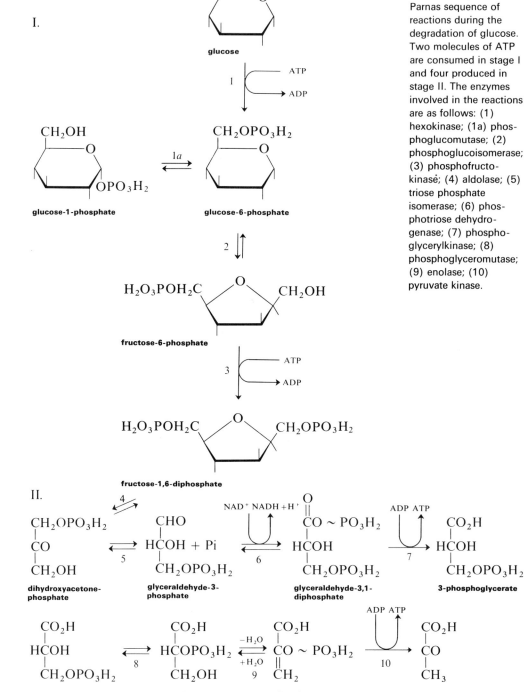

figure 9.1 ::
Embden-Meyerhof-
Parnas sequence of
reactions during the
degradation of glucose.
Two molecules of ATP
are consumed in stage I
and four produced in
stage II. The enzymes
involved in the reactions
are as follows: (1)
hexokinase; (1a) phos-
phoglucomutase; (2)
phosphoglucoisomerase;
(3) phosphofructo-
kinase; (4) aldolase; (5)
triose phosphate
isomerase; (6) phos-
photriose dehydro-
genase; (7) phospho-
glycerylkinase; (8)
phosphoglyceromutase;
(9) enolase; (10)
pyruvate kinase.

final intermediates in the process. Pyruvate and acetaldehyde are the most common acceptors of H from NADH but they are not the only ones. There is great diversity in the living world in the manner in which NAD^+ is regenerated during anaerobic glycolysis, particularly among microorganisms and invertebrates.

Another characteristic of anaerobic glycolysis is the accumulation of the reduced product: lactate in muscle and ethanol in yeast. The final disposition of the end product varies considerably from one organism to another.

The breakdown of glucose through the sequence of reactions shown in Figure 9.1 is known as the *Embden-Meyerhof-Parnas scheme*, after three of several investigators who contributed greatly to our present understanding (G. Embden, O. Meyerhof, and J. Parnas).

Before discussing each individual reaction, some comments should be made on the overall scheme. First, the starting material in the scheme is glucose but in the cell free glucose need not be formed if glycogen is present. Glycogen splits into glucose-1-phosphate by the action of phosphorylase.

If glucose is the starting material, it must first be phosphorylated by ATP; the reaction proceeds with a large decrease in free energy, and its reversal is almost impossible at the concentration of reactants present in the cell. The same situation is observed in two other reactions in which there is a large decrease in free energy: reactions 3 and 10.

Despite the irreversibility of three reactions, glucose can be formed in the cell from pyruvate by reversing all other reactions. The energy barrier of the three reactions just mentioned is overcome in the cell by utilizing another route. For example, in reaction 1, glucose-6-phosphate is dephosphorylated by a different enzyme: a phosphatase. Thus glucose-6-phosphate does not need to react with ADP to yield glucose. A similar phosphatase dephosphorylates fructose-1,6-diphosphate (reaction 3).

The energy barrier in reaction 10 is overcome by a more roundabout set of reactions, which will be discussed in more detail later.

Other features of the Embden-Meyerhof-Parnas scheme stand out. Note that reactions 1 to 4 consume two molecules of ATP, one for each of the two phosphorylations. The process up to this point yields no energy but actually consumes energy. In reaction 4 one molecule of phosphorylated hexose cleaves into two phosphorylated trioses. When the two trioses are oxidized in steps 5 and 6, the energy of oxidation is coupled to the phosphorylation of two molecules of ATP. Generation of two molecules of ATP in stage II of glycolysis at this point cancels the utilization of the two molecules of ATP in the first stage of glycolysis. A net gain of two ATP molecules per glucose molecule accrues in reaction 9 when phosphoenolpyruvate reacts with ADP.

Now we shall proceed to discuss briefly each reaction in the glycolytic scheme (Figure 9.1).

1. PHOSPHORYLATION OF GLUCOSE : Glucose is phosphorylated in the cell by ATP in a reaction mediated by either a *hexokinase* or a *glucokinase*. Hexokinase is an enzyme of relatively broad specificity; it attacks in addition to glucose: mannose, fructose, 2-deoxyglucose, and glucosamine. Glucokinase, on the other hand, is specific for D-glucose. The reaction

is, as already indicated, an exergonic reaction with a ΔF^0 of about -5 kcal and therefore not easily reversed. The K_{eq} for the reaction is 6.5×10^3.

1*a*. INTERCONVERSION OF GLUCOSE-6-PHOSPHATE AND GLUCOSE-1-PHOSPHATE : Glucose-6-phosphate and glucose-1-phosphate are readily interconvertible in the presence of the enzyme *phosphoglucomutase*. The importance of this reaction is that in the cell glucose-1-phosphate is formed from glycogen (in animals) and starch (in plants), and it becomes the starting material for glycolysis. The reaction

is reversible but it favors the formation of glucose-6-phosphate. The K_{eq} of the reaction (glucose-6-phosphate/glucose-1-phosphate) is 19 at pH 7.

2. ISOMERIZATION OF GLUCOSE-6-PHOSPHATE : In reaction 2, glucose-6-phosphate undergoes isomerization to fructose-6-phosphate by the action of the enzyme *phosphoglucoisomerase*. This is a metalloprotein with a rather high degree of specificity:

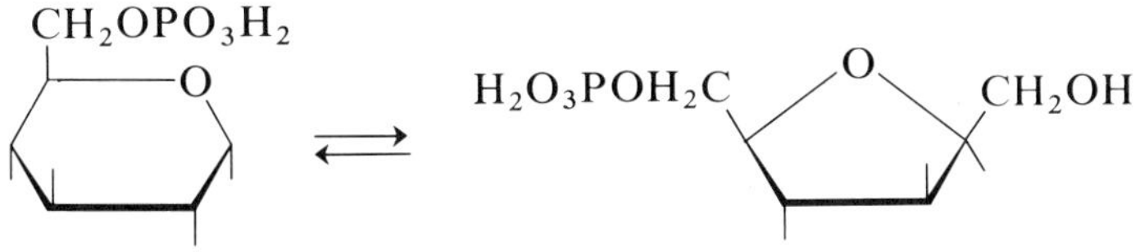

$CH_2OPO_3H_2$

glucose-6-phosphate

$H_2O_3POH_2C$ CH_2OH

fructose-6-phosphate

There is no known cofactor involved in this reaction; the reaction is freely reversible ($K_{eq} = 0.5$).

A mechanism (discussed in Chapter 7) for this reaction involves the formation of an intermediate *cis*-ene-diol.

3. PHOSPHORYLATION OF FRUCTOSE-6-PHOSPHATE : The second phosphorylation in glycolysis is catalyzed by a specific kinase: *phosphofructokinase*; like other kinases catalyzing phosphorylations by ATP it requires Mg^{2+}.

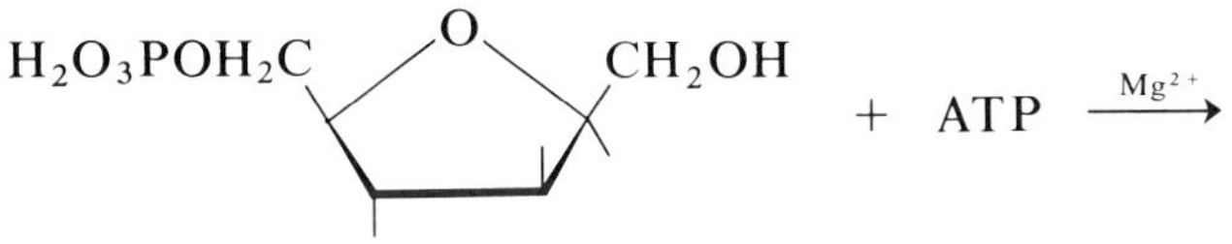

$H_2O_3POH_2C$ CH_2OH +   ATP $\xrightarrow{Mg^{2+}}$

fructose-6-phosphate

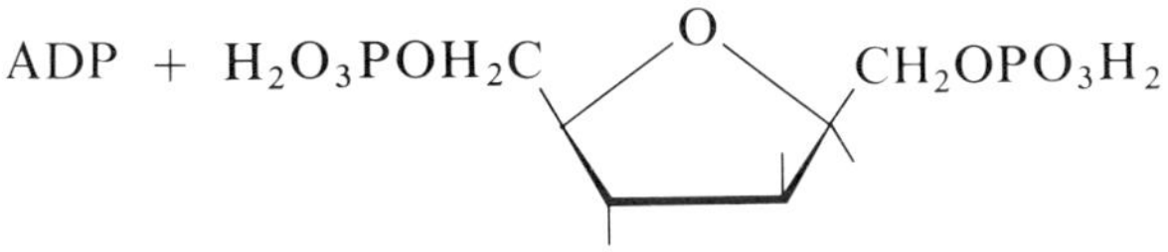

ADP + $H_2O_3POH_2C$ $CH_2OPO_3H_2$

fructose-1,6-diphosphate

Phosphofructokinase has been studied extensively, as it represents a key enzyme in the regulation of glycolysis. As pointed out at the beginning of the chapter, metabolic pathways are regulated within the cell by a number of devices. For example, phosphofructokinase is inhibited by high concentration of ATP and also by citrate. If ATP is produced abundantly by oxidations in the mitochondria, the excess ATP inhibits glycolysis at this point by inhibiting phosphorylation of fructose-6-phosphate; when glycolysis is blocked, glucose is synthesized. The reverse is also true;

when ATP is in short supply, the concentration of ADP increases and ADP is known to activate phosphofructokinase.

4. FRAGMENTATION OF FRUCTOSE-1,6-DIPHOSPHATE : The formation of a hexose diphosphate completes the first stage of glycolysis, which may be regarded as a preparatory stage. Cleavage of fructose-1,6-diphosphate into two triose phosphates is the beginning of a second stage, which leads to the oxidoreduction reaction. The cleavage of fructose-1,6-diphosphate is catalyzed by the enzyme *aldolase*:

$H_2O_3POH_2C$ 　 O 　 $CH_2OPO_3H_2$

$$
\begin{array}{c}
CH_2OPO_3H_2 \\
| \\
C=O \\
| \\
HOCH \\
| \\
HCOH \\
| \\
HCOH \\
| \\
CH_2OPO_3H_2
\end{array}
\rightleftharpoons
\begin{array}{c}
CH_2OPO_3H_2 \\
| \\
C=O \\
| \\
CH_2OH
\end{array}
+
\begin{array}{c}
CHO \\
| \\
HCOH \\
| \\
CH_2OPO_3H_2
\end{array}
$$

dihydroxyacetone phosphate **glyceraldehyde-3-phosphate**

fructose-1,6-diphosphate

The K_{eq} for the reaction is 9.1×10^{-5}, and it favors the formation of the hexose diphosphate over its cleavage. This is no problem in the cell, as the products are rapidly removed by subsequent reactions.

The cleavage is regarded as a reverse aldol condensation similar to acid-base–catalyzed aldol condensations of this type:

$$
\begin{array}{c}
R_1 \\
| \\
C=O \\
| \\
HOCH \\
H
\end{array}
+ B^-
\rightleftharpoons
\begin{array}{c}
R_1 \\
| \\
C=O \\
| \\
HOCH \\
\bar{\ }
\end{array}
+ BH
$$

$$
\begin{array}{c}
R_1 \\
| \\
C=O \\
| \\
HOCH \\
\end{array}
+ \overset{\delta^+}{H}-\overset{\delta^-}{C}=O \quad R_2
\rightleftharpoons
\begin{array}{c}
R_1 \\
| \\
C=O \\
| \\
HOCH \\
| \\
HCO^- \\
| \\
R_2
\end{array}
+ BH
\rightleftharpoons
\begin{array}{c}
R_1 \\
| \\
C=O \\
| \\
HOCH \\
| \\
HCOH \\
| \\
R_2
\end{array}
+ B^-
$$

5. ISOMERIZATION OF TRIOSE PHOSPHATES : The two products of reaction 4 are readily interconvertible. The enzyme *triose phosphate isomerase* catalyzes the conversion of dihydroxyacetone phosphate into glyceraldehyde-3-phosphate:

$$
\begin{array}{lcl}
\text{CH}_2\text{OH} & & \text{CHO} \\
| & & | \\
\text{C}{=}\text{O} & \rightleftharpoons & \text{HCOH} \\
| & & | \\
\text{CH}_2\text{OPO}_3\text{H}_2 & & \text{CH}_2\text{OPO}_3\text{H}_2
\end{array}
$$

dihydroxyacetone phosphate   **glyceraldehyde-3-phosphate**

There is little difference, mechanistically, between this reaction and reaction 2. At equilibrium, dihydroxyacetone phosphate predominates ($K_{eq} = 22$), but here also glyceraldehyde-3-phosphate is removed rapidly by a subsequent reaction.

It should be remembered that dihydroxyacetone phosphate serves as a hydrogen acceptor from NADH and in this way serves as a shuttle between cytoplasmic and mitochondrial oxidoreductions (Chapter 8).

6. THE OXIDATION-REDUCTION STEP : In all subsequent reactions two molecules of triose phosphate are implied, since dihydroxyacetone phosphate is readily converted to glyceraldehyde-3-phosphate.

Oxidation of glyceraldehyde-3-phosphate to 3-phosphoglycerate is catalyzed by the enzyme *phosphotriose dehydrogenase*. The enzyme has been purified extensively, and it has been found that it contains firmly attached NAD^+, in contrast to other dehydrogenases in which NAD^+ is easily dissociated from the apoenzyme. The activity of the enzyme is inhibited by iodoacetate and other reagents known to attack the $-SH$ groups.

On the basis of all available information, a mechanism for the action of phosphotriose dehydrogenase has been proposed.

The reactions overleaf clearly show that NAD^+ and H_3PO_4 are necessary. In reaction 3 the intermediate has a high group-transfer potential and utilizes H_3PO_4 to transfer the acyl group. The product, 1,3-diphosphoglycerate, is an energy-rich compound; it can transfer its phosphate group from position 1 to a suitable acceptor such as ADP, as will be shown below.

The oxidation-reduction step in glycolysis is an example of oxidative phosphorylation at the substrate level in distinction to oxidative phosphorylation by electron transfer in the respiratory assembly. In the oxidation of 3-phosphoglyceraldehyde, the energy

1.
$$\begin{array}{c} O \\ \parallel \\ CH \\ HCOH \\ \mid \\ CH_2OPO_3H_2 \end{array} + HS-enzyme-NAD^+ \rightleftharpoons \begin{array}{c} O \\ \parallel \\ C-S-enzyme-NADH + H^+ \\ HCOH \\ \mid \\ CH_2OPO_3H_2 \end{array}$$

2.
$$\begin{array}{c} O \\ \parallel \\ C-S-enzyme-NADH + H^+ \\ HCOH \\ \mid \\ CH_2OPO_3H_2 \end{array} + NAD^+ \rightleftharpoons$$

$$\begin{array}{c} O \\ \parallel \\ C-S-enzyme-NAD^+ \\ HCOH \\ \mid \\ CH_2OPO_3H_2 \end{array} + NADH + H^+$$

3.
$$\begin{array}{c} O \\ \parallel \\ C-S-enzyme-NAD^+ \\ HCOH \\ \mid \\ CH_2OPO_3H_2 \end{array} + H_3PO_4 \rightleftharpoons$$

$$\begin{array}{c} O \\ \parallel \\ CO \sim PO_3H_2 \\ HCOH \\ \mid \\ CH_2OPO_3H_2 \end{array} + HS-enzyme-NAD^+$$

of oxidation is conserved in the form of a mixed anhydride bond between phosphate and a carboxylic acid. The high chemical potential of 1,3-diphosphoglycerate makes it possible to generate ATP.

7. ATP GENERATION : ADP is phosphorylated to ATP by 1,3-diphosphoglycerate in a reaction catalyzed by *phosphoglyceryl kinase*:

$$\begin{array}{c} O \\ \parallel \\ CO \sim PO_3H_2 \\ HCOH \\ \mid \\ CH_2OPO_3H_2 \end{array} + ADP \xrightleftharpoons{Mg^{2+}} ATP + \begin{array}{c} CO_2H \\ \mid \\ HCOH \\ \mid \\ CH_2OPO_3H_2 \end{array}$$

1,3-diphosphoglycerate   3-phosphoglycerate

8. ISOMERIZATION OF 3-PHOSPHOGLYCERATE : The conversion of 3-phosphoglycerate to 2-phosphoglycerate is catalyzed by the enzyme *phosphoglyceromutase*. The reaction resembles reaction 1a, in which the phosphate group migrates from position 1 to position 6 of glucose. The enzyme utilizes 2,3-diphosphoglyceric acid as a cofactor, as was shown in Section 7.2.

The reaction

$$
\begin{array}{ccc}
CO_2H & & CO_2H \\
| & & | \\
HCOH & \rightleftharpoons & HCOPO_3H_2 \\
| & & | \\
CH_2OPO_3H_2 & & CH_2OH \\
\text{\scriptsize 3-phosphoglycerate} & & \text{\scriptsize 2-phosphoglycerate}
\end{array}
$$

is readily reversible.

9. FORMATION OF PHOSPHOENOLPYRUVATE (PEP) : Removal of water from 2-phosphoglycerate is catalyzed by *enolase*:

$$
\begin{array}{ccc}
CO_2H & & CO_2H \\
| & \xrightarrow{Mg^{2+}} & | \\
HCOPO_3H_2 & \rightleftharpoons & CO \sim PO_3H_2 + H_2O \\
| & & || \\
CH_2OH & & CH_2 \\
\text{\scriptsize 3-phosphoglycerate} & & \text{\scriptsize PEP}
\end{array}
$$

The phosphate in PEP has a high group-transfer potential (ΔF^0 of hydrolysis, -12 kcal). In the above reaction the removal of water results in a redistribution of energy, leading to the formation of an energy-rich compound.

10. GENERATION OF ATP AND FORMATION OF PYRUVATE : In this step of glycolysis pyruvate is formed when phosphoenolpyruvate transfers its phosphate to ADP; the reaction is catalyzed by *pyruvate kinase*:

$$
\begin{array}{ccc}
CO_2H & & CO_2H \\
| & \xrightarrow{Mg^{2+}} & | \\
CO \sim PO_3H_2 + ADP & & CO + ATP \\
|| & & | \\
CH_2 & & CH_3 \\
\text{\scriptsize phosphoenolpyruvate} & & \text{\scriptsize pyruvate}
\end{array}
$$

The energy of hydrolysis of PEP is more than adequate for the generation of ATP. The two molecules of ATP (from two molecules of PEP) represent the net gain in the breakdown of glucose to pyruvate.

As pointed out earlier, the equilibrium of the last reaction greatly favors pyruvate formation. The energy barrier in the reverse reaction is overcome in the cell by utilizing different routes for the formation of PEP from pyruvate.

In one such route a *pyruvate carboxylase* or *malic enzyme* catalyzes the carboxylation of pyruvate to oxalacetate. Pyruvate carboxylase, for example, catalyzes the reaction

$$
\begin{array}{c}
CO_2H \\
| \\
CO \\
| \\
CH_3
\end{array}
+ CO_2 + ATP
\xrightarrow{\text{acetyl-CoA, Mg}^{2+}}
\begin{array}{c}
CO_2H \\
| \\
CO \\
| \\
CH_2 \\
| \\
CO_2H
\end{array}
+ ADP + P_i
$$

pyruvate   oxalacetate

The oxalacetate thus formed gives rise to phosphoenolpyruvate by a reaction catalyzed by the enzyme PEP-carboxykinase:

$$
\begin{array}{c}
CO_2H \\
| \\
CO \\
| \\
CH_2 \\
| \\
CO_2H
\end{array}
+ ITP\dagger
\xrightleftharpoons{\text{Mg}^{2+}}
\begin{array}{c}
CO_2H \\
| \\
CO \sim PO_3H_2 \\
|| \\
CH_2
\end{array}
+ IDP\dagger + CO_2
$$

oxalacetate   phosphoenolpyruvate

The formation of PEP by this route is no less expensive in terms of energy than by reaction 10. The advantage here is that by utilizing another set of reactions the formation of PEP can be driven by coupled reactions.

OXIDATION OF NADH : During the oxidation of glyceraldehyde-3-phosphate (reaction 6) two molecules of NAD^+ are reduced. If the process is to continue in the absence of oxygen, the resulting NADH must be oxidized. In skeletal muscle as well as in many other tissues pyruvate serves as the hydrogen acceptor:

$$
\begin{array}{c}
CO_2H \\
| \\
CO \\
| \\
CH_3
\end{array}
+ NADH + H^+
\rightleftharpoons
\begin{array}{c}
CO_2H \\
| \\
HCOH \\
| \\
CH_3
\end{array}
+ NAD^+
$$

pyruvate   lactate

† ITP, inosine triphosphate; IDP, inosine diphosphate.

The reaction is catalyzed by *lactic dehydrogenase*, a widely distributed enzyme.

Lactic acid is, in this instance, the end product of glycolysis and would accumulate unless removed from the cell or oxidized. In the animal both processes operate; lactic acid is removed by the blood and carried from muscle to other organs, where it can be oxidized. It can also be oxidized in muscle by reverting to pyruvate and entering into the citrate cycle during periods when muscle has an ample supply of oxygen.

In yeast, pyruvate undergoes decarboxylation to produce acetaldehyde, which becomes the hydrogen acceptor:

$$\begin{array}{c} CO_2H \\ | \\ CO \\ | \\ CH_3 \end{array} \quad \xrightarrow[\text{TPP}]{\text{Mg}^{2+}} \quad \begin{array}{c} CHO \\ | \\ CH_3 \end{array} + CO_2$$

pyruvate   acetaldehyde

This reaction is catalyzed by a thiamine pyrophosphate enzyme, *pyruvic decarboxylase*, which is present in yeast. Acetaldehyde reacts with NADH to produce ethanol:

$$\begin{array}{c} CHO \\ | \\ CH_3 \end{array} + NADH + H^+ \rightleftarrows \begin{array}{c} CH_2OH \\ | \\ CH_3 \end{array} + NAD^+$$

The last reaction is catalyzed by alcohol dehydrogenase, a widely distributed enzyme.

The production of two molecules of pyruvate from one molecule of glucose by the Embden-Meyerhof-Parnas pathway is accompanied by the production of two molecules of ATP, which is a *relatively poor yield.* A large amount of chemical potential remains in the end product, so we may view the production of pyruvate from glucose as a means of generating fuel for the mitochondrion.

conversion of glucose to pyruvate: pentose phosphate pathway :: 9.3

The production of pyruvate from glucose by the sequence of reactions just outlined is a process common to many organisms. It is by no means the only process by which pyruvate is produced from glucose.

It was suspected for a long time that glucose must undergo other degradative reactions in the cell. One of the reasons for suspecting another pathway was the observation by the German biochemist Otto Warburg that glucose-6-phosphate was oxidized to 6-phosphogluconate in yeast. The product of oxidation is not an intermediate of glycolysis, and some other pathway had to be invoked to account for its final breakdown.

Other reasons include the need to explain the utilization of pentoses by microorganisms or their biosynthesis from glucose. The search for another pathway for glucose degradation ended with the discovery of new reaction sequences and new enzymes that could account for the formation of pyruvate from glucose by an alternative route.

The reactions involved in this new scheme, which is known as the pentose phosphate pathway, will be discussed in turn.

1. FORMATION OF 6-PHOSPHOGLUCONATE: Starting with glucose-6-phosphate, the first step is its oxidation catalyzed by the enzyme glucose-6-phosphate dehydrogenase, which utilizes $NADP^+$ as a coenzyme:

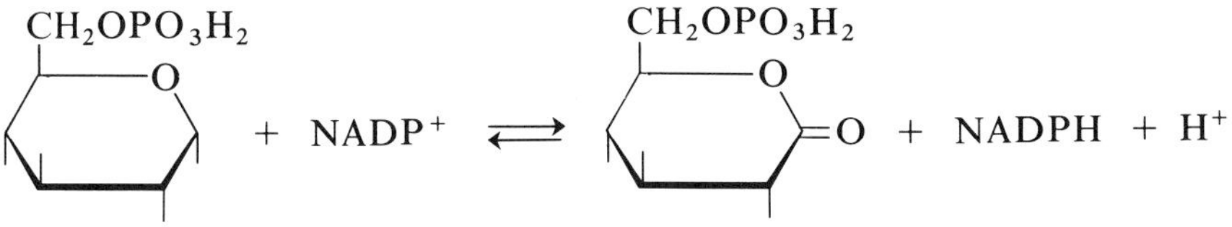

glucose-6-phosphate   6-phosphoglucono-δ-lactone

The immediate product of oxidation, as shown above, is 6-phosphoglucono-δ-lactone rather than the acid. Lactones are notoriously unstable and hydrolyze without difficulty into the acid. However, in the cell rapid hydrolysis is ensured by the action of a *6-phosphogluconolactonase*, which catalyzes the reaction:

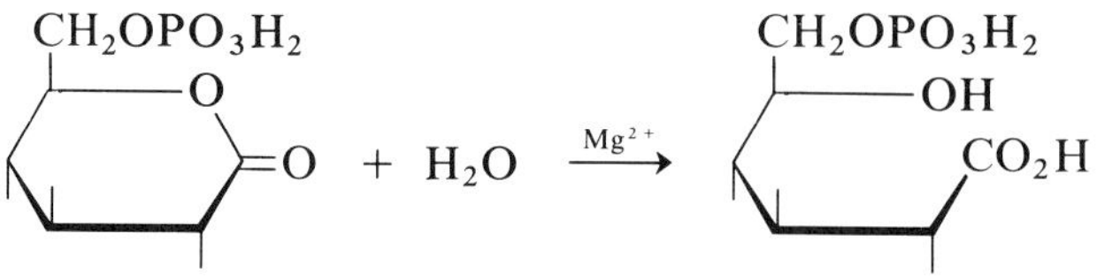

6-phosphoglucono-δ-lactone   6-phosphogluconate

2. FORMATION OF RIBULOSE-5-PHOSPHATE : A second $NADP^+$-dependent enzyme catalyzes the conversion of 6-phosphogluconate to ribulose-5-phosphate. The reaction involves an oxidation and decarboxylation:

$$
\begin{array}{c}
\text{CO}_2\text{H} \\
| \\
\text{HCOH} \\
| \\
\text{HOCH} \\
| \\
\text{HCOH} \\
| \\
\text{HCOH} \\
| \\
\text{CH}_2\text{OPO}_3\text{H}_2
\end{array}
\quad + \text{NADP}^+ \xrightarrow{\text{Mg}^{2+}}
\left[
\begin{array}{c}
\text{CO}_2\text{H} \\
| \\
\text{HCOH} \\
| \\
\text{C}=\text{O} \\
| \\
\text{HCOH} \\
| \\
\text{HCOH} \\
| \\
\text{CH}_2\text{OPO}_3\text{H}_2
\end{array}
\right]
\longrightarrow
$$

6-phosphogluconate   3-keto-6-phosphohexonic acid

$$
\begin{array}{c}
\text{CO}_2 \\
+ \\
\text{CH}_2\text{OH} \\
| \\
\text{C}=\text{O} \qquad + \text{NADPH} + \text{H}^+\\
| \\
\text{HCOH} \\
| \\
\text{HCOH} \\
| \\
\text{CH}_2\text{OPO}_3\text{H}_2
\end{array}
$$

ribulose-5-phosphate

The enzyme, *6-phosphogluconate dehydrogenase*, catalyzes the oxidation of C_3 to give rise to a postulated intermediate (in brackets above), sufficiently unstable to decarboxylate as shown, yielding pentose phosphate as the final product.

Another possibility is that the enzyme catalyzes the simultaneous oxidation and decarboxylation of 6-phosphogluconate without the necessity to form an intermediate.

The two oxidations outlined result in the reduction of two molecules of NADP^+. This is one important source of the reduced coenzymes necessary in a multitude of biosynthetic reactions driven specifically by NADPH.

3. FORMATION OF XYLULOSE-5-PHOSPHATE AND RIBOSE-5-PHOS-PHATE : Ribulose-5-phosphate undergoes two possible reactions:

$$
\begin{array}{ccc}
\text{CH}_2\text{OH} & & \text{CHO} \\
| & & | \\
\text{C}=\text{O} & & \text{HCOH} \\
| & \rightleftharpoons & | \\
\text{HCOH} & & \text{HCOH} \\
| & & | \\
\text{HCOH} & & \text{HCOH} \\
| & & | \\
\text{CH}_2\text{OPO}_3\text{H} & & \text{CH}_2\text{OPO}_3\text{H}_2
\end{array}
$$

1.   ribulose-5-phosphate   ribose-5-phosphate

$$
2.\ \begin{array}{c} CH_2OH \\ | \\ C=O \\ | \\ HCOH \\ | \\ HCOH \\ | \\ CH_2OPO_3H_2 \end{array} \quad \rightleftharpoons \quad \begin{array}{c} CH_2OH \\ | \\ C=O \\ | \\ HOCH \\ | \\ HCOH \\ | \\ CH_2OPO_3H_2 \end{array}
$$

ribulose-5-phosphate   **xylulose-5-phosphate**

Reaction (1) is an isomerization similar to that of reaction (2) in glycolysis; it is catalyzed by *phosphoribose isomerase*. Reaction (2), catalyzed by *phosphoketopentoisomerase*, results in epimerization at C_3 to yield xylulose-5-phosphate.

The formation of any of the three pentose phosphates from one molecule of glucose presents no difficulty. It becomes somewhat confusing to trace the carbons from pentose phosphate to pyruvate because more than one molecule of pentose phosphate is needed in the formulation. Before dealing with the stoichiometry of the sequence, two new reactions must be introduced.

TRANSKETOLASE : *Transketolase* is a thiamine pyrophosphate (TPP) enzyme catalyzing the scission of a C—C bond in compounds with the structure

$$
\begin{array}{c} CH_2OH \\ | \\ C=O \\ | \\ HOCH \\ | \\ R \end{array}
$$

and condensing the ketol group (bold) to an aldehyde. The reaction can be represented in general terms by

$$
1.\ \begin{array}{c} \mathbf{CH_2OH} \\ | \\ \mathbf{C=O} \\ | \\ HOCH \\ | \\ R_1 \end{array} + \text{TPP}-\text{enzyme} \xrightarrow{\text{Mg}^{2+}} \begin{array}{c} \mathbf{CH_2OH} \\ | \\ \mathbf{C=O} \\ | \\ \text{TPP}-\text{enzyme} \end{array} + \begin{array}{c} H-C=O \\ | \\ R_1 \end{array}
$$

$$
2.\ \begin{array}{c} CH_2OH \\ | \\ C=O \\ | \\ \text{TPP}-\text{enzyme} \end{array} + \begin{array}{c} H-C=O \\ | \\ R_2 \end{array} \xrightarrow{\text{Mg}^{2+}} \begin{array}{c} CH_2OH \\ | \\ C=O \\ | \\ HOCH \\ | \\ R_2 \end{array} + \text{TPP}-\text{enzyme}
$$

Xylulose-5-phosphate and ribose-5-phosphate are representatives of R_1 and R_2, respectively.

TRANSALDOLASE : The enzyme transaldolase catalyzes the transfer of the dihydroxyacetone portion of fructose-6-phosphate or sedohepulose-7-phosphate to a suitable aldose such as glyceraldehyde-3-phosphate:

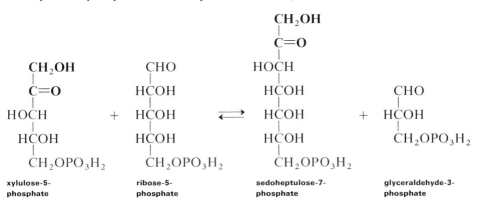

CH₂OH		CH₂OH	
C=O		C=O	CHO
HOCH	+ HC=O ⇌	HOCH	+ HCOH
HCOH	HCOH	HCOH	HCOH
HCOH	CH₂OPO₃H₂	HCOH	CH₂OPO₃H₂
HCOH		CH₂OPO₃H₂	
CH₂OPO₃H₂			
sedoheptulose-7-phosphate	glyceraldehyde-3-phosphate	fructose-6-phosphate	erythrose-4-phosphate

4. BALANCE OF CARBONS : The pentose phosphate pathway is represented in Figure 9.2. It is not immediately clear from the flow diagram how the carbons of glucose-6-phosphate are balanced. To account for the total oxidation of one glucose molecule, it is necessary to start the scheme with six glucose molecules. At the end of the sequence, five molecules of glucose are regenerated for each one oxidized to $6CO_2$. The process can be represented schematically as in Figure 9.3.

The formation of the pentoses, in the scheme needs no further explanation (*a*). In (*b*) the reaction catalyzed by transketolase occurs between xylulose-5-phosphate and ribose-5-phosphate (all three pentose phosphates are easily interconverted):

		CH₂OH	
		C=O	
CH₂OH	CHO	HOCH	
C=O	HCOH	HCOH	CHO
HOCH	+ HCOH ⇌	HCOH	+ HCOH
HCOH	HCOH	HCOH	CH₂OPO₃H₂
CH₂OPO₃H₂	CH₂OPO₃H₂	CH₂OPO₃H₂	
xylulose-5-phosphate	ribose-5-phosphate	sedoheptulose-7-phosphate	glyceraldehyde-3-phosphate

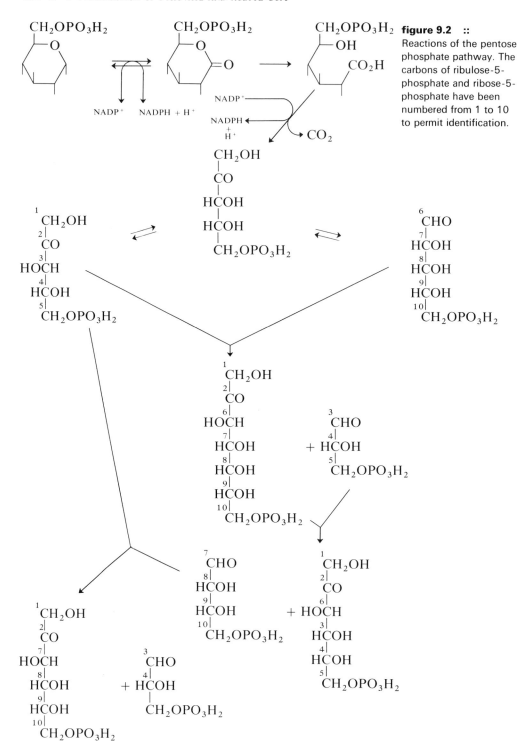

figure 9.2 :: Reactions of the pentose phosphate pathway. The carbons of ribulose-5-phosphate and ribose-5-phosphate have been numbered from 1 to 10 to permit identification.

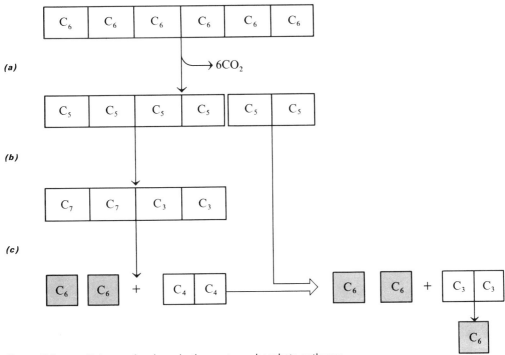

figure 9.3 :: Balance of carbons in the pentose phosphate pathway. For every six glucose molecules at the start, one glucose molecule is oxidized while five hexoses are regenerated.

In (c), transaldolase catalyzes the formation of two fructose-6-phosphates (as already shown), leaving behind two erythrose-4-phosphates. These are aldehyde acceptors in the transketolase reaction, and they react with two xylulose molecules to form two fructose-6-phosphates and leave behind two triose phosphates (Figure 9.3). Aldolase catalyzes their condensation to fructose-1,6-diphosphate.

Fructose esters are intermediates in the Embden-Meyerhof-Parnas sequence; all six carbons can flow into pyruvate by this roundabout pathway.

The two pathways coexist in many types of cells, sometimes sharing the degradation of glucose to the same degree, but in some cells one or the other pathway predominates.

As mentioned briefly, an important feature of the pentose phosphate pathway is that it generates NADPH. The potential in NADPH is utilized in the biosynthesis of fatty acids, steroids, and other substances. It is apparent that a number of biosynthetic reactions are driven specifically by NADPH rather than by NADH.

conversion of amino acids to pyruvate :: **9.4**

Amino acids are deaminated in most cells by the action of specific deaminases and transaminases. The resulting carbon framework (an α-keto acid) of some amino acids reacts to yield pyruvate and in some cases acetyl-CoA directly. Amino acids such as alanine, serine, and cysteine (three-carbon amino acids) yield pyruvate by a single reaction. Others must follow more roundabout pathways.

It should be noted that some amino acids can be synthesized by reversing some of the degradative reactions leading to pyruvate, because their carbon frameworks are often intermediates in the degradation of glucose or intermediates in the citrate cycle. For example, alanine, aspartate, and glutamate are readily formed by transamination (or amination) of pyruvate, oxalacetate, and α-ketoglutarate, respectively.

Although the present discussion is limited to sources of pyruvate as mitochondrial fuel, it should be kept in mind that the carbon framework of some amino acids can enter the citrate cycle directly, as is the case with the three amino acids listed above. Several amino acids undergo reactions that yield one of the three amino acids in tandem with the citrate cycle, thus providing substrates for mitochondrial oxidations.

CONVERSION OF ALANINE, CYSTEINE, AND SERINE TO PYRUVATE : There is a close relationship between the three amino acids and pyruvate and also a mutual relationship among all three amino acids. Several enzymes are known to catalyze the deamination of alanine, serine, and cysteine. Alanine is deaminated mainly by transmination (1), but it can be deaminated also by the action of L-*amino acid oxidase* (2):

$$
\begin{array}{l}
\text{1.} \quad
\begin{array}{l}
CH_3 \\
\mid \\
CHNH_2 \\
\mid \\
CO_2H
\end{array}
+
\begin{array}{l}
CO_2H \\
\mid \\
CH_2 \\
\mid \\
CH_2 \\
\mid \\
CO \\
\mid \\
CO_2H
\end{array}
\quad \rightleftharpoons \quad
\begin{array}{l}
CH_3 \\
\mid \\
CO \\
\mid \\
CO_2H
\end{array}
+
\begin{array}{l}
CO_2H \\
\mid \\
CH_2 \\
\mid \\
CH_2 \\
\mid \\
CHNH_2 \\
\mid \\
CO_2H
\end{array}
\end{array}
$$

    alanine α-ketoglutarate   pyruvate   glutamate

$$
\text{2.} \quad
\begin{array}{l}
CH_3 \\
\mid \\
CHNH_2 \\
\mid \\
CO_2H
\end{array}
+ FAD \rightleftharpoons FADH_2 +
\begin{array}{l}
CH_3 \\
\mid \\
CO \\
\mid \\
CO_2H
\end{array}
+ NH_3
$$

The last reaction is catalyzed by the enzyme L-amino acid oxidase, which has a broad specificity; it attacks several other L-amino acids but at rates too slow to play a significant role in deamination.

Serine is deaminated mainly by the action of *serine dehydrase*, an enzyme functioning with pyridoxal phosphate. Quite analogous to serine dehydrase is *cysteine desulfhydrase*, which also functions with pyridoxal phosphate. In both instances elimination of the α hydrogen and the β substituent ($-OH$ in serine, $-SH$ in cysteine) yield the same products:

$$
\begin{array}{c}
CH_2OH \\
| \\
CHNH_2 \\
| \\
CO_2H
\end{array}
\xrightarrow{-H_2O}
\left[
\begin{array}{c}
CH_2 \\
\| \\
C-NH_2 \\
| \\
CO_2H
\end{array}
\rightleftharpoons
\begin{array}{c}
CH_3 \\
| \\
C=NH \\
| \\
CO_2H
\end{array}
\right]
\longrightarrow
\begin{array}{c}
CH_3 \\
| \\
CO \\
| \\
CO_2H
\end{array}
+ NH_3
$$

serine   aminoacrylic acid   pyruvate

$$
\begin{array}{c}
CH_2SH \\
| \\
CHNH_2 \\
| \\
CO_2H
\end{array}
\xrightarrow{-H_2S}
\left[
\begin{array}{c}
CH_2 \\
\| \\
C-NH_2 \\
| \\
CO_2H
\end{array}
\rightleftharpoons
\begin{array}{c}
CH_3 \\
| \\
C=NH \\
| \\
CO_2H
\end{array}
\right]
\longrightarrow
\begin{array}{c}
CH_3 \\
| \\
CO \\
| \\
CO_2H
\end{array}
+ NH_3
$$

cysteine   aminoacrylic acid   pyruvate

Aminoacrylic acid, the postulated intermediate, is too unstable to exist in aqueous solution; it reacts with water to yield pyruvate and ammonia.

Other reactions are known in which the carbons of cysteine and serine become the carbons of pyruvate. Those in which cysteine is involved will be discussed in Chapter 11. Reactions of serine other than the one just discussed include transamination:

$$
\begin{array}{c}
CH_2OH \\
| \\
CHNH_2 \\
| \\
CO_2H
\end{array}
+
\begin{array}{c}
CO_2H \\
| \\
CH_2 \\
| \\
CH_2 \\
| \\
CO \\
| \\
CO_2H
\end{array}
\rightleftharpoons
\begin{array}{c}
CH_2OH \\
| \\
C=O \\
| \\
CO_2H
\end{array}
+
\begin{array}{c}
CO_2H \\
| \\
CH_2 \\
| \\
CH_2 \\
| \\
CHNH_2 \\
| \\
CO_2H
\end{array}
$$

serine   α-ketoglutarate   hydroxy-pyruvate   glutamate

The product of interest here, hydroxypyruvate, finds its way into the glycolytic pathway and its carbons become the carbons of pyruvate.

CONVERSION OF GLYCINE TO PYRUVATE : The two carbons of glycine flow into pyruvate by first being incorporated into serine. Serine and glycine are interconvertible in many cells:

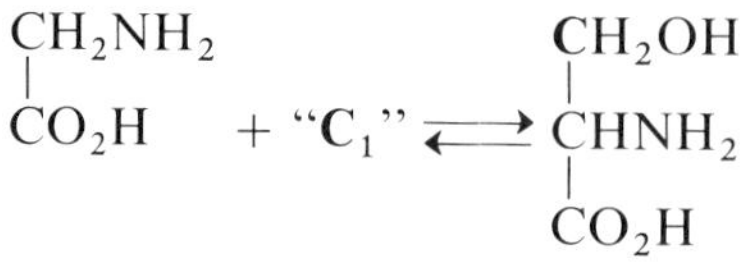

$$
\begin{array}{c}
CH_2NH_2 \\
| \\
CO_2H
\end{array}
+ \text{``}C_1\text{''} \rightleftharpoons
\begin{array}{c}
CH_2OH \\
| \\
CHNH_2 \\
| \\
CO_2H
\end{array}
$$

The reaction between glycine and an "active one-carbon compound" is not a simple one. The one-carbon compound is methylene-N_{5-10}-tetrahydrofolic acid:

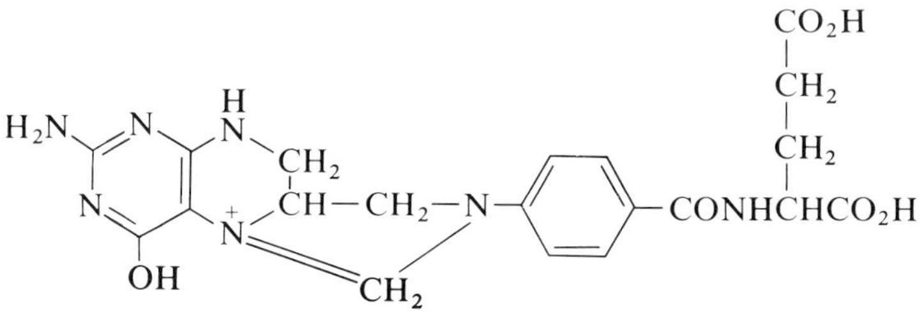

It is produced in the cell from tetrahydrofolic acid (FH_4) and formate; ring closure and reduction gives rise to an active $-CH_2OH$ that condenses with glycine. Formate is not a foreign substance in most cells; it is a product of several enzymatic degradations, and it is an important starting material in biosynthetic reactions.

CONVERSION OF GLUTAMATE AND ASPARTATE TO PYRUVATE : Both amino acids are in tandem with the citrate cycle. Deamination of glutamate is catalyzed by a number of transaminases and also by *gluatamic dehydrogenase*. The resulting α-ketoglutarate undergoes reactions of the citrate cycle and four of the five carbons become the carbons of oxalacetate. Oxalacetate, also the product of aspartate deamination, decarboxylates into pyruvate:

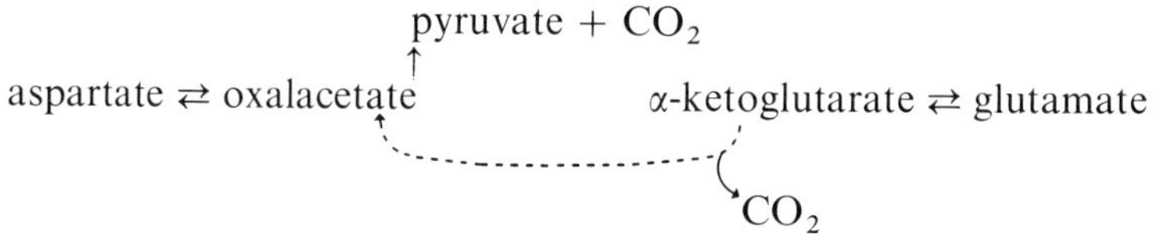

By means of this sequence, it is possible for carbons from intermediates of the citrate cycle to flow into glucose. It would be impossible otherwise because acetyl-CoA is produced from pyruvate irreversibly.

PROLINE–HYDROXYPROLINE : The conversion of proline and hydroxyproline to pyruvate proceeds through several reactions:

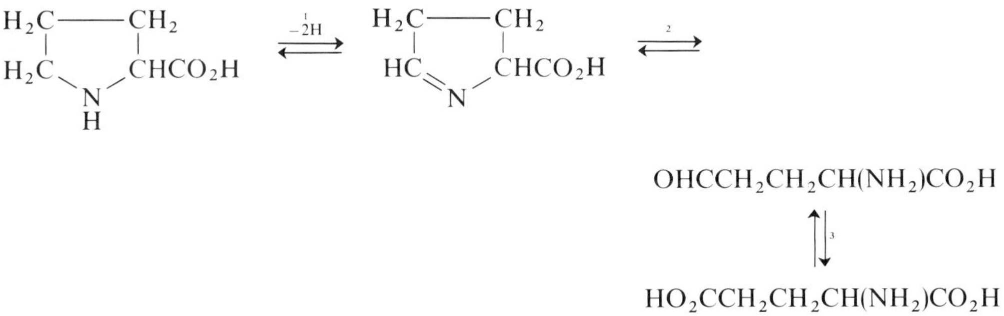

$$H_2C\!-\!\!-\!\!-\!CH_2 \quad \underset{-2H}{\overset{1}{\rightleftharpoons}} \quad H_2C\!-\!\!-\!\!-\!CH_2 \quad \overset{2}{\rightleftharpoons}$$

(proline ring: H_2C, $CHCO_2H$, N, H)

(pyrroline ring: HC, $CHCO_2H$, N)

$$OHCCH_2CH_2CH(NH_2)CO_2H$$
$$\updownarrow{\scriptstyle 3}$$
$$HO_2CCH_2CH_2CH(NH_2)CO_2H$$

1. Oxidation to Δ'-pyrroline-5-carboxylic acid by the action of an oxidase that requires oxygen.
2. Nonenzymatic ring cleavage, producing glutamic acid-γ-semialdehyde.
3. Oxidation of the aldehyde to glutamate by the action of a dehydrogenase.
   The product of the above reactions, glutamate, is converted to pyruvate by reactions already discussed.
   Hydroxyproline undergoes similar reactions but the product is γ-hydroxyglutamate:

$$HO_2CCHOHCH_2CH(NH_2)CO_2H$$

When γ-hydroxyglutamate transaminates, it yields α-keto-γ-hydroxyglutarate, which is enzymatically cleaved into glyoxylate and pyruvate:

$$HO_2C\overset{\downarrow}{C}HOHCH_2COCO_2H \rightleftharpoons HO_2CCHO + CH_3COCO_2H$$

$$\text{glyoxylate} \qquad\qquad \text{pyruvate}$$

HISTIDINE : The carbon atoms of histidine appear as the carbons of pyruvate by reactions that first yield glutamate:

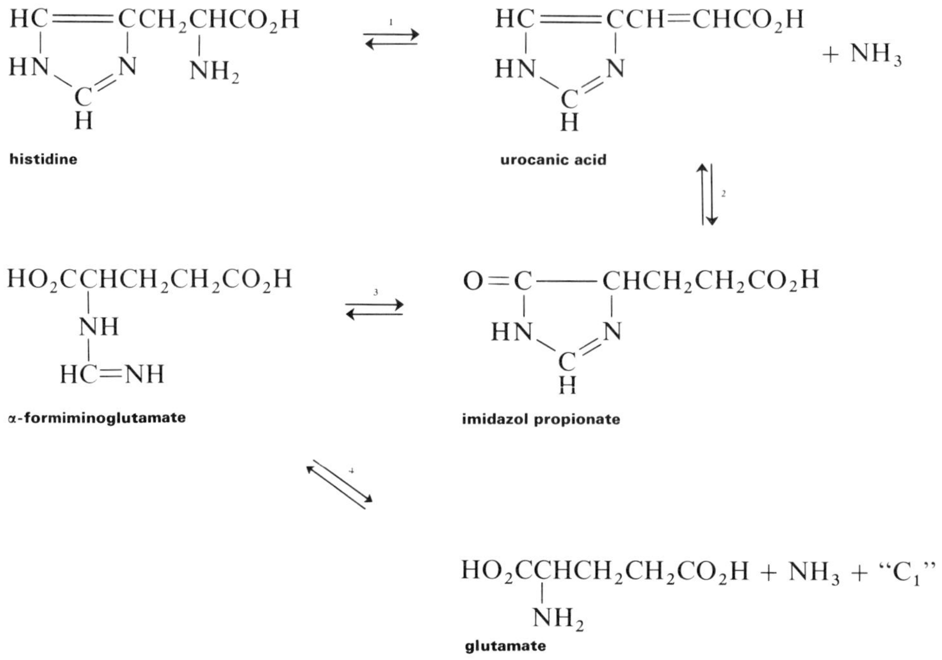

$$HC=\!\!=\!\!CCH_2CHCO_2H$$

(histidine structure with ring: HN, N, NH$_2$, C, H)

$\rightleftharpoons$ (1)

$$HC=\!\!=\!\!CCH=CHCO_2H \quad + NH_3$$

(urocanic acid structure with ring: HN, N, C, H)

histidine

urocanic acid

$\updownarrow$ (2)

$$HO_2CCHCH_2CH_2CO_2H$$

$$|$$
$$NH$$
$$|$$
$$HC=NH$$

$\rightleftharpoons$ (3)

$$O=C\!-\!\!-\!\!CHCH_2CH_2CO_2H$$

(imidazol propionate structure with ring: HN, N, C, H)

α-formiminoglutamate

imidazol propionate

$\nwarrow\!\!\!\searrow$ (4)

$$HO_2CCHCH_2CH_2CO_2H + NH_3 + \text{``}C_1\text{''}$$
$$|$$
$$NH_2$$

glutamate

1. α, β Elimination of NH_3 results in the formation of urocanic acid. The enzyme histidase catalyzes the reaction.

2. The enzyme urocanase catalyzes the conversion of urocanic acid into imidazol propionate. The mechanism of the reaction is not known.

3. Ring opening is catalyzed by a hydrolase to yield α-formimino-glutamate.

4. The final reaction produces glutamate, which is connected to pyruvate by the familiar reactions. Formate finds its way into pyruvate through serine as already shown.

THREONINE : A C—C bond in threonine is cleaved by the action of *threonine aldolase* to yield glycine and acetaldehyde. Glycine finds its way into pyruvate through serine:

$$CH_3CHOHCH(NH_2)CO_2H \rightleftharpoons CH_3CHO + CH_2(NH_2)CO_2H$$

threonine   acetaldehyde   glycine

VALINE : The degradation of valine is an interesting example of diversity of enzymatic reactions to complete its conversion into pyruvate. The steps in this conversion are:

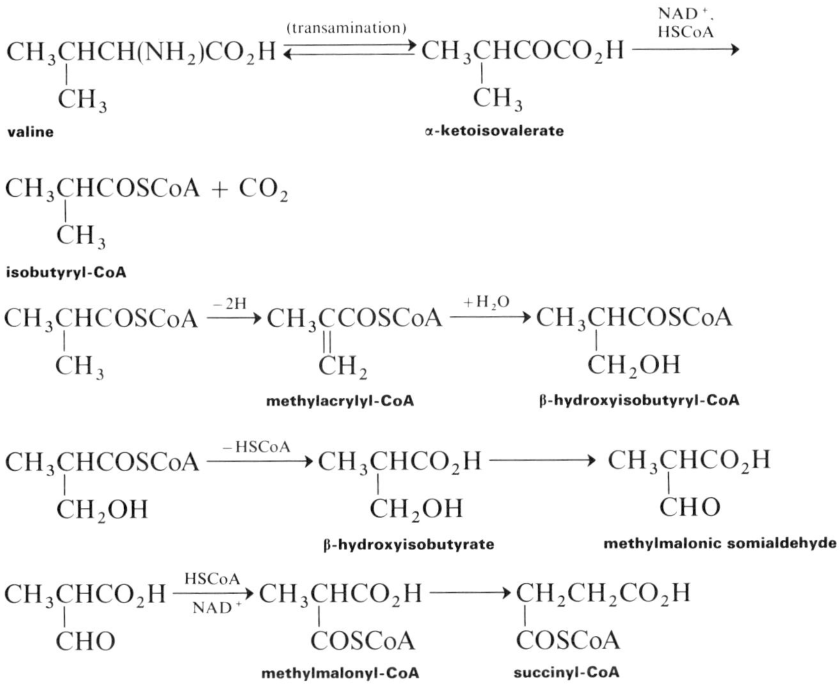

$$CH_3CHCH(NH_2)CO_2H \underset{\text{(transamination)}}{\rightleftharpoons} CH_3CHCOCO_2H \xrightarrow{\overset{NAD^+,}{HSCoA}}$$
$$\quad\quad |\qquad\qquad\qquad\qquad\qquad\qquad |$$
$$\quad\quad CH_3 \qquad\qquad\qquad\qquad\qquad CH_3$$

valine   α-ketoisovalerate

$$CH_3CHCOSCoA + CO_2$$
$$\quad\quad |$$
$$\quad\quad CH_3$$

isobutyryl-CoA

$$CH_3CHCOSCoA \xrightarrow{-2H} CH_3CCOSCoA \xrightarrow{+H_2O} CH_3CHCOSCoA$$
$$\quad\quad |\qquad\qquad\qquad\qquad ||\qquad\qquad\qquad\qquad |$$
$$\quad\quad CH_3 \qquad\qquad\qquad CH_2 \qquad\qquad\qquad CH_2OH$$

methylacrylyl-CoA   β-hydroxyisobutyryl-CoA

$$CH_3CHCOSCoA \xrightarrow{-HSCoA} CH_3CHCO_2H \longrightarrow CH_3CHCO_2H$$
$$\quad\quad |\qquad\qquad\qquad\qquad |\qquad\qquad\qquad\qquad |$$
$$\quad\quad CH_2OH \qquad\qquad\quad CH_2OH \qquad\qquad\quad CHO$$

β-hydroxyisobutyrate   methylmalonic somialdehyde

$$CH_3CHCO_2H \xrightarrow[NAD^+]{HSCoA} CH_3CHCO_2H \longrightarrow CH_2CH_2CO_2H$$
$$\quad\quad |\qquad\qquad\qquad\qquad |\qquad\qquad\qquad\qquad |$$
$$\quad\quad CHO \qquad\qquad\qquad COSCoA \qquad\qquad COSCoA$$

methylmalonyl-CoA   succinyl-CoA

The end product, succinyl-CoA, is a member of the citrate cycle that undergoes the familiar reactions to yield oxalacetate and finally pyruvate by decarboxylation.

OTHER AMINO ACIDS : A portion of the tryptophan molecule can, under certain circumstances, find its way into pyruvate. Some of the carbons of methionine and arginine also appear as pyruvate. These reactions, however, will be better discussed in relation to the metabolic flow of sulfur and nitrogen.

conversion of amino acids to acetyl-CoA :: 9.5

Although some amino acids produce acetyl-CoA by first being converted to pyruvate, other amino acids produce acetyl-CoA without first being converted to pyruvate. These will be discussed next.

LEUCINE AND ISOLEUCINE : The degradation of leucine and isoleucine is in many ways similar in its reactions to the degradation of valine. All undergo an initial transamination to yield their keto acid analogue. They also have in common the decarboxylation and acyl-CoA formation steps. The pathways of degradation of leucine and isoleucine are shown below:

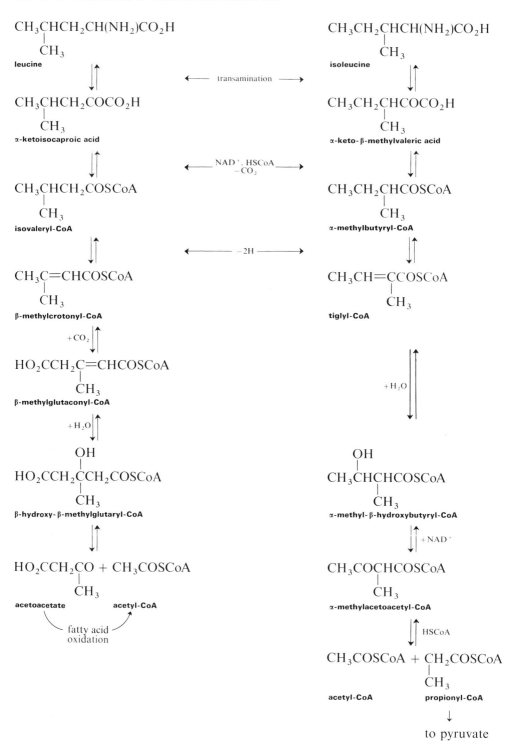

Whereas leucine is converted exclusively into acetyl-CoA, isoleucine yields acetyl-CoA and propionyl-CoA. The latter finds its way into pyruvate by other reactions not to be discussed here but they involve the citrate cycle.

PHENYLALANINE AND TYROSINE : The degradation of these two aromatic amino acids is by a common pathway, because phenylalanine is easily converted to tyrosine by oxidation (hydroxylation). The end products of tyrosine degradation are acetyl-CoA and fumarate:

phenylalanine   tyrosine

p-hydroxyphenylpyruvate   homogentisic acid

4-maleyl acetoacetate   4-fumaryl acetoacetate

$$HO_2CCH + HO_2CCH_2COCO_2H$$
$$\parallel$$
$$HCCO_2H$$

fumarate   acetoacetate

to citrate cycle   to acetyl-CoA through
                                  fatty acid oxidation pathway

As with isoleucine, part of the carbons flow into acetyl-CoA directly and part indirectly through the citrate cycle and into pyruvate.

In Figure 9.4 are summarized the pathways of carbon flow from glucose and amino acids into pyruvate and acetyl-CoA. The flow diagram clearly demonstrates the versatility of the living

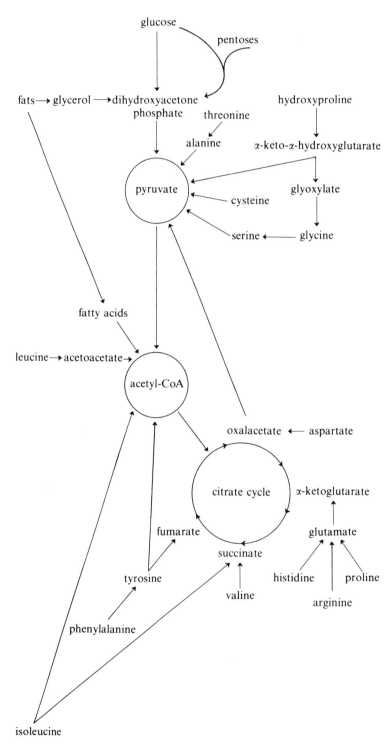

figure 9.4 :: Flow diagram showing the main sources of pyruvate and acetyl-CoA. Only key intermediates are shown.

cell and its ability to simplify its operation. By transforming a variety of organic compounds to acetyl-CoA, the cell deals with one major oxidizable substrate when it reaches the mitochondria.

references ::

GREENBERG, D., ed., in *Metabolic Pathways* (2nd ed.), Vol. I. New York: Academic Press, Inc., 1960.

HOLLMANN, S., AND O. TOUSTER, *Non-Glycolytic Pathways of Metabolism of Glucose.* New York: Academic Press, Inc., 1964.

HORECKER, B. L., "Interdependent Pathways of Carbohydrate Metabolism," in *Harvey Lectures*, Vol. 57, p. 35 (1961–1962). New York: Academic Press, Inc., 1963.

KREBS, H. A., AND H. L. KORNBERG, *Energy Transformations in Living Matter.* Berlin: Springer-Verlag, 1957.

MEISTER, A., *Biochemistry of Amino Acids* (2nd ed.). New York: Academic Press, Inc., 1965.

FOODSTUFFS PROVIDE ALL THE ORGANIC AND INORGANIC SUBSTANCES
needed by organisms to grow and sustain life. The organic substances include potential precursors of pyruvate, acetyl-CoA, and
other citrate-cycle intermediates which, as we know, are completely
burned by the organism. The energy requirements are thus met by
the foodstuffs. In addition, foodstuffs furnish essential organic
compounds that the organisms themselves are unable to synthesize. The vitamins, for example, are in this category.

Foodstuffs that originate in plants and animals are made mostly
of proteins, nucleic acids, carbohydrates, and lipids. Organisms
do not normally assimilate these components intact; if they did,
they could not be utilized to build cell substances. The reason is
that organisms must synthesize substances unique to the organism,
tissue, or even cell. It is known, for example, that proteins are
specific for each organism. It is therefore of no value to assimilate
proteins from the environment. Instead, the proteins in the foodstuffs are cleaved into their component amino acids, which are
then reassembled by the organism into its own proteins.

The same situation applies to other macromolecules; it also

applies to some compounds of low molecular weight, as is the case with nucleotides that are synthesized from readily available and relatively simple precursors.

Generally, the extent to which an organism utilizes the components of the diet without first changing them depends on the organism. Plants and bacteria, for example, are known to be almost self-sufficient; they have the capacity to synthesize the most complex molecules from the simplest compounds. Man and the higher mammals, on the other hand, must feed upon complex molecules that they are unable to produce from simple precursors.

As a general rule, macromolecular substances are first degraded as far as they can be degraded by hydrolysis before being taken in by the cells. This function—the function of hydrolizing macromolecules and also lipids—has become the special function of the digestive enzymes. These are, unlike most other enzymes, excreted by the cells that produce them. Their action upon foodstuffs is carried on outside the cell, either in digestive systems or in their surroundings, depending on whether we are dealing with a multicellular or a unicellular organism.

Even the most complex foodstuffs becomes a mixture of mostly amino acids, a few glycoses, fatty acids, glycerol, pyrimidines, purines, and a few inorganic elements when processed by the digestive enzymes.

Before discussing the breakdown of foodstuffs by digestive enzymes, it is important to recognize that once a molecule originating in the diet enters a cell it becomes indistinguishable from other molecules already present in the cell. As we shall see, the only way to distinguish a dietary molecule is by "tagging" it with an isotope.

dynamic state of cell constituents :: 10.1

When an amino acid, for example, leucine, which originates in dietary protein, enters the cell, it mixes with all other leucine molecules in the cell. Some of them are the product of the breakdown of cell protein. Because any leucine molecule is like any other leucine molecule, it would be impossible to distinguish those which came from the diet from those which were already present in the cell. As a consequence of this technical difficulty, it would have been impossible to trace the path of dietary products as soon as they were absorbed by the tissues or cells.

The cells were once believed to be static systems that undergo some wear and tear, but this idea gave way to the concept of *dynamic equilibrium*, first proposed in 1939 by R. Schoenheimer. The concept of dynamic equilibrium was born from a conclusive experiment in which leucine tagged with heavy N (^{15}N) was fed to rats. The presence of ^{15}N in the synthetic leucine molecule gives it a distinctive property that can be detected in the mass spectrometer, and therefore it can be distinguished from other leucine molecules.

After feeding leucine tagged with ^{15}N to rats for several days, the leucine ^{15}N was found as part of tissue protein. But because the animals gained no weight (in fact, their total protein content did not change), Schoenheimer was led to conclude that protein synthesis had to be attended by protein breakdown. He suggested that dietary leucine (^{15}N) had mixed with leucine in the cell to form a "leucine pool." From this pool the cells draws leucine for protein synthesis and to this pool the cell contributes leucine when tissue protein breaks down (Figure 10.1).

The concept of dynamic equilibrium has been extended to other cell constituents. According to present theories, the living cell is looked upon as a steady state in which many, if not all, of the constituents are in a constant state of flux. The balance between biosynthetic and degradative reactions is well regulated, so that at any time the composition of the cell is the same.

In Section 10.2, we shall be concerned with the breakdown of foodstuffs before they enter the cells. As already discussed in Chapter 9, the products of the digestive breakdown (fatty acids, amino acids, sugars) find their way into acetyl-CoA and citrate-cycle intermediates, forming part of their respective pools, which provide the precursors of biosynthetic reactions as well as mitochondrial fuel.

If we consider only degradative reactions, a diagram such as Figure 10.2 can be drawn. In the diagram are represented three stages in the breakdown of foodstuffs. The second and third stages have been discussed already. The first stage will be discussed next.

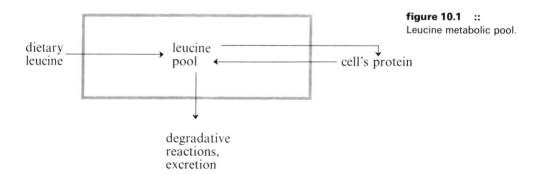

figure 10.1 ::
Leucine metabolic pool.

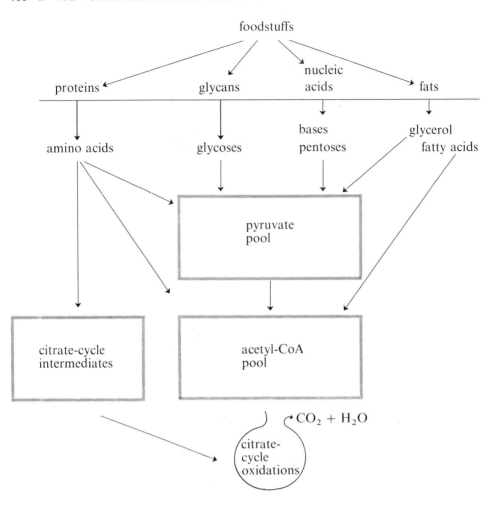

figure 10.2 :: Carbon flow from foodstuffs to CO_2.

extracellular breakdown of macromolecules :: **10.2**

Proteins, glycans, nucleic acids, and fats make up the bulk of the solid matter of most foodstuffs. Other substances of low molecular weight present in the diet normally do not represent a significant supply of nutrients for the organism.

The breakdown of the three major groups of macromolecular substances and fats is hydrolytic in the first stage. This is in reference to the digestive process. But we should also consider their intra-cellular breakdown. The two processes are mechanistically very similar, in some instances identical. They differ, however, in the nature of the enzymes that catalyze their hydrolysis. The digestive and intracellular hydrolases are quite different in properties.

Let us consider first the digestive enzymes.

PROTEASES (PROTEOLYTIC ENZYMES) : Digestive *proteases* have been known for a long time. They are among the best studied enzymes and they continue to hold attention as models of enzyme catalysis. They catalyze the hydrolytic cleavage of peptide bonds, but each protease has a preference for specific bonds. Some attack preferentially peptide bonds at the ends of the polypeptide chain (*exopeptidases*) and others prefer to attack internal bonds (*endopeptidases*). In Table 10.1 we have listed some of the known digestive proteases (or peptidases).

Proteolytic enzymes are widely distributed in the living world but not all have received the same amount of attention. Those discussed here are primarily enzymes obtained from the digestive system of mammals. It is, however, probable that the mode of action of proteolytic enzymes is similar, regardless of source.

Pepsin. Most digestive enzymes are produced within specialized cells in the form of inactive precursors or *zymogens. Pepsin*, for example, is made in the *chief cells* of the gastric mucosa as pepsinogen, which has no proteolytic activity. It becomes active *autocatalytically*, that is, by its own catalytic action when the pH is low. As a matter of fact, in the mammal the pH of the stomach contents is nearly 2, and at this pH pepsinogen is fast converted to pepsin.

The enzyme, which has been obtained in crystalline form, has a molecular weight of about 36,000 and consists of a single polypeptide chain. It functions optimally at unusually low pH values (1 to 3).

Pepsin attacks internal bonds but has a preference for those peptide bonds formed by two hydrophobic amino acids: Phe-Leu, Phe-Phe; Phe-Tyr, Leu-Ala. Also, it seems to be more active with peptide bonds established between a hydrophobic and a dicarboxylic amino acid such as Glu-Tyr, Leu-Glu.

table 10.1 :: Proteases

Endopeptidases:	Exopeptidases:
Pepsin	Carboxypeptidases
Trypsin	Aminopeptidases
Chymotrypsin	Tripeptidases
Cathepsins	Dipeptidases
Papain (plants)	

The autocatalytic transition of pepsinogen to pepsin is accompanied by the loss of a polypeptide from the pepsinogen molecule. The polypeptide, which has a molecular weight of 3,000, is large enough to accommodate 30 amino acid residues. According to present theory, the polypeptide is an inhibitor of pepsin. The autocatalytic reaction can then be represented by the following reaction:

$$\text{pepsinogen} \xrightarrow[\text{pepsin}]{\text{H}^+} \text{pepsin} + \text{peptide}$$

The products of peptic action upon proteins are mixtures of peptides and uncombined amino acids. In most animals, however, pepsin is in contact with dietary protein only the relatively short time that food remains in the stomach. And since the breakdown to the amino acid stage is slow, few amino acids are liberated during this phase of digestion.

Trypsin and chymotrypsin. These two enzymes are produced in the *acinar cells* of the pancreas. Similar enzymes are produced by bacteria and excreted into their surroundings.

As is the case with pepsin, both trypsin and chymotrypsin are produced as inactive precursors: *trypsinogen* and *chymotrypsinogen*. Their conversion to active enzymes involves partial proteolytic digestion of the zymogens. In the case of trypsinogen, it is evident that a hexapeptide is split off from its chain; this event is attended in all probability by conformational changes of the molecule (Figure 10.3).

A similar situation exists in the conversion of chymotrypsinogen to chymotrypsin but the process is stepwise. Autodigestion and digestion by other proteolytic enzymes (trypsin, for example) leads to the liberation of a dipeptide from chymotrypsinogen, but the remainder of the chymotrypsinogen molecule undergoes additional loss of small peptide fragments, leaving behind several active forms of the enzyme.

Trypsin and chymotrypsin have been investigated extensively and in great detail. But we are only concerned at this point with their action on foodstuffs, so that details of their mechanism and properties will not be discussed here. Their specificity, however, merits attention. The two are endopeptidases that attack specific internal bonds. Pancreatic trypsin principally attacks lysyl and arginyl bonds:

$$H_2N-C=NH$$
$$|$$
$$NH$$
$$|$$
$$(CH_2)_3$$
$$|$$
$$-HN-CH-CO-NH-$$
$$\uparrow$$

$$NH_2$$
$$|$$
$$(CH_2)_4$$
$$|$$
$$-HN-CH-CO-NH-$$
$$\uparrow$$

arginyl bond   **lysyl bond**

Chymotrypsin has a preference for peptide bonds in which aromatic amino acids participate as acyl residues: Try, Tyr, and Phe. It also has a certain activity toward bonds formed by Met, Leu, and His.

Exopeptidases. In distinction to the endopeptidases, or *proteinases*, are the exopeptidases, which attack the terminal peptide

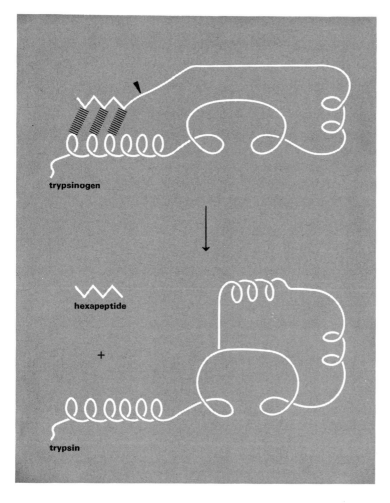

figure 10.3 ::
Conversion of
trypsinogen to trypsin.

(a) ---Gly-Ala-Phe-Lys-Met-Leu-Phe-Phe-Ileu---COOH

 ↑ ↑ ↑ ↑

 pepsin trypsin pepsin chymotrypsin

(b) H$_2$N---Ala-Glu-Leu-Met-Tyr (C terminal)

 ↑

 carboxypeptidase A

figure 10.4 :: Some typical peptide bonds attacked by endopeptidases (*a*) and carboxypeptidase (*b*).

bonds of polypeptides. They are also called simply *peptidases* and include aminopeptidases, carboxypeptidases, and dipeptidases.

In the animal, most peptidases are metalloproteins made as inactive precursors in the intestinal mucosa. In their active form they attack specifically bonds at the C-terminal (carboxypeptidase) or N-terminal (amino peptidase) portion of the peptide chain. They do not attack indiscriminately all terminal amino acids; they are somewhat specific for selected terminal amino acids. For example, carboxypeptidase A removes C-terminal phenylalanine, tyrosine, tryptophan, leucine, methionine, and isoleucine but at different rates; phenylalanine is cleaved fastest; isoleucine is cleaved at a much slower rate. Other amino acids (except Pro, Lys, and Arg) are also hydrolyzed at quite appreciable, but nevertheless slower, rates.

The concerted action of all these proteolytic enzymes on proteins from foodstuffs leads to the production of uncombined amino acids. These are absorbed by the organism and transported to the cell, where they mix into their respective pools. The specific action of proteases is depicted in Figure 10.4.

GLYCOSIDASES : The hydrolytic breakdown of polysaccharides or glycans is important—from a nutritional aspect—only with regard to glucans. Of these, starch is by far the most abundant of the nutrient polysaccharides. Although cellulose is the most abundant organic substance on earth, its nutritive value is limited to the few organisms that have enzymes to break it down.

In addition to starch and glycogen, glycans with fewer units also merit attention, because of their wide use in human nutrition. Of those, sucrose and lactose (milk sugar) will be mentioned.

Amylases—the enzymes responsible for the hydrolytic breakdown of starch and glycogen—are specific for α-1,4-glycosidic bonds. Two types are known: α-amylases and β-amylases, depending on their mode of action. α-Amylase, also called an endoamylase in similarity to endopeptidases, cleaves glucans into smaller units containing several sugar units. After prolonged action of the enzyme on starch it produces largely α-maltose. The enzyme simply does not attack α-1,6-glycosidic bonds present on the branched points.

β-Amylases, also called exoamylases, attack the linear portion of starch (amylose) from one end and cleave a maltose unit while an inversion yielding β-maltose is taking place. It should be remembered that β-amylase does not attack β-glycosidic bonds nor the branched points in starch (or glycogen) with their α-1,6-glycosidic bonds. The mode of action of the two amylases is depicted schematically in Figure 10.5.

The final step in the breakdown of starch is the cleavage of maltose by the enzyme maltase, which was mentioned in Chapter 5.

Other disaccharides ordinarily present in foodstuffs (we have already mentioned sucrose and lactose) are hydrolyzed by the

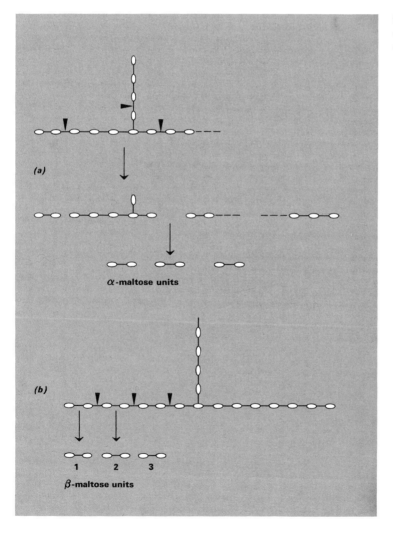

figure 10.5 :: Mode of action of (*a*) α-amylase and (*b*) β-amylase.

action of specific hydrolases. Sucrose, for example, is a substrate for *invertase* or *sucrase*, which is present in the intestinal juice. It catalyzes the cleavage of sucrose into fructose and glucose. Other glycosidases cause the breakdown of lactose into galactose and glucose and so on.

Hexoses and some pentoses are the final breakdown products of most carbohydrate from foodstuffs. Hexoses are interconvertible in the cell and pentoses give rise to glucose. It is not an exaggeration when we say that nearly all carbohydrate in food can be represented by glucose.

NUCLEASES : Nucleic acids are from the point of view of nutrition among the least important components of foodstuffs. The organism relies almost entirely on its own capacity to synthesize DNA and RNA from the simplest possible precursors. Even in man and the mammals in whom biosynthetic capabilities are limited, DNA and RNA are made from simple and readily available compounds.

In this sense nucleic acids ingested by the organism are of little value for the synthesis of DNA and RNA. They undergo instead degradative reactions in which the end products become excretory products. Parts of the nucleic acid molecules are utilized for other purposes, but in general their contribution to the nutrition of the organism is minimal.

Digestive enzymes that cleave nucleic acids are mostly in the esterase group, specifically *phosphatases*. The name *nuclease* indicates that these are phosphatases specific for the phosphodiester bonds of polynucleotides.

When nucleases such as pancreatic ribonuclease attack RNA, the products formed are nucleotides and oligonucleotides. The mode of action of ribonuclease was briefly discussed in Chapter 3. We repeat here that when RNA is hydrolyzed by the action of ribonuclease, a cyclization of the phosphodiester bond occurs. The process is similar to that observed during alkali hydrolysis. However, the products are 3'-phosphoesters, because, unlike the process in alkali hydrolysis, ribonuclease cleaves the cyclic phosphodiester through only one bond :

Nucleases degrade nucleic acids to the nucleotide stage. But nucleotides still have a phosphoester bond and a N-glycosidic bond, both of which are susceptible to hydrolytic cleavage.

The name *nucleotidase* is used to describe phosphatases that cleave the phosphate group from a nucleotide and the name *nucleosidases* to describe enzymes that cause cleavage of the N-glycosidic bond. Neither of these groups of enzymes has received sufficient attention; relatively little is known of their distribution and properties.

The pentoses from nucleic acids can find their way into other metabolic pathways so that their carbon atoms become part of the general carbon pool. The purines and pyrimidines, however, are degraded into such products as uric acid, allantoin, urea, β-alanine, and some others. A few of these find their way into general pools, but in the main they are excreted.

extracellular breakdown of lipids :: 10.3

A distinction should be made between those lipids with chemical bonds susceptible to hydrolysis and those that are resistant to hydrolysis.

In the first stage of food breakdown, only lipids with hydrolizable bonds are considered: fats, oils, and glycerophosphatides; all produce long-chain fatty acids and glycerol as their most important nutritional products.

The enzymatic hydrolysis of fats and oils presents an interesting situation in which a water-soluble enzyme must attack a water-insoluble substrate. Organisms have resolved this apparent difficulty by bringing the fats and oils into an emulsion. In animals emulsions are obtained during intestinal digestion by the action of the bile salts, which are excellent emulsifiers.

As pointed out in the discussion on enzyme specificity (Chapter 6), esterases are among the least specific of enzymes. Lipases, which are esterases of a special type, attack the ester bonds in triglycerides with little preference for the type of acyl group participating in the formation of the bond.

A higher degree of specificity is noted in the *phosphatidases*, which are the enzymes that attack glycerophosphatides. For example, there are several such enzymes acting on lecithin but each attacks a different bond, giving different products.

The hydrolysis products of fats, oils, and glycerophosphatides are transported into the cells, where they are converted into pyruvate and acetyl-CoA. Pyruvate is the product of glycerol breakdown by reactions of the Embden-Meyerhof-Parnas scheme, whereas acetyl-CoA, as discussed in Chapter 9, results from successive degradations of the long-chain fatty acid molecules.

intracellular breakdown of macromolecules :: 10.4

In distinction to the digestive enzymes discussed, there are the intracellular enzymes that also catalyze the breakdown of macro-molecules. The difference is not only in their site of action but in their properties. For example, the amylases, which function outside the cell, cleave starch and glycogen into maltose. But their counter-parts in the cell, the *phosphorylases*, produce glucose-1-phosphate from starch or glycogen. In effect, phosphorylases catalyze "phos-pholysis" rather than hydrolysis.

Intracellular proteases and nucleases are also known, and these will be discussed.

PHOSPHORYLASES : Starch in plant cells and glycogen in animal cells are reserve nutritional glucans that break into glucose as the need arises. Their breakdown and biosynthesis are well-regulated processes in the cell.

The breakdown is catalyzed by the enzyme phosphorylase. This enzyme has been purified from various sources and its mode of action studied in some detail. Phosphorylases obtained in pure form from heart muscle and skeletal muscle exist in two inter-convertible forms, a and b. They differ in molecular weight; accord-ing to the best estimates, the molecular weight of phosphorylase a is twice the molecular weight of phosphorylase b. Moreover, phosphorylase b is an *inactive* molecule that gives rise to the active enzyme phosphorylase a, at the expense of ATP. The process can be represented by

$$\text{2 phosphorylase b} + \text{4ATP} \xrightarrow{\text{kinase}} \text{phosphorylase a} + \text{4ADP}$$

in which a specific kinase intervenes. What actually occurs is that two molecules of b dimerize into one molecule of a.

The breakdown of a into b is also a catalytic process; a phosphat-ase has been found in tissues which catalyzes the following reaction :

$$\text{phosphorylase a} \xrightarrow{\text{phosphatase}} \text{2 phosphorylase b} + \text{4P}_i$$

Phosphorylase a is specific for α-1,4-glycosidic bonds and in-effectual in attacking α-1,6 bonds. This means that neither starch nor glycogen can be brought to the stage of glucose-1-phosphate by the exclusive action of phosphorylase. Phosphorylase attacks only the linear molecules of starch, amylose, and part of the branches of amylopectin. This is depicted schematically in Figure 10.6. The α-1,6-glycosidic bonds of the branching points are cleaved by enzymes specific for these sites. Once a branched point is cleaved, phosphorylase renews its attack of the linear portion.

Phosphorylase initiates phosphorolysis at the nonreducing end of a linear glucan:

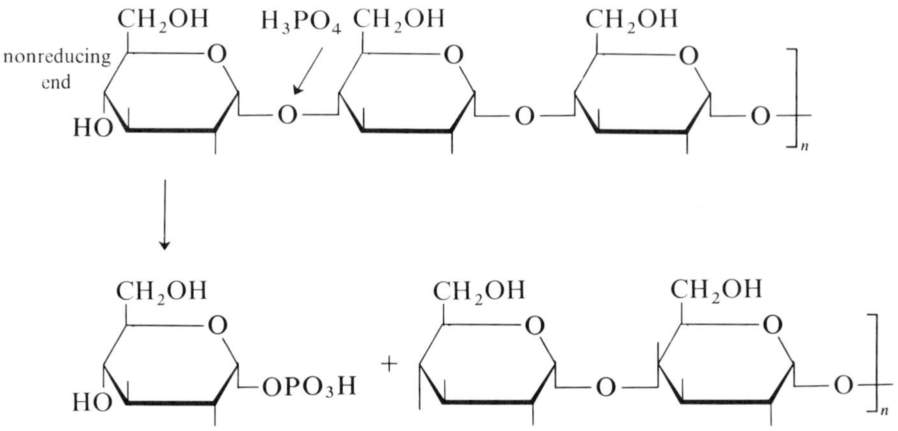

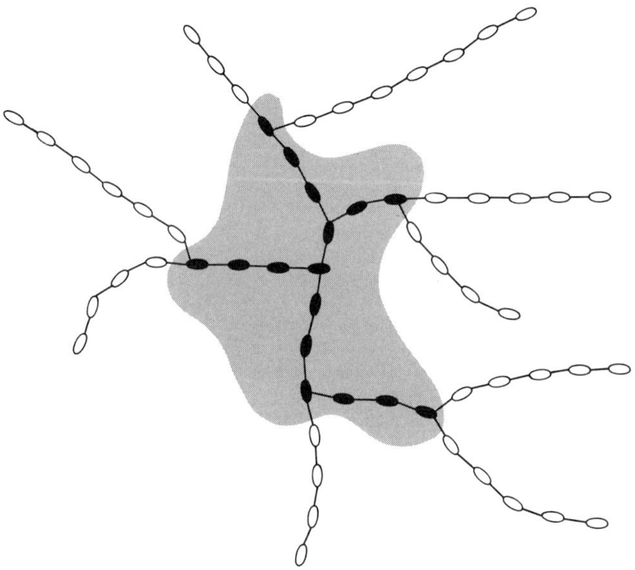

figure 10.6 :: Action of phosphorylase on a branched glucan.

and continues to catalyze in successive steps the cleavage of one glucose molecule from that end.

Glucose-1-phosphate is isomerized into glucose-6-phosphate when attacked by the enzyme *phosphoglucomutase,*

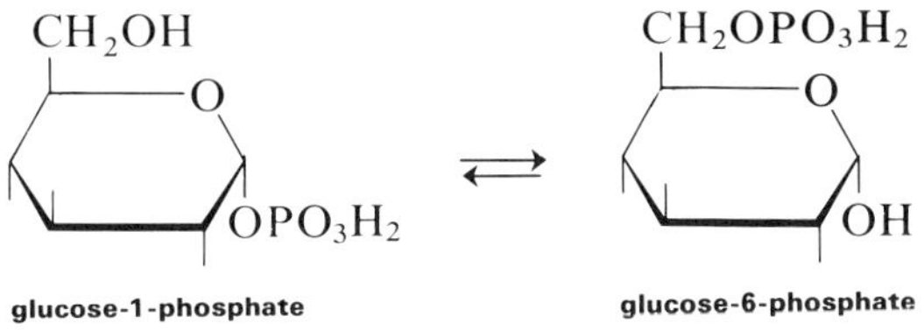

glucose-1-phosphate   glucose-6-phosphate

and in this way glucose units from starch and glycogen find their way into the Embden-Meyerhof-Parnas scheme or the pentose phosphate pathway.

Although glucans are the major sources of glucose, hexoses and pentoses also give rise to glucose. Of the hexoses, galactose will be discussed, because it introduces us to some interesting reactions.

Galactose is the product of hydrolysis of lactose or milk sugar. It cannot be converted directly to glucose by epimerization, that is, inversion of the $-OH$ group in position 4:

galactose   glucose

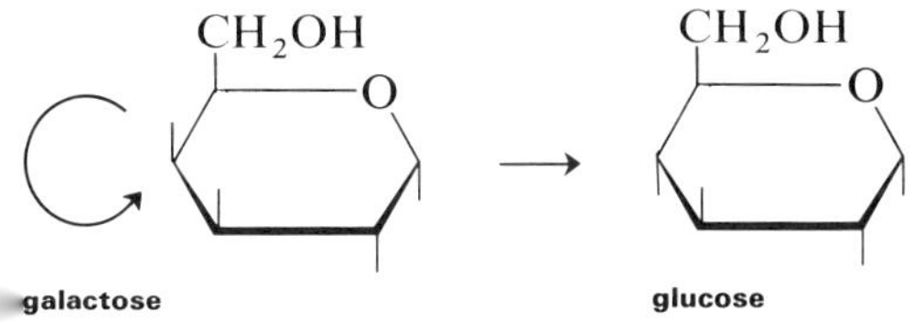

Galactose must first form a "sugar nucleotide," uridine diphosphate galactose:

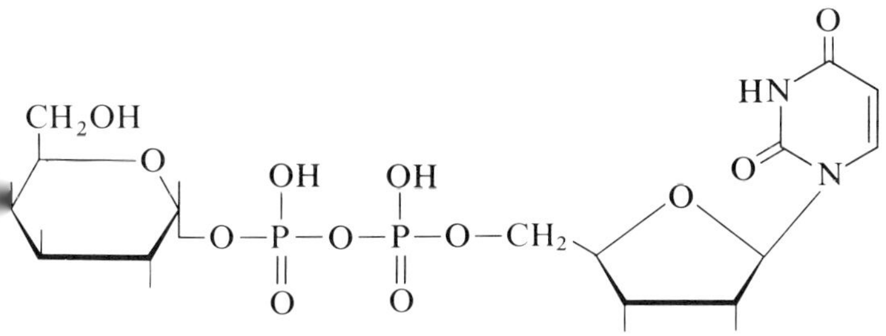

In the form of this derivative, galactose becomes the substrate of diphosphoglycosyl-4-epimerase, which catalyzes the inversion of the $-OH$ group in position 4 to yield *uridine diphosphate glucose* (UDPG). The latter is an interesting intermediate in many reactions but a reaction of interest is its reversible conversion to glucose-1-phosphate:

UDPG ... $+ PP_i \rightleftharpoons$

glucose-1-phosphate + **UTP**

Thus the original galactose molecule becomes glucose-1-phosphate, which as already seen, is converted to glucose-6-phosphate.

Sugar nucleotides are reactive substances that serve as precursors of polymeric structures. They are formed at the expense of ATP from sugar phosphates. For example, galactose is first converted to galactose-1-phosphate by phosphorylation with ATP and a kinase:

$$\text{galactose} + \text{ATP} \xrightarrow{Mg^{2+}} \text{galactose-1-phosphate} + \text{ADP}$$

Galactose-1-phosphate reacts with nucleotide-5′-triphosphates such as uridine triphosphate (UTP) to yield the sugar nucleotide:

$$\text{galactose-1-phosphate} + \text{UTP} \rightarrow \text{UDP-galactose} + PP_i$$

Many other sugar nucleotides are known in nature, all produced by reactions similar to the formation of UDP-galactose. Reference to these substances will be made again in relation to biosynthetic reactions.

INTRACELLULAR PROTEASES : In contrast to the vast amount of information on the properties and mode of action of digestive proteases, there is only limited knowledge of the intracellular proteases. They are classified under the name *cathepsins*. Plant proteases have been easier to obtain and have been studied to a greater extent, especially *papain* from the unripe fruit of the papaya.

The cathepsins, together with many plant proteases, belong to the group of enzymes that function best in the presence of reducing agents; these enzymes are also designated as *thiol proteases* because of their strict requirement for intact —SH groups.

The cathepsins seem to be present in all tissues of animals, but they are more abundant in organs such as the kidney, spleen, liver, and lung. Their substrate specificity lacks clear definition, but from studies with synthetic substrates several cathepsins have been distinguished broadly.

Very little can be said about this group of enzymes, which must play some role in the physiology of the cell. It is known that they are most active at acid pH (about 4) and that they are responsible for tissue autolysis, the breakdown of tissue after death.

The cathepsins are localized within the cell in particles called *lysosomes*, which also contain a variety of other hydrolases. It has been suggested that the lysosome's activities are not manifested until they are disrupted and release their contents. As long as the enzymes are bounded within the lysosomes, they are ineffective, because they do not make contact with their corresponding substrates.

Besides the cathepsins, aminopeptidases are also found widely distributed in cells from animal tissues and plants and also in microorganisms. One of the best studied of these is leucine aminopeptidase.

INTRACELLULAR NUCLEASES : Besides pancreatic ribonuclease, which is a well-studied digestive enzyme, a variety of intracellular ribonucleases have been detected, isolated, and purified. They originate in organs such as the spleen and liver, and in microorganisms and plants.

Deoxyribonucleases are also widely distributed. They vary in properties, and the products of their action differ from one deoxyribonuclease to another. Some will attack 3'-phosphoester bonds to yield 5'-phosphates. Other deoxyribonucleases attack only the 5'-phosphoester bond, and the expected products in this case are 3'-phosphates.

intracellular breakdown of lipids :: **10.5**

Hydrolytic breakdown of fats and glycerophosphatides in the cell is a prerequisite for their degradation. The intracellular lipases (which hydrolyze fats) and phosphatidases (which hydrolyze glycerophosphatides) are the responsible enzymes.

 As seems to always be the case, the best studied enzymes are those the most easily obtained. For this reason pancreatic lipases and phosphatidases have received much attention, while the intra-cellular enzymes remain poorly defined. It is known, however, that both types of enzymes are widely distributed in animal and plant tissues as well as in microorganisms. Their mode of action upon their substrates can be guessed to be the same for all carboxyl esterases.

nutritional requirements of man :: **10.6**

The relative ease by which organisms convert one type of metabolite into another simplifies to a great extent the search for selected foodstuffs. The energy requirements of the organisms are satisfied by an adequate quantity of oxidizable substances. It does not matter greatly if the substances are supplied in the form of starch, fat, or protein.

		table 10.2 ::
Essential:	Nonessential:	Essential and nonessential amino acids
Isoleucine	Alanine	
Leucine	Arginine†	
Lysine	Aspartic acid	
Methionine	Asparagine	
Phenylalanine	Cystine‡	
Threonine	Glutamic acid	
Tryptophan	Glutamine	
Valine	Glycine	
	Histidine†	
	Proline and hydroxyproline	
	Serine	
	Tyrosine§	

† Arginine and histidine are essential to the rat but not to man.
‡ Cystine is nonessential when adequate amounts of methionine are supplied in the diet.
§ Tyrosine is nonessential when adequate amounts of phenylalanine are supplied in the diet.

Nutritionists at the turn of the century became preoccupied with defined diets, that is, diets of known composition. It soon became apparent that animals need more than an adequate supply of food in a caloric sense. The discoveries of the two great nutritionists T. B. Osborne and L. B. Mendel pointed the way to the study of trace elements and essential organic compounds. The vitamins were recognized early as nutritional factors necessary for life. But Osborne and Mendel established that all proteins did not possess the same nutritional value when fed to growing rats on equal weight bases. Some proteins were found unable to support growth no matter what amount fed. Despite the crude analytical tools of the time, Osborne and Mendel were able to recognize that the nutritional value of a protein was directly related to its amino acid composition. They established that the absence of some amino acid(s) in a protein made it unsuitable to induce growth or to maintain weight. From this they concluded that some amino acids are absolutely essential to the rat, whereas others are not essential.

The quality of protein, not just the quantity, became an important factor in nutrition. In man, according to the elaborate investigations of W. C. Rose, 8 of the 20 amino acids of proteins must be present in the diet in adequate amounts. A deficiency in any of the 8 amino acids results in the impairment of growth and good health.

The amino acids essential to man are listed in Table 10.2, together with the 12 nonessential amino acids.

Although man lacks the necessary enzymes to synthesize vitamins, essential amino acids, and some other vital substances, plants and microorganisms are nearly self-sufficient. They synthesize the most complex molecules when provided with a source of carbon, nitrogen, and sulfur in the form of very simple molecules. Much of the biosynthetic potential of plants and microorganisms is lost in the higher forms and in man.

references ::

BOYER, P. D., H. LARDY, AND K. MYRBACK, eds., *The Enzymes*, Vol. IV. New York: Academic Press, Inc., 1960.

CUNNINGHAM, L., in *Comprehensive Biochemistry*, Vol. 16, M. Florkin and E. H. Stotz, eds. Amsterdam: Elsevier Publishing Company, 1965.

FISHER, R. B., *Protein Metabolism*. London: Methuen & Co., Ltd., 1954.

DURING THE BREAKDOWN OF FOODSTUFFS IN THE ANIMAL, SULFUR and nitrogen are cleaved at some stage while carbon flows into oxidizable substrates, as shown in Figure 10.2.

The disposition of sulfur and nitrogen is not a simple process; it involves numerous enzymatic reactions—some endergonic—before the two elements make their appearance in molecules suitable for excretion, such as sulfate, ammonia, and urea.

Keeping in mind that sulfur and nitrogen constitute important metabolic pools—mainly as amino acids—their disposition will be discussed here in terms of their catabolic flow and final excretion.

Nitrogen excretion deserves a few comments. Most of the nitrogen excreted by animals is in the form of ammonia, urea, or uric acid. The amount excreted is greatly dependent upon the dietary intake of nitrogen: in man, for example, there is a balance between intake and output of nitrogen. In the adult, intake and output are about the same, but in children, because of their growth, the output is less than the intake. We speak here of a positive nitrogen balance. A negative balance is observed when there is excessive tissue breakdown or starvation.

Because of the dynamic state of tissue components, the nitrogen excreted represents metabolic-pool nitrogen in excess of the needs of the organism.

sources of sulfur :: **11.1**

Animals require sulfur for the biosynthesis of proteins and muco-polysaccharides and also for the biosynthesis of low-molecular-weight sulfur compounds.

The sulfur requirement in higher animals is met by ʟ-methionine, ʟ-cysteine, and ʟ-cystine, together with the vitamins thiamin and biotin:

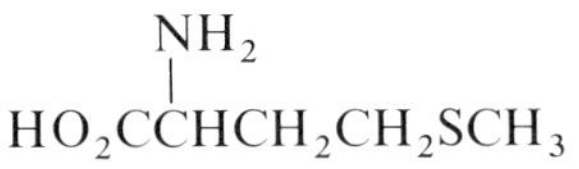

methionine

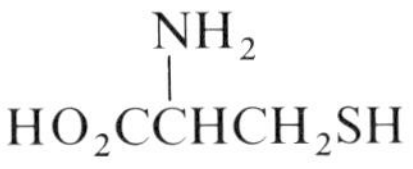

cysteine

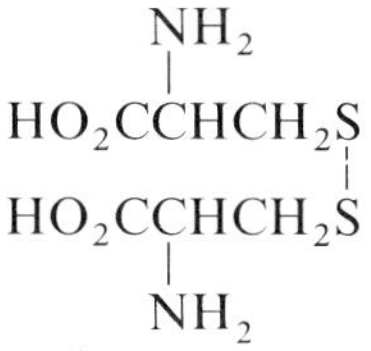

cystine

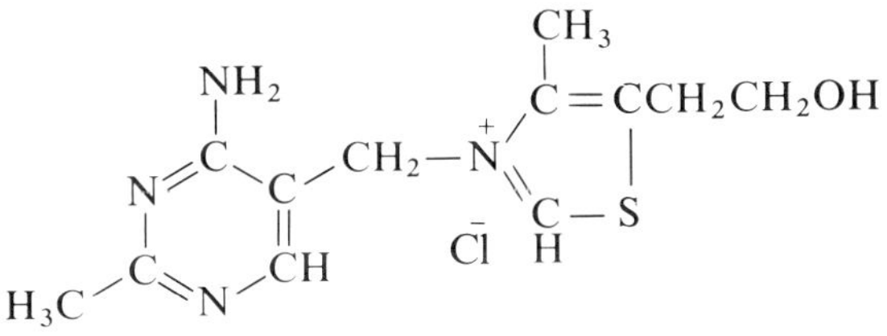

thiamine chloride

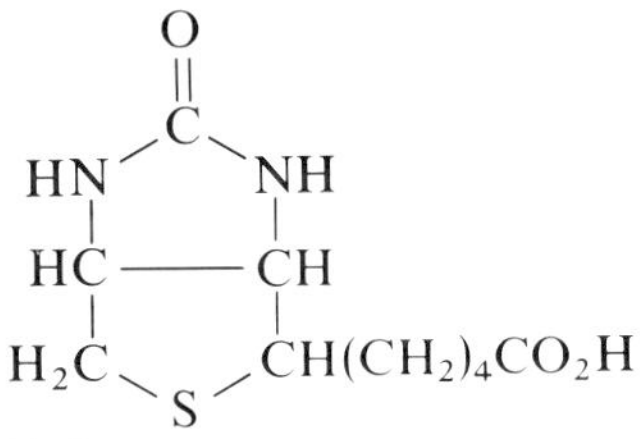

biotin

Sulfur in sulfate has no nutritional value for the majority of animals because they lack the necessary enzymes to catalyze the reduction of sulfate. Sulfate, however, reacts with ATP, and in this form it has a high group-transfer potential, allowing it to form sulfate esters with many substrates.

Methionine alone could satisfy all the sulfur needs of the animal (except for the two vitamins thiamin and biotin) if supplied in sufficient amount. Methionine gives rise to cysteine, which is readily oxidized to cystine. These two amino acids are not essential in man if methionine is provided in the diet, but neither cysteine nor cystine can replace methionine.

Because methionine sulfur flows into nearly all other sulfur compounds in the animal, the flow pattern will start with methionine.

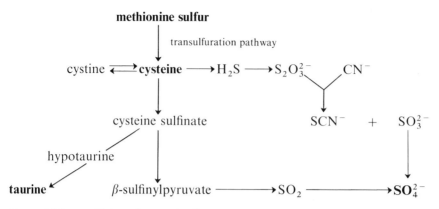

figure 11.1 :: Main pathways of sulfur.

The flow of sulfur from methionine to other compounds is depicted in Figure 11.1. Two main stages can be recognized : (1) flow of methionine sulfur to cysteine, and (2) flow of cysteine sulfur to other compounds.

In the first stage, methionine sulfur is not cleaved in the reaction ; methionine first loses its methyl group by methylating a suitable substrate A while the resulting homocysteine enters into a sequence of reactions known as *transulfuration*. The reactions involved are shown here :

1. $$\underset{\text{methionine}}{HO_2C\overset{\overset{\displaystyle NH_2}{|}}{C}HCH_2CH_2SCH_3} + ATP \rightleftharpoons \underset{\text{S-adenosylmethionine}}{HO_2C\overset{\overset{\displaystyle NH_2}{|}}{C}HCH_2CH_2\overset{+}{\underset{\underset{\displaystyle CH_3}{|}}{S}}{-}adenosine} + P_i + PP_i$$

2. $$HO_2C\overset{\overset{\displaystyle NH_2}{|}}{C}HCH_2CH_2\overset{+}{\underset{\underset{\displaystyle CH_3}{|}}{S}}{-}adenosine + A$$

$$\updownarrow$$

$$CH_3{-}A + \underset{\text{homocysteine}}{HO_2C\overset{\overset{\displaystyle NH_2}{|}}{C}HCH_2CH_2SH} + adenosine$$

3. $$\underset{\text{homocysteine}}{HO_2C\overset{\overset{\displaystyle NH_2}{|}}{C}HCH_2CH_2SH} + \underset{\text{serine}}{HOCH_2\overset{\overset{\displaystyle NH_2}{|}}{C}HCO_2H}$$

$$\updownarrow$$

$$\underset{\text{cystathionine}}{HO_2C\overset{\overset{\displaystyle NH_2}{|}}{C}HCH_2CH_2SCH_2\overset{\overset{\displaystyle NH_2}{|}}{C}HCO_2H} + H_2O$$

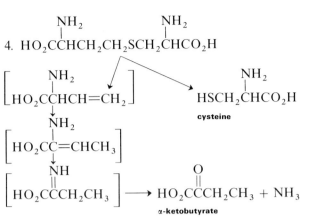

4.

Reactions (1) and (2) have been discussed in Chapter 7. It can only be added that the conversion of methionine into homocysteine requires a methyl-group acceptor A and that the thioether in methionine becomes a mercaptan.

In reactions (3) and (4), homocysteine condenses with L-serine; the reaction, which is catalyzed by *cystathionine synthetase*, requires pyridoxal phosphate as a cofactor. Cystathionine undergoes cleavage in a reaction catalyzed by *cystathionase*. One product of the cleavage is cysteine, the other vinyl glycine, which undergoes intramolecular rearrangement and is finally hydrolyzed into ammonia and α-ketobutyric acid.

One interesting feature of the enzyme cystathionase is that it catalyzes two reactions. One is the cleavage of cystathionine without releasing one of the products—vinyl glycine; associated with the enzyme, vinyl glycine undergoes the reactions just described.

Note that all the carbons in cysteine originate in L-serine; only the sulfur of methionine appears in the newly synthesized cysteine by this pathway. Cysteine, as already mentioned, is autoxidizable; that is, the thiol undergoes oxidation in the presence of molecular oxygen to yield the disulfide cystine.

In the second stage, the C—S bond is broken to produce inorganic sulfur compounds or it is maintained to yield stable final products such as taurine. The C—S bond is broken in cysteine directly to yield H_2S + pyruvate + NH_3 or it is broken after sulfur has been oxidized. The cleavage of H_2S from cysteine is comparable to a dehydration reaction; the reaction catalyzed by a pyridoxal phosphate enzyme was discussed in Chapter 9.

Oxidation of cysteine merits further attention. First it should be said that cysteine and cystine are readily interconvertible in the cell. Cystine in the presence of thiols (such as glutathione) is converted into cysteine. In many organisms, however, cysteine undergoes oxidation to the sulfinate stage:

$$\underset{\text{cysteine}}{HO_2CCHCH_2SH} \overset{\underset{\text{ATP, NADP}^+}{}}{\underset{Mg^{2+}, O_2}{\longrightarrow}} \underset{\text{cysteine sulfinate}}{HO_2CCHCH_2SO_2H}$$

with NH_2 groups above the respective CCH carbons.

Cysteine sulfinate oxidation has been demonstrated but the nature of the reaction or the enzyme involved are not known. It is beyond dispute that cysteine sulfinate is a transient intermediate in the degradation of sulfur amino acids.

Cysteine sulfinate undergoes decarboxylation or transamination, with simultaneous breaking of the C—S bond:

1.
$$\underset{\text{cysteine sulfinate}}{HO_2\overset{NH_2}{C}CHCH_2SO_2H} \xrightarrow{\text{pyridoxal phosphate}} \underset{\text{"hypotaurine"}}{H_2NCH_2CH_2SO_2H} + CO_2$$

2.
$$HO_2\overset{NH_2}{C}CHCH_2SO_2H + R\overset{O}{C}CO_2H \rightleftharpoons R\overset{NH_2}{C}HCO_2H + \left[\underset{\text{β-sulfinylpyruvate}}{HO_2\overset{O}{C}CCH_2SO_2H}\right]$$

$$\downarrow$$

$$\underset{\text{pyruvate}}{HO_2\overset{O}{C}CCH_3} + SO_2$$

In reaction (1) cysteine sulfinate is decarboxylated to 2-aminoethane sulfinate (hypotaurine); this compound undergoes oxidation to the sulfonate, which is taurine:

$$H_2NCH_2CH_2SO_2H \xrightarrow{\frac{1}{2}O_2} H_2NCH_2CH_2SO_3H$$

Taurine is very stable in most organs and occurs in relatively high concentration in the free state. In the liver, taurine is attacked by cholyl-CoA, making an amide bond; the product taurocholate is one of the known bile salts.

In the heart and brain, taurine is somehow deaminated to yield 2-hydroxyethane sulfonate (isethionic acid). The rate of conversion is extremely slow:

$$\underset{\text{taurine}}{H_2NCH_2CH_2SO_3H} \longrightarrow \underset{\text{isethionic acid}}{HOCH_2CH_2SO_3H}$$

Taurine represents one of the final products that contain sulfur originated in cysteine (or methionine). It can be regarded as one of the terminals in the flow of sulfur because it is excreted in significant amounts in the urine and seems to undergo no additional reaction in most tissues.

The alternative pathway (2) involves transamination, primarily with α-ketoglutarate. The postulated intermediate is β-sulfinyl pyruvate, which if formed decomposes spontaneously into pyruvate and SO_2. In the cell SO_2 is expected to form sulfite, HSO_3^-, which is rapidly oxidized to sulfate by an oxidase. Sulfate represents the major form of sulfur excreted by animals.

Other inorganic forms of sulfur are known in animals: $S_2O_3^{2-}$ and SCN^-. Their formation has been accounted for by enzymatic reactions. Thiosulfate, $S_2O_3^{2-}$, is the product of the following reactions:

$$-HSO_3^- + RSSR \longrightarrow RSH + RSSO_3^-$$

$$RSSO_3^- + {}^-HS \longrightarrow S_2O_3^{2-} + RSH$$

$$2RSH^- + \tfrac{1}{2}O_2 \longrightarrow RSSR + H_2O$$

Thiosulfate is interconvertible with thiocyanate; the latter is produced by the action of *rhodanase*, an enzyme catalyzing the reaction

$$S_2O_3^{2-} + CN^- \longrightarrow SCN^- + SO_3^{2-}$$

The other product, SO_3^{2-}, is oxidized to sulfate.

Most of the sulfate produced from sulfur amino acids is excreted in the urine. A part of the sulfate is utilized in the biosynthesis of compounds with sulphate ester functions, for example, the sulfated mucopolysaccharides. As mentioned previously, sulfate forms an active nucleotide derivative:

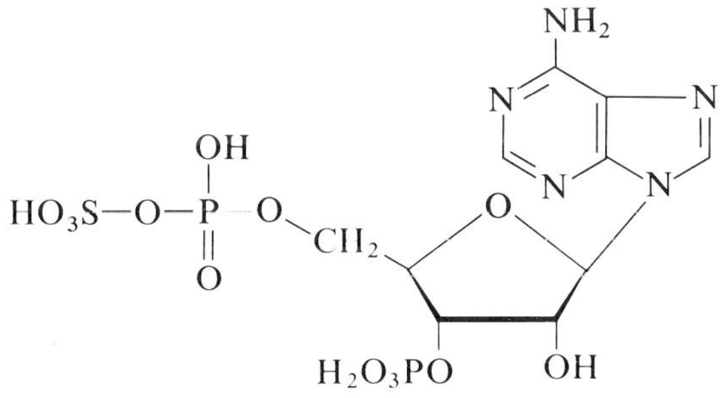

3'-phosphoadenosine-5'-phosphosulfate

which is formed by a two-step reaction:

1. $SO_4^{2-} + ATP \xrightarrow{Mg^{2+}}$ adenosine-5'-phosphosulfate + PP_i

2. adenosine-5'-phosphosulfate + ATP $\xrightarrow{Mg^{2+}}$ 3'-phosphoadenosine-5'-phosphosulfate

$$+ ADP$$

The nitrogen content of proteins and nucleic acids is relatively high; as degradation of these two groups of substances proceeds in the animal the nitrogen is detached from the carbon. The C—N bond is cleaved in most amino acids by the action of transaminases or deaminases. The amino nitrogen is also cleaved from aminated purines and pyrimidines, but the ring nitrogens are not. In most animals the C—N bonds from the rings remain intact in the final products.

Because the flow of nitrogen from proteins is different from the flow of nitrogen from nucleic acids, the two processes will be discussed separately.

FLOW OF PROTEIN NITROGEN : As shown in Figure 10.2, proteins release amino acids (by the action of peptidases). Amino nitrogen from glutamine and asparagine is released as ammonia when the bond is cleaved by the respective enzymes.

Several enzymes are known that catalyze deamination of amino acids; the amino acid oxidases release ammonia but they do not account for most of the deamination that takes place in the organism. Amino acid oxidases do not attack all amino acids, and several amino acids are attacked at insignificant rates.

A mechanism that could account for most deamination involves transaminases and glutamate dehydrogenase. Transaminases are distributed widely and most of them catalyze reactions at a substantial rate. Glutamate dehydrogenase also has a relatively wide distribution and where present in the tissues occurs in high concentration.

The combination of the reactions can be depicted schematically as

$$NH_3$$

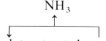

amino acids + α-ketoglutarate ⇄ glutamate + α-keto acids

Glutamic acid is readily formed by transamination of most if not all amino acids with α-ketoglutarate; the product glutamate is readily deaminated by glutamate dehydrogenase and α-ketoglutarate is regenerated.

In this catalytic scheme ammonia is produced from glutamate only. The rate of ammonia production is too great to be tolerated by most animals, because ammonia is quite toxic, even at low concentration. Many invertebrates successfully dispose of their ammonia directly. Freshwater teleosts also excrete ammonia by way of the urine. Most other animals have evolved biochemical mechanisms to remove ammonia as rapidly as it is formed by reactions in which the final product is harmless. Those animals in which ammonia goes into urea are known as *ureotelic animals*, and those in which it goes into uric acid are known as *uricotelic animals*. Animals that excrete ammonia directly are *ammonotelic animals*.

FLOW OF NUCLEIC ACID NITROGEN : Deamination of adenine, guanine, cytosine, and its derivatives is catalyzed by specific deaminases and ammonia is produced in each case.

Pyrimidines and purines do not release their ring nitrogen; instead they undergo reactions yielding products that are finally excreted. Adenine and guanine give rise to uric acid, which is the normal excretion product in numerous animals. The reactions are

Uric acid is attacked by other enzymes present in some animals to yield other products:

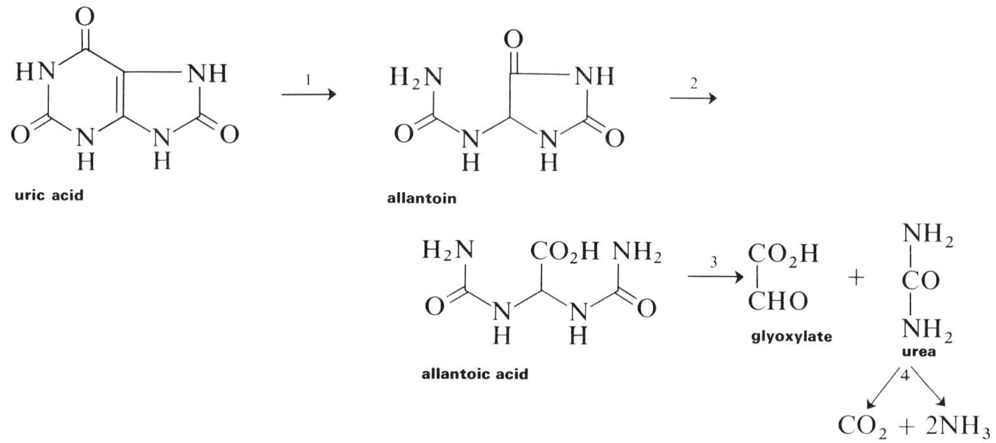

uric acid

allantoin

allantoic acid

glyoxylate

urea

$$CO_2 + 2NH_3$$

The enzymes involved are (1) uricase, (2) allantoinase, (3) allantoicase, and (4) urease.

It is of considerable comparative interest that the end product(s) of purine breakdown is unique to a given species. For example, man and the primates excrete uric acid. Teleost fishes have allantoinase, which cleaves the imidazole ring of allantoin to yield allantoic acid. Amphibia have allantoicase, which breaks allantoic acid into glyoxylic acid and urea. Finally, crustaceans, mollusks, and some other species have urease, which catalyzes the breakdown of urea into $CO_2 + NH_3$.

The pyrimidines also undergo reactions that yield products with one of the original ring nitrogens. Two reactions have been studied in some detail: the breakdown of uracil:

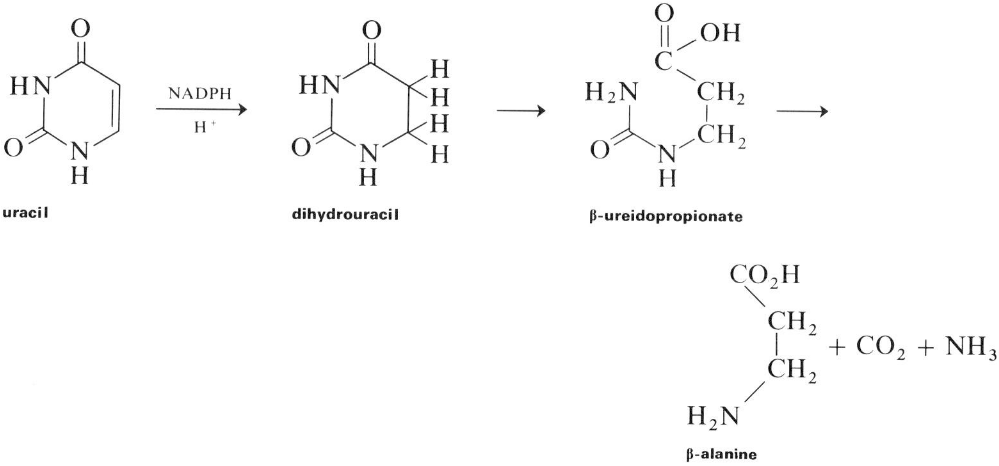

uracil

dihydrouracil

β-ureidopropionate

$+ CO_2 + NH_3$

β-alanine

and the breakdown of thymine:

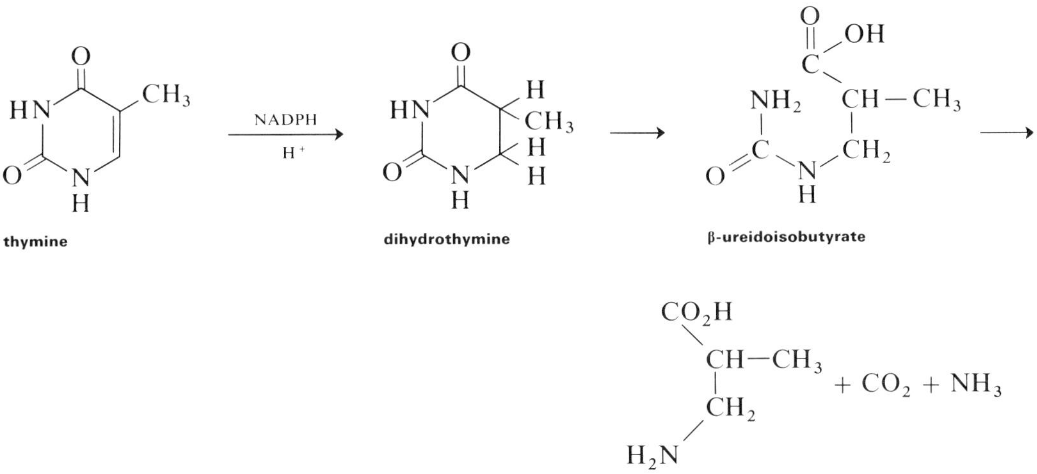

thymine   dihydrothymine   β-ureidoisobutyrate

β-aminoisobutyrate

The breakdown of cytosine remains obscure. One possibility is that cytosine is deaminated to yield uracil:

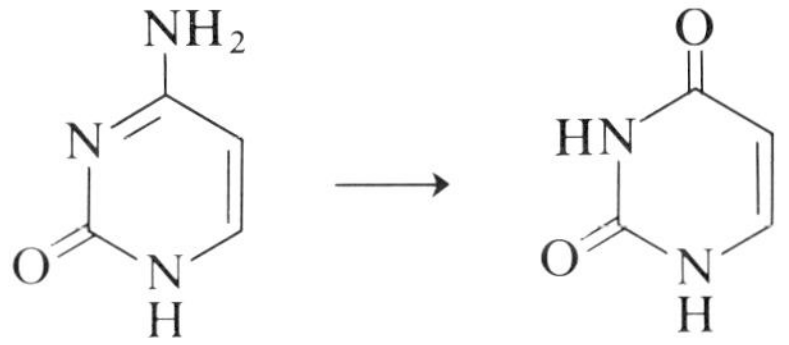

The known products of pyrimidine degradation, β-alanine and β-aminoisobutyric acid, are normally excreted in the urine.

Both these substances undergo deamination to a limited extent by way of a transamination reaction:

β-alanine + α-ketoglutarate ⇌ glutamate + malonate semialdehyde

β-aminoisobutyric acid + α-ketoglutarate ⇌ glutamate + methyl malonate semialdehyde

β-Alanine is degraded more extensively by a variety of tissues. One reaction of relatively wide scope is

$$H_2NCH_2CH_2CO_2H \xrightarrow{-NH_3} [OHCCH_2CO_2H] \longrightarrow \begin{array}{c} CO_2 \\ + \\ CH_3CHO \end{array}$$

The flow of nitrogen in the animal ends with ammonia. As already mentioned, ammonia is very toxic and animals have evolved biochemical reactions to remove it rapidly in the form of nontoxic substances.

Urea is one such substance. Its synthesis from NH_3, NH_4^+, and $^-HCO_3$ is under physiologic conditions a highly endergonic process; it requires 14 kcal/mole at the low concentration of reactants normally present in the cell. As is the case with most endergonic reactions, urea formation is driven by ATP.

The formation of urea involves several enzymes and coenzymes to catalyze the sequence of reactions depicted in Figure 11.2. Each reaction in this cyclic process will be discussed in turn.

FORMATION OF CARBAMYL PHOSPHATE : A nonenzymatic reaction between CO_2 and NH_3 yields carbamic acid:

$$NH_3 + CO_2 \rightleftharpoons H_2NC \overset{\displaystyle O}{\underset{\displaystyle OH}{\big\Vert}}$$

which is quite unstable and decomposes into $CO_2 + NH_3$. Carbamate reacts with ATP in the presence of an enzyme, carbamate kinase, to yield carbamyl phosphate:

$$H_2NC\overset{O}{\underset{OH}{\big\Vert}} + ATP \underset{}{\overset{enzyme}{\rightleftharpoons}} H_2NC\overset{O}{\underset{O \sim PO_3H_2}{\big\Vert}} + ADP$$

Unfortunately the enzyme seems to be present only in some strains of bacteria. The absence of the enzyme in animals makes this mechanism unlikely.

Other mechanisms have been proposed. In one such mechanism, the formation of a hypothetical active CO_2 is postulated. The active CO_2 is formed in the presence of a very low concentration of N-acetyl glutamate, which seems to be an absolute requirement in addition to ATP.

The active CO_2 combines with NH_4^+, forming carbamyl phosphate while ATP hydrolyzes. The overall reaction is

$$CO_2 + NH_4^+ + 2ATP \longrightarrow 2ADP + P_i + H_2NC\overset{O}{\underset{O \sim PO_3H_2}{\big\Vert}}$$

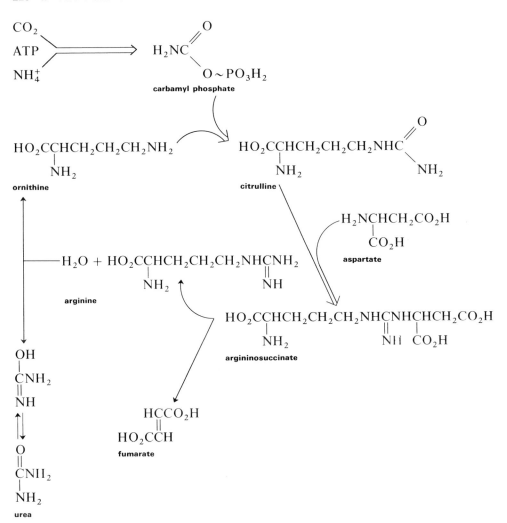

figure 11.2 :: Urea cycle.

The formation of carbamyl phosphate by this mechanism is still not clear. The nature of the active CO_2 remains to be explained.

It should be said that carbamyl phosphate synthesis is an important step not only in urea biosynthesis but also in the biosynthesis of pyrimidines (Chapter 12). Also, since arginine is formed during the urea cycle, carbamyl phosphate formation is also a first step in the biosynthesis of arginine.

FORMATION OF CITRULLINE : Citrulline is produced in the animal from ornithine and carbamyl phosphate:

$$\underset{\substack{| \\ NH_2}}{HO_2CCHCH_2CH_2CH_2NH_2} + H_2NC\overset{\displaystyle O}{\underset{\displaystyle O \sim PO_3H_2}{\diagdown}} \rightleftharpoons$$

ornithine

$$\underset{\substack{| \\ NH_2}}{HO_2CCHCH_2CH_2CH_2NHC}\overset{\displaystyle O}{\underset{\displaystyle NH_2}{\diagdown}} + P_i$$

citrulline

The enzyme catalyzing the reaction, *ornithine transcarbamylase*, is found in the liver of ureotelic animals, including elasmobranch fishes. It is absent from the liver of other fish, and from birds and reptiles.

FORMATION OF ARGININE : Arginine is produced from citrulline by a two-step reaction requiring two enzymes, aspartic acid and ATP. The intermediate, arginosuccinic acid, has been isolated.

In the first step, citrulline condenses with aspartate in the presence of ATP and the enzyme *argininosuccinate synthetase*:

$$\underset{\substack{| \\ NH_2}}{HO_2CCHCH_2CH_2CH_2NHC}\overset{\displaystyle OH}{\underset{\displaystyle NH}{\diagup}} + \underset{\substack{| \\ CO_2H}}{H_2NCHCH_2CO_2H} \underset{\substack{\text{ATP}}}{\overset{-H_2O}{\rightleftharpoons}}$$

citrulline (lactim) aspartate

$$\underset{\substack{| \\ NH_2}}{HO_2CCHCH_2CH_2CH_2NHCNHCHCH_2CO_2H} + AMP + PP_i$$
$$\qquad\qquad\qquad\qquad\quad \underset{NH}{\|}\ \underset{CO_2H}{|}$$

argininosuccinate

Note that the ureido portion of citrulline is written as the lactim (enol) form.

Arginosuccinate is cleaved by the action of a second enzyme, *argininosuccinase*, yielding arginine and fumarate:

$$\underset{\substack{| \\ NH_2}}{HO_2CCHCH_2CH_2CH_2NHCNHCHCH_2CO_2H} \longrightarrow$$
$$\qquad\qquad\qquad\qquad \underset{NH}{\|}\ \underset{CO_2H}{|}$$

$$\underset{\substack{| \\ NH_2}}{HO_2CCHCH_2CH_2CH_2NHCNH_2} + \underset{\substack{\| \\ HO_2CCH}}{HCCO_2H}$$
$$\qquad\qquad\qquad\qquad\quad \underset{NH}{\|}$$

arginine fumarate

FORMATION OF UREA : Urea formation from arginine takes place by the hydrolytic action of arginase:

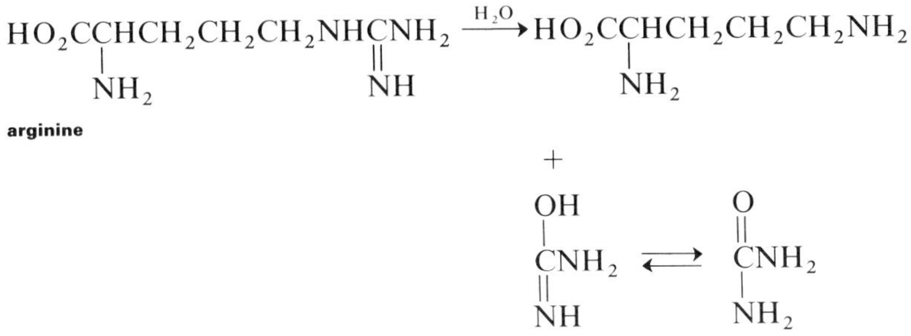

$$HO_2CCHCH_2CH_2CH_2NHCNH_2 \xrightarrow{H_2O} HO_2CCHCH_2CH_2CH_2NH_2$$

with NH_2 below the first carbon, NH below the C (double bond), and NH_2 below on the product.

arginine

$$+$$

$$\begin{array}{ccc} OH & & O \\ | & & || \\ CNH_2 & \rightleftharpoons & CNH_2 \\ || & & | \\ NH & & NH_2 \end{array}$$

urea

Ornithine is produced in the last reaction, so the entire process can be visualized as a cycle. The overall process consumes NH_3, CO_2, and ATP; all other intermediates are regenerated at the turn of each cycle.

The formation of urea in ureotelic animals is the main process by which ammonia is removed. It is interesting to note that urea formation takes place in the liver. Ammonia produced in other organs must be transported to the liver for its final disposition.

The formation of uric acid from NH_3 entails numerous reactions that will be discussed in Chapter 12 in connection with the biosynthesis of purines.

references ::

COHEN, P. P., AND H. J. SALLACH, in D. Greenberg, ed., *Metabolic Pathways* (3rd ed.), Vol. 2. New York: Academic Press, Inc., 1966.

YOUNG, L., AND G. A. MAW, *The Metabolism of Sulfur Compounds.* London: Methuen & Co., Ltd., 1958.

THE TERM LOW MOLECULAR WEIGHT AS USED HERE APPLIES TO organic substances other than macromolecules. It can be a simple amino acid such as glycine or a complex molecule such as cholesterol or heme.

But because the number of different organic molecules synthesized in nature is staggering, this chapter will deal only with the biosynthesis of a few typical cell constituents. From these few examples we can learn about the general plan for most biosynthesis. The devices the cell utilizes are based on a few basic principles. One is that the energy to make bonds is funneled from oxidation reactions by means of energy-rich compounds. Reactants are generally "activated." This means that the transfer potential of a reactant is raised by forming a derivative. For example, acetate, which has a low transfer potential, becomes active in the form of acetyl-CoA. Phosphorylation by ATP will also raise the potential of a number of reactants.

Specific enzymes take over at this point. From acetyl-CoA, for example, cells make fatty acids, steroids, terpenes, and many other substances. We shall confine our discussion to the biosynthesis of nucleotides, lipids, and porphyrins.

biosynthesis of purine nucleotides :: 12.1

Organisms do not normally depend on dietary sources of ribo- and deoxyribonucleotides for the synthesis of the vital nucleic acids. Only on rare occasions will an organism become dependent on exogenous nucleotides or the free bases. Most of the time these substances are synthesized from simple-precursors readily available to the cell.

The purine ring is built up in the cell from carbon and nitrogen atoms originating in aspartate, glutamine, formate, glycine, and CO_2, all of which are readily available. The precursor-product relation was discovered by using compounds labeled with radioactive carbon (^{14}C) and heavy nitrogen (^{15}N). For example, if an animal is fed formate, labelled with ^{14}C, the carbon can be traced to uric acid and by chemical degradation its position in the uric acid molecule established. With similar procedures all the atoms in the purine ring were traced to the precursors listed above:

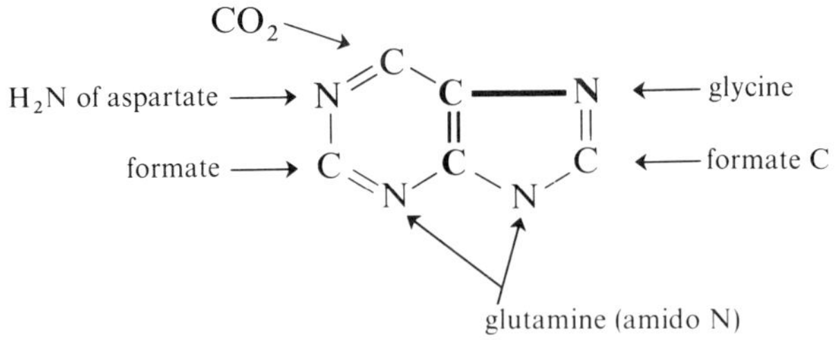

The purine ring is not synthesized as such; it is synthesized around a ribose phosphate to yield a nucleotide. The first product in purine biosynthesis is inosinic acid; from inosinic acid arise adenine and guanine by further enzymatic reactions. First we shall concern ourselves with the biosynthesis of inosinic acid.

FORMATION OF INOSINIC ACID : The key compound in the biosynthesis of purines is 5-phosphoribosyl-1-pyrophosphate (PRPP). Its discovery made it possible to elucidate all the steps in the synthesis of purines. It is produced from ribose-5-phosphate, which as we know is a product of glucose (see pentose phosphate pathway):

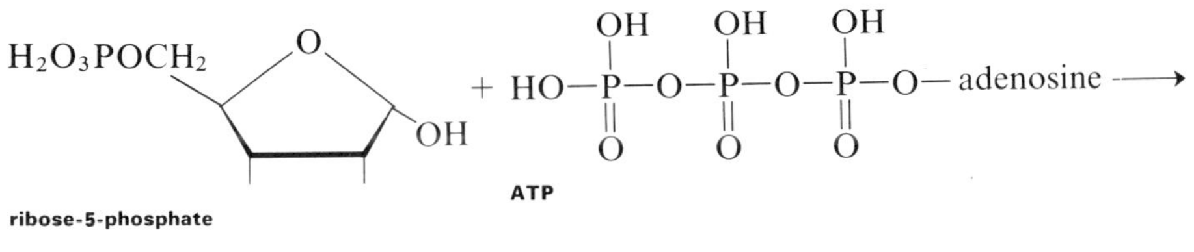

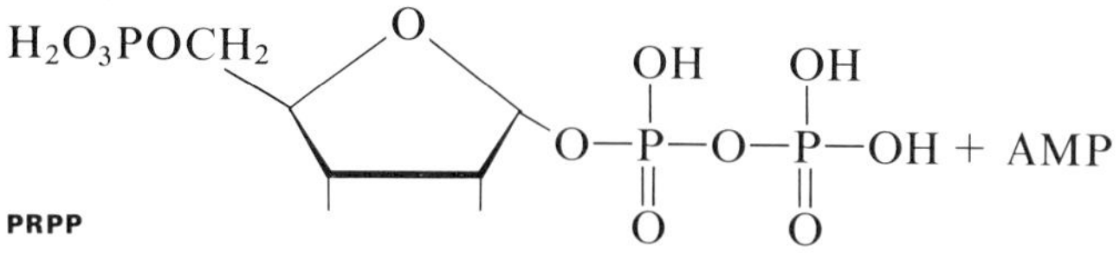

$$H_2O_3POCH_2 \quad \begin{array}{c} O \\ \end{array} \quad O-\underset{\underset{O}{\parallel}}{\overset{OH}{\underset{|}{P}}}-O-\underset{\underset{O}{\parallel}}{\overset{OH}{\underset{|}{P}}}-OH + AMP$$

PRPP

The next step is the formation of an amine from PRPP. The reaction is with glutamine, which supplies its amido nitrogen while pyrophosphate splits off:

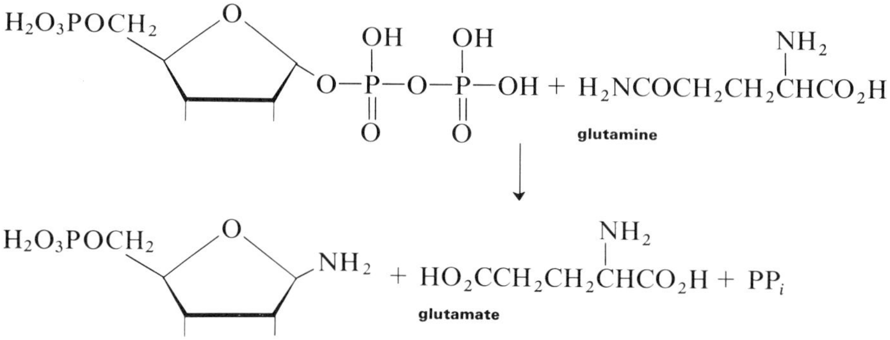

$$H_2O_3POCH_2 \quad \begin{array}{c} O \\ \end{array} \quad O-\underset{\underset{O}{\parallel}}{\overset{OH}{\underset{|}{P}}}-O-\underset{\underset{O}{\parallel}}{\overset{OH}{\underset{|}{P}}}-OH + H_2NCOCH_2CH_2\overset{NH_2}{\underset{|}{C}}HCO_2H$$

glutamine

$$\downarrow$$

$$H_2O_3POCH_2 \quad \begin{array}{c} O \\ \end{array} \quad NH_2 \; + \; HO_2CCH_2CH_2\overset{NH_2}{\underset{|}{C}}HCO_2H + PP_i$$

glutamate

5-phosphoribosyl-1-amine

Condensation of 5-phosphoribosyl-1-amine with glycine yields a glycine amide ribonucleotide. The amide bond is formed at the expense of ATP:

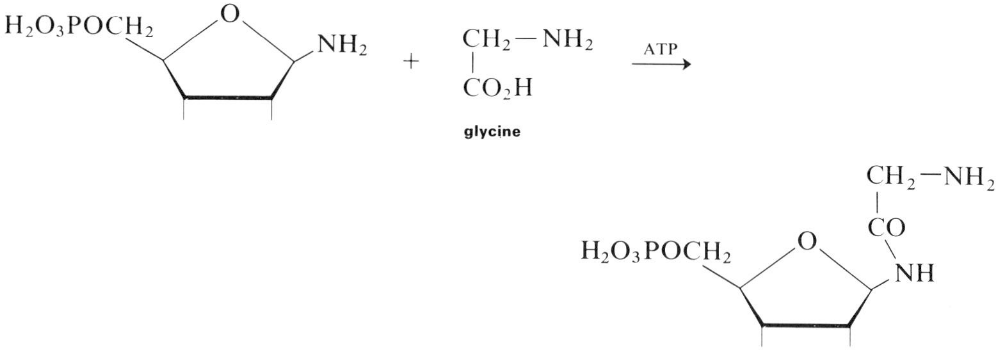

$$H_2O_3POCH_2 \quad \begin{array}{c} O \\ \end{array} \quad NH_2 \quad + \quad \begin{array}{c} CH_2-NH_2 \\ | \\ CO_2H \end{array} \quad \xrightarrow{ATP}$$

glycine

$$H_2O_3POCH_2 \quad \begin{array}{c} O \\ \end{array} \quad \begin{array}{c} CH_2-NH_2 \\ | \\ CO \\ \diagdown NH \end{array}$$

glycinamide ribonucleotide

From here on, we shall simplify the writing of the structures by representing ribose phosphate by —RP. Formylation of glycine amide-RP is the next step. It is made possible by formyl tetrahydrofolic acid (active formate, or F—CH):

$$\underset{\underset{O}{\parallel}}{}$$

$$
\begin{array}{c}
\underset{|}{CH_2-NH_2} \\
\underset{\diagdown}{CO} \\
\quad \underset{|}{NH} \\
\quad RP
\end{array}
\quad + \quad
\underset{\underset{O}{\parallel}}{F-CH}
\quad \longrightarrow \quad
\begin{array}{c}
\underset{|}{CH_2\!-\!\!-\!\!-NH} \\
\underset{\diagdown}{CO} \quad \underset{H}{C=O} \\
\quad \underset{|}{NH} \\
\quad RP
\end{array}
$$

N-formyl glycinamide
ribonucleotide

Glutamine again supplies the amido $-NH_2$ group for amination in a reaction requiring ATP:

$$
\begin{array}{c}
\underset{|}{CH_2\!-\!\!-\!\!-NH} \\
\underset{\diagdown}{CO} \quad \underset{H}{C=O} \\
\quad \underset{|}{NH} \\
\quad RP
\end{array}
+ \; H_2NCOCH_2CH_2\underset{\underset{NH_2}{|}}{C}HCO_2H \xrightarrow{\text{ATP}}
$$

$$
\begin{array}{c}
\quad \underset{|}{CH_2\!-\!\!-\!\!-NH} \\
\underset{HN}{\diagup}\!\!\!C \quad \underset{H}{C=O} \\
\qquad \underset{|}{NH} \\
\qquad RP
\end{array}
+ \; HO_2CCH_2CH_2\underset{\underset{NH_2}{|}}{C}HCO_2H + ADP + P_i
$$

N-formyl glycinamidine
ribonucleotide

Ring closure to yield the imidazol portion of the purine is promoted by ATP.

$$
\begin{array}{c}
\quad \underset{|}{CH_2\!-\!\!-\!\!-NH} \\
\underset{HN}{\diagup}\!\!\!C \quad \underset{\parallel}{C=O} \\
\qquad \underset{|}{NH} \\
\qquad RP
\end{array}
\quad \rightleftharpoons \quad
\begin{array}{c}
\quad CH\!-\!\!-\!N \\
\quad \parallel \qquad \parallel \\
\underset{H_2N}{\diagup}\!\!\!\underset{H}{C}\underset{N}{\diagdown}\;\underset{H}{C}-OH \\
\qquad \underset{|}{N} \\
\qquad RP
\end{array}
$$

$$
\text{ATP} \diagup -H_2O \searrow
$$

$$
\begin{array}{c}
\quad CH\!-\!\!-\!N \\
\quad \parallel \qquad \parallel \\
\underset{H_2N}{\diagup}\!\!\!C\underset{N}{\diagdown}\;CH \\
\qquad \underset{|}{N} \\
\qquad RP
\end{array}
$$

5-aminoimidazole ribonucleotide

The formation of the pyrimidine ring portion of purine begins by making a C—C bond on position 4. CO_2 supplies the carbon in a reaction not well understood:

$$
\begin{array}{c}
\text{HC} \longrightarrow \text{N} \\
\| \quad\quad \| \\
\text{C} \quad\quad \text{CH} \\
\text{H}_2\text{N} \diagdown \text{N} \diagup \\
| \\
\text{RP}
\end{array}
\; + \; \text{CO}_2 \longrightarrow
\begin{array}{c}
\text{HO}_2\text{C} - \text{C} \longrightarrow \text{N} \\
\| \quad\quad \| \\
\text{C} \quad\quad \text{CH} \\
\text{H}_2\text{N} \diagdown \text{N} \diagup \\
| \\
\text{RP}
\end{array}
$$

5-aminoimidazole-4-carboxylic acid

Aspartate supplies the —NH₂ group in the next step. The condensation of aspartate and release of fumarate is somewhat similar to the formation of arginine via argininosuccinate:

$$
\begin{array}{c}
\text{HO}_2\text{CCH}_2\text{CHCO}_2\text{H} \\
| \\
\text{NH}_2 \\
+ \\
\text{HO}_2\text{C} - \text{C} \longrightarrow \text{N} \\
\| \quad\quad \| \\
\text{C} \quad\quad \text{CH} \\
\text{H}_2\text{N} \diagdown \text{N} \diagup \\
| \\
\text{RP}
\end{array}
\xrightarrow{\text{ATP}}
\begin{array}{c}
\text{HO}_2\text{CCH}_2\text{CHCO}_2\text{H} \\
| \\
\text{HN} - \text{CO} \\
\diagdown \\
\text{C} \longrightarrow \text{N} \\
\| \quad\quad \| \\
\text{C} \quad\quad \text{CH} \\
\text{H}_2\text{N} \diagdown \text{N} \diagup \\
| \\
\text{RP}
\end{array}
$$

Cleavage of the condensation product is nonhydrolytic:

$$
\begin{array}{c}
\text{H} \quad \text{CO}_2\text{H} \\
| \quad | \\
\text{C} = \text{C} \\
| \quad \text{H} \\
\text{HO}_2\text{C}
\end{array}
\; + \;
\begin{array}{c}
\quad\quad \text{O} \\
\quad\quad \| \\
\quad\quad \text{C} \\
\text{H}_2\text{N} \diagup \quad \text{C} \longrightarrow \text{N} \\
\| \quad\quad \| \\
\text{C} \quad\quad \text{CH} \\
\text{H}_2\text{N} \diagdown \text{N} \diagup \\
| \\
\text{RP}
\end{array}
$$

**5-aminoimidazole-4-carboxamide
ribonucleotide**

A second formylation, akin to the first one shown, is carried on with formyl tetrahydrofolate:

$$
\begin{array}{c}
\quad\quad \text{O} \\
\quad\quad \| \\
\quad\quad \text{C} \\
\text{H}_2\text{N} \diagup \quad \text{C} \longrightarrow \text{N} \\
\| \quad\quad \| \\
\text{C} \quad\quad \text{CH} \\
\text{H}_2\text{N} \diagdown \text{N} \diagup \\
| \\
\text{RP}
\end{array}
\; + \;
\begin{array}{c}
\text{F} - \text{CH} \\
\| \\
\text{O}
\end{array}
\longrightarrow
\begin{array}{c}
\quad\quad \text{O} \\
\quad\quad \| \\
\quad\quad \text{C} \\
\text{H}_2\text{N} \diagup \quad \text{C} \longrightarrow \text{N} \\
\| \quad\quad \| \\
\text{O} = \text{C} \quad\quad \text{C} \quad\quad \text{CH} \\
\text{H} \diagdown \text{N} \diagdown \text{N} \diagup \\
\quad | \quad\quad | \\
\quad \text{H} \quad\quad \text{RP}
\end{array}
$$

**5-formamidoimidazol-4-carboxamide
ribonucleotide**

Ring closure yields inosinic acid:

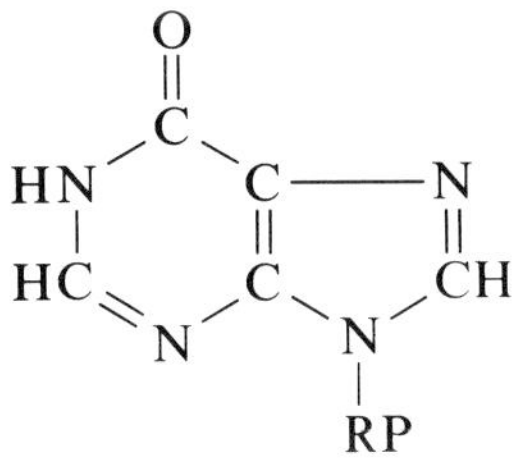

inosinic acid

FORMATION OF ADENYLIC AND GUANYLIC ACIDS : Inosinic acid, the first product in the biosynthetic pathway of purine nucleotides, yields adenylic acid by first forming adenylosuccinate:

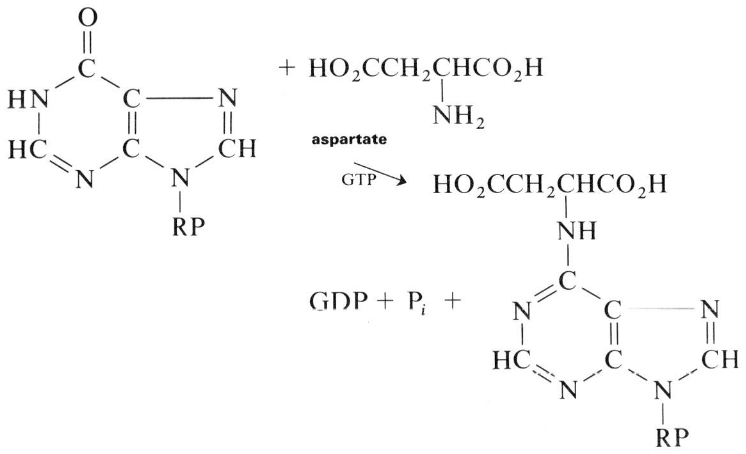

$+ HO_2CCH_2CHCO_2H$

NH_2

aspartate

GTP →

$HO_2CCH_2CHCO_2H$

NH

$GDP + P_i +$

Condensation is driven by the energy-rich compound GTP, which seems to be specific for the reaction. Nonhydrolytic cleavage of adenosyl succinate yields adenylic acid and fumarate:

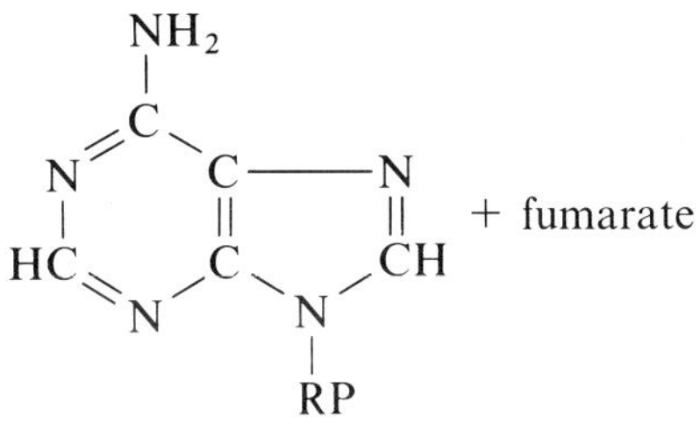

$+ fumarate$

adenylic acid

Guanylic acid is formed by amination of xanthylic acid, which is an oxidation product of inosinic acid. The oxidation requires NAD^+:

$$\text{inosinic acid} \xrightarrow{NAD^+} \text{xanthylic acid} + NADH + H^+$$

inosinic acid   xanthylic acid

Amination is mediated by glutamine similarly to reactions described previously:

$$\text{xanthylic acid} \xrightarrow{glutamine} \text{guanylic acid}$$

guanylic acid

The routes for the biosynthesis of the two purine nucleotides (5′-phosphates) just described represent the primary mechanism in the cell. The other pathway reported does not represent total synthesis; it entails reactions of existing purines to form nucleotides. In this sense it does not qualify as a biosynthetic pathway.

The requirement for folic acid in two of the steps is another example of the key position occupied by the vitamins in the economy of the cell. In the absence of folic acid, synthesis would stop at an intermediate stage. Without purine nucleotides neither RNA nor DNA can be produced.

biosynthesis of pyrimidine nucleotides :: 12.2

Pyrimidines are synthesized as their nucleotides rather than as free bases. The key substance in pyrimidine biosynthesis is orotic acid, which is in itself a pyrimidine derivative (4-carboxyuracil). First, dihydroorotic acid is synthesized by ring closure of N-carbamyl aspartate, which is formed by carbamylation of aspartate. Reduction catalyzed by an NAD^+ enzyme yields orotic acid:

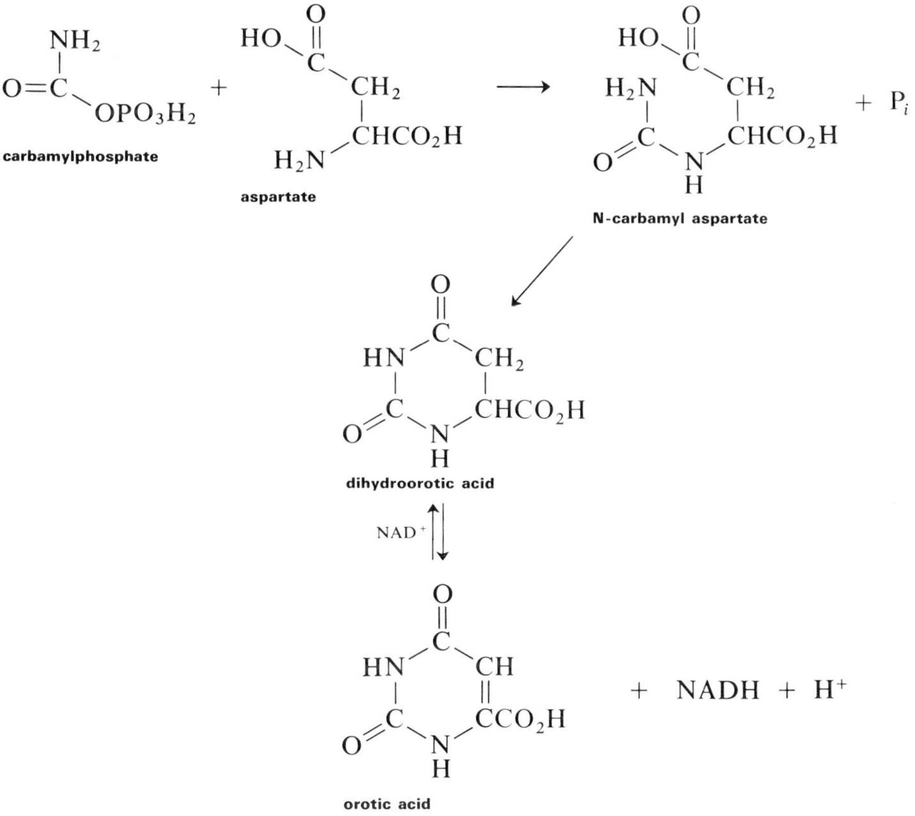

carbamylphosphate + aspartate → N-carbamyl aspartate + P_i

dihydroorotic acid

orotic acid + NADH + H⁺

Orotic acid itself does not give rise to the other pyrimidines. It condenses with 5-phosphoribosyl-1-pyrophosphate (PRPP) to yield orotidine-5′-phosphate, which is the intermediate precursor of the known pyrimidine nucleotides:

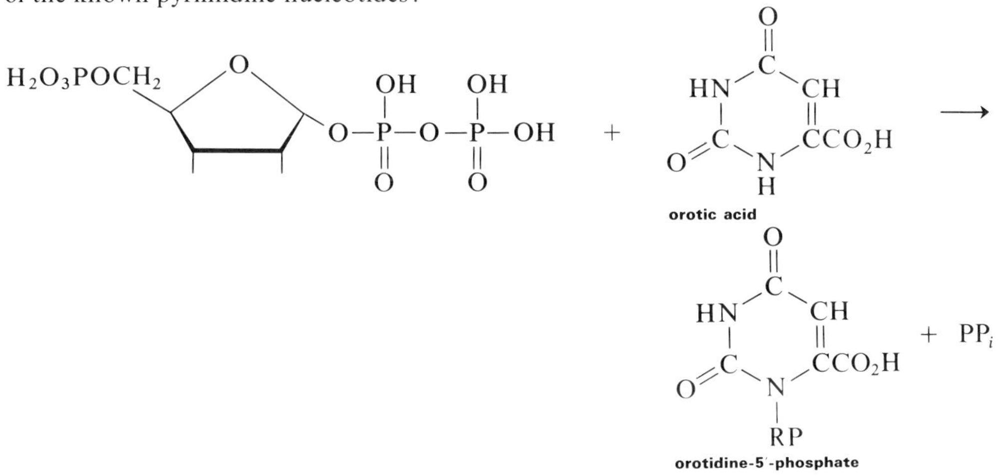

orotic acid

orotidine-5′-phosphate + PP_i

Orotidine-5'-phosphate is decarboxylated, yielding uridine-5'-phosphate (UMP):

$$
\begin{array}{c}
\text{O} \\
\parallel \\
\text{C} \\
\text{HN} \diagup \quad \diagdown \text{CH} \\
| \qquad\qquad \parallel \\
\text{O}{=}\text{C} \diagdown \quad \diagup \text{CH} \\
\text{N} \\
| \\
\text{RP}
\end{array}
\quad + \quad \text{CO}_2
$$

UMP

UMP gives rise to cytidine phosphates indirectly: UMP is first phosphorylated to uridine triphosphate (UTP) by two successive phosphorylations:

$$\text{UMP} + \text{ATP} \rightleftharpoons \text{UDP} + \text{ADP}$$

$$\text{UDP} + \text{ATP} \rightleftharpoons \text{UTP} + \text{ADP}$$

and then amination of UTP proceeds in the presence of NH_3 to yield cytidine triphosphate (CTP):

$$
\begin{array}{c}
\text{O} \\
\parallel \\
\text{C} \\
\text{HN} \diagup \quad \diagdown \text{CH} \\
| \qquad\qquad \parallel \\
\text{O}{=}\text{C} \diagdown \quad \diagup \text{CH} \\
\text{N} \\
| \\
\text{RPPP}
\end{array}
\; + \; \text{NH}_3 \; \xrightarrow{\text{ATP}} \;
\begin{array}{c}
\text{NH}_2 \\
| \\
\text{C} \\
\text{N} \diagup \quad \diagdown \text{CH} \\
| \qquad\qquad \parallel \\
\text{O}{=}\text{C} \diagdown \quad \diagup \text{CH} \\
\text{N} \\
| \\
\text{RPPP}
\end{array}
\; + \; \text{ADP} \; + \; \text{P}_i
$$

conversions to deoxyribonucleotides :: **12.3**

Loss of oxygen on $C_{,2}$ of ribonucleotides would be the most direct way to form deoxyribonucleotides. Proof that this is the process that takes place in the cell is not easily obtained. It is generally accepted that deoxyadenylic and deoxyguanylic acids are obtained by direct deoxygenation of AMP and GMP, respectively.

With pyrimidine nucleotides the situation appears to be somewhat different. It is almost certain that the immediate precursors of the deoxyribonucleotides are the diphosphates.

Diphosphates of pyrimidine nucleosides are not difficult to obtain by enzymatic phosphorylation of the monophosphates or dephosphorylation of the triphosphates. This step presents no problem.

The loss of oxygen from the 2′—OH group is another matter; it is apparent that a protein cofactor called *thioredoxin* is needed for the reduction of the 2′—OH group of the ribose portion in addition to $NADPH^+$. Thioredoxin behaves as a reducing agent by virtue of its —SH group. No more will be said about this reaction.

Thymidylic acid, which is a component of DNA, is made from deoxyuridine monophosphate by methylation:

deoxyuridine monophosphate
(dUMP)

thymidylic acid

The coenzyme carrying the active carbon serves here not only as a carrier but as a reducing agent to form the methyl group. This method of methylation is quite different from the one described in which S-adenosylmethionine is the methylating agent.

formation of polyphosphates :: **12.4**

It is quite apparent that nucleotides undergo numerous phosphorylation reactions yielding di- and triphosphates. Enzymes are known that catalyze transphosphorylations among ribonucleotides. The formation of deoxyribonucleotide triphosphates from the monophosphates proceeds generally in two stages; ATP supplies the phosphate in each case:

$$dAMP + ATP \rightleftharpoons dADP + ADP$$
$$dADP + ATP \rightleftharpoons dATP + ADP$$
$$dGDP + ATP \rightleftharpoons dGTP + ADP$$

and so on.

The necessity to synthesize triphosphates will become apparent in the biosynthesis of DNA and RNA. The enzymes catalyzing polymerizations are, as we shall see, specific for the triphosphates. They are in effect active forms (one with a high transfer potential) of nucleotides.

The biosynthesis of fats, glycerophosphatides, and other complex lipids begins with the synthesis of long-chain fatty acids. It would seem that a fatty acid can be made in the cell by simply reversing its degradation, as discussed in Chapter 8. But as we shall see in a moment in the cell there are two independent pathways to produce fatty acids. One, localized in the mitochondria, starts with an existing fatty acid and is simply elongated by condensations with acetyl-CoA. The other pathway, which is probably the major one, represents total synthesis of fatty acids in the cytoplasm, where soluble enzymes catalyze successive condensations starting with acetyl-CoA and malonyl-CoA. It is, therefore, important to consider first the sources of cytoplasmic acetyl-CoA and malonyl-CoA.

FORMATION OF ACETYL-CoA AND MALONYL-CoA : The supply of acetyl-CoA in the cytoplasm is limited by the fact that this substance is located in the mitochondria and does not normally diffuse into the cytoplasm proper where fatty acid synthesis takes place by the total pathway. One good source of acetyl-CoA is citrate; formed in the mitochondria during the operation of the citrate cycle it diffuses into the cytoplasm proper, where acetyl-CoA is produced by the following reaction:

$$\text{citrate} + \text{ATP} + \text{HSCoA} \rightleftharpoons \text{acetyl-CoA} + \text{oxalacetate} + \text{ADP} + P_i$$

Malonyl-CoA is produced by the carboxylation of acetyl-CoA. The reaction, catalyzed by a biotin enzyme, requires ATP as shown here:

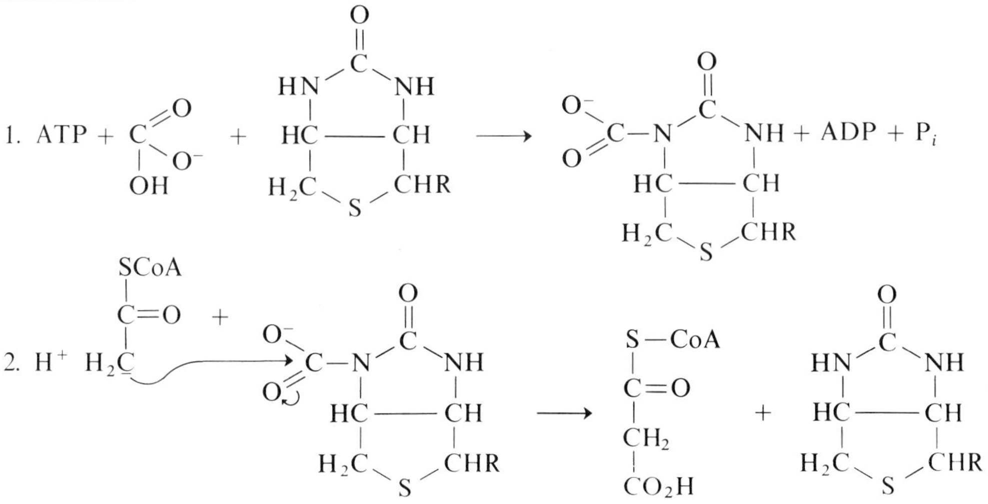

TOTAL SYNTHESIS : The soluble enzymes catalyzing the synthesis of fatty acids in the cytoplasm are associated as a multienzyme system ("synthetase").

Synthetases have been purified from plants, animals, and bacteria, but the latter are better understood systems. In the bacterial synthetase is found a heat-stable protein that has been given the name *acyl carrier protein* (ACP). It is a protein of molecular weight 9,500 to which is bound a molecule of 4'-phosphorylpantheteine. In subsequent reactions, the acyl carrier protein will be represented by ACP—SH.

The —SH group of the 4'-phosphorylpantheteine reacts with the substrates and intermediates of fatty acid synthesis to form thiolesters, which are the substrates of the fatty acid synthetase.

The reactions in fatty acid synthesis in bacteria are shown in the following sequence:

1.
$$\overset{\text{ACP}}{\underset{|}{\text{SH}}} + \underset{\textbf{acetyl-CoA}}{CH_3COSCoA} \xrightarrow[\text{transacylase}]{\text{acetyl}} \overset{\text{ACP}}{\underset{|}{\text{S—COCH}_3}} + HSCoA$$

2.
$$\overset{\text{SH}}{\underset{|}{\text{ACP}}} + \underset{\textbf{malonyl-CoA}}{HO_2CCH_2COSCoA} \xrightarrow[\text{transacylase}]{\text{malonyl}} \overset{\text{S—COCH}_2CO_2H + HSCoA}{\underset{|}{\text{ACP}}}$$

3.
$$\overset{\text{ACP}}{\underset{|}{\text{S—COCH}_3}} \quad \overset{CO_2}{\nearrow} \quad \xrightarrow[\text{ACP synthetase}]{\beta\text{-ketoacyl}} \quad \underset{\textbf{acetoacetyl-S-ACP}}{\overset{\text{S—COCH}_2COCH_3}{\underset{|}{\text{ACP}}}}$$

$$\overset{\text{S—COCH}_2CO_2H}{\underset{|}{\text{ACP}}} \qquad \overset{\text{SH}}{\underset{|}{\text{ACP}}}$$

4.
$$\overset{\text{S—COCH}_2COCH_3}{\underset{|}{\text{ACP}}} \xrightarrow[\text{ACP reductase}]{\substack{NADPH + H^+ \\ \beta\text{-ketoacyl} \\ \searrow NADP^+}} \underset{\textbf{D(−)}\boldsymbol{\beta}\textbf{-hydroxybutyryl-S-ACP}}{\overset{\text{S—COCH}_2\overset{H}{\underset{|}{\text{C}}}CH_3}{\underset{\underset{OH}{|}}{\underset{|}{\text{ACP}}}}}$$

5.
$$\overset{\text{S—COCH}_2\overset{H}{\underset{|}{\text{C}}}CH_3}{\underset{\underset{OH}{|}}{\underset{|}{\text{ACP}}}} \xrightarrow[\text{hydrase}]{\text{enoyl ACP}} \underset{\textbf{crotonyl-S-ACP}}{\overset{\text{S—COCH}=CHCH_3 + H_2O}{\underset{|}{\text{ACP}}}}$$

6.
$$\overset{\text{S—COCH}=CHCO_2H}{\underset{|}{\text{ACP}}} \xrightarrow[\text{reductase}]{\substack{NADPH + H^+ \\ \text{enoyl ACP} \\ \searrow NADP^+}} \underset{\textbf{butyryl-S-ACP}}{\overset{\text{S—COCH}_2CH_2CH_3}{\underset{|}{\text{ACP}}}}$$

The process starts again with butyryl-S-ACP, which like all intermediates remains bonded to the synthetase through the thiol ester bond. At the end of each sequence of reactions a new molecule of malonyl-CoA enters into the sequence and starts the process again, so that at each passage two carbons from malonyl-CoA are added to the fatty acid molecule; the process of elongation continues until the final product dissociates from the synthetase as the acyl-CoA derivative. The final reaction involves HS-CoA:

$$\underset{\substack{|| \\ R-C-S-ACP}}{O} + HSCoA \rightleftharpoons \underset{\substack{|| \\ R-C-SCoA}}{O} + HS-ACP$$

INTRODUCTION OF DOUBLE BONDS : The reactions just discussed yield a saturated fatty acid. The formation of olefinic acids by introducing one or several double bonds is not as simple as it seems. Although it was known for a long time that saturated acids give rise to olefinic acids, the exact steps were not known. Konrad Bloch, who has made a study of the process, has shown that oxidation of saturated acids is brought about by an $NADP^+$ enzyme acting on acyl-CoA. But the oxidation, according to Bloch, seems to be confined to aerobic organisms. Anaerobic organisms utilize a more complicated device. For example, synthesis proceeds as follows:

$$CH_3(CH_2)_nCH_2CH_2CO_2H$$

$\downarrow C_2$

$$CH_3(CH_2)_nCH_2CH_2\overset{\overset{\textstyle O}{\textstyle ||}}{C}CH_2CO_2H$$

$\downarrow$

$$CH_3(CH_2)_nCH_2CH_2\overset{\overset{\textstyle OH}{\textstyle |}}{\underset{\underset{\textstyle H}{\textstyle |}}{C}}CH_2CO_2H \rightarrow \alpha,\beta\text{-enoic acids}$$

$\downarrow$ $\downarrow$ saturated acids

$$CH_3(CH_2)_nCH_2CH=CHCH_2CO_2H$$

$\downarrow$

$$CH_3(CH_2)_nCH_2CH=CH(CH_2)_xCO_2H$$

biosynthesis of triglycerides and glycerophosphatides :: 12.6

The glycerol of triglycerides and glycerophosphatides is a product of glucose degradation. Converted to L-glycerophosphate, it reacts with acyl derivatives of CoA, which as we know have a high transfer potential:

$$
\begin{array}{c}
\text{CH}_2\text{OH} \\
| \\
\text{HOCH} \\
| \\
\text{CH}_2\text{OPO}_3\text{H}_2
\end{array}
\;+\;
\left\{
\begin{array}{c}
\overset{\displaystyle O}{\overset{\|}{\text{R}'\text{CSCoA}}} \\[2ex]
\overset{\displaystyle O}{\overset{\|}{\text{R}''\text{CSCoA}}}
\end{array}
\right.
\longrightarrow
\begin{array}{c}
\qquad\quad \overset{\displaystyle O}{\overset{\|}{}} \\
\text{O}\;\;\text{CH}_2\text{OCR}' \\
\|\;\;| \\
\text{R}''\text{COCH} \\
| \\
\text{CH}_2\text{OPO}_3\text{H}_2
\end{array}
\;+\;2\text{HSCoA}
$$

To introduce the third acyl group to yield a triglyceride, phosphatidic acid is first hydrolyzed:

$$
\begin{array}{c}
\qquad \overset{\displaystyle O}{\overset{\|}{}} \\
\text{O}\;\;\text{CH}_2\text{OCR}' \\
\|\;\;| \\
\text{R}''\text{COCH} \\
| \\
\text{CH}_2\text{OPO}_3\text{H}_2
\end{array}
\longrightarrow
\begin{array}{c}
\qquad \overset{\displaystyle O}{\overset{\|}{}} \\
\text{O}\;\;\text{CH}_2\text{OCR}' \\
\|\;\;| \\
\text{R}''\text{COCH} \\
| \\
\text{CH}_2\text{OH}
\end{array}
\;+\;\text{P}_i
$$

α, β-diglyceride

The resulting α,β-diglyceride is esterified to a triglyceride:

$$
\begin{array}{c}
\qquad \overset{\displaystyle O}{\overset{\|}{}} \\
\text{O}\;\;\text{CH}_2\text{OCR}' \\
\|\;\;| \\
\text{R}''\text{COCH} \\
| \\
\text{CH}_2\text{OH}
\end{array}
\;+\;\text{R}'''\text{CSCoA}
\longrightarrow
\begin{array}{c}
\qquad \overset{\displaystyle O}{\overset{\|}{}} \\
\text{O}\;\;\text{CH}_2\text{OCR}' \\
\|\;\;| \\
\text{R}''\text{COCH} \\
| \\
\text{CH}_2\text{OCR}''' \\
\|\\
\text{O}
\end{array}
\;+\;\text{HSCoA}
$$

Glycerophosphatides with choline, ethanolamine, and serine are also derived from phosphatidic acid. The introduction of choline is not direct, but it must first form a derivative with cytidine diphosphate:

$$
\text{cytidine}-\text{O}-\overset{\displaystyle \text{OH}}{\underset{\displaystyle \text{O}}{\overset{|}{\underset{\|}{\text{P}}}}}-\text{O}-\overset{\displaystyle \text{O}^-}{\underset{\displaystyle \text{O}}{\overset{|}{\underset{\|}{\text{P}}}}}-\text{OCH}_2\text{CH}_2\overset{+}{\text{N}}(\text{CH}_3)_3
$$

cytidine diphosphate choline

Its formation involves two steps:

$$
\text{choline}\;+\;\text{ATP}\;\rightleftharpoons\;{}^-\text{O}-\overset{\displaystyle \text{OH}}{\underset{\displaystyle \text{O}}{\overset{|}{\underset{\|}{\text{P}}}}}-\text{OCH}_2\text{CH}_2\cdot\overset{+}{\text{N}}(\text{CH}_3)_3\;+\;\text{ADP}
$$

phosphorylcholine

$$\text{phosphorylcholine} + \text{cytidine}-\text{O}-\overset{\overset{\text{OH}}{|}}{\underset{\underset{\text{O}}{||}}{\text{P}}}-\text{O}-\overset{\overset{\text{OH}}{|}}{\underset{\underset{\text{O}}{||}}{\text{P}}}-\text{O}-\overset{\overset{\text{OH}}{|}}{\underset{\underset{\text{O}}{||}}{\text{P}}}-\text{OH} \rightleftharpoons$$

$$\text{cytidine}-\text{O}-\overset{\overset{\text{OH}}{|}}{\underset{\underset{\text{O}}{||}}{\text{P}}}-\text{O}-\overset{\overset{\text{O}^-}{|}}{\underset{\underset{\text{O}}{||}}{\text{P}}}-\text{OCH}_2\text{CH}_2\overset{+}{\text{N}}(\text{CH}_3)_3 + \text{PP}_i$$

Condensation with α,β-diglyceride yields phosphatidyl choline (lecithin):

$$
\begin{array}{c}
\overset{\overset{\text{O}}{||}}{\text{O}}\ \overset{\overset{}{}}{\text{CH}_2\text{OCR}'}\\
\overset{\overset{\text{O}}{||}}{\text{R}''\text{COC}}\\
|\\
\text{CH}_2\text{OH}
\end{array}
\quad + \text{cytidine}-\text{O}-\overset{\overset{\text{OH}}{|}}{\underset{\underset{\text{O}}{||}}{\text{P}}}-\text{O}-\overset{\overset{\text{O}^-}{|}}{\underset{\underset{\text{O}}{||}}{\text{P}}}-\text{OCH}_2\text{CH}_2\overset{+}{\text{N}}(\text{CH}_3)_3
$$

$$
\begin{array}{c}
\overset{\overset{\text{O}}{||}}{}\\
\text{CH}_2\text{OCR}'\\
|\\
\text{R}''\text{COCH} \qquad \text{O}^-\\
|\qquad\quad |\\
\text{CH}_2\text{O}-\overset{}{\underset{\underset{\text{O}}{||}}{\text{P}}}-\text{OCH}_2\text{CH}_2\overset{+}{\text{N}}(\text{CH}_3)_3
\end{array}
\ + \ \text{cytidine}-\text{O}-\overset{\overset{\text{OH}}{|}}{\underset{\underset{\text{O}}{||}}{\text{P}}}-\text{OH}
$$

The production of phosphatidyl serine and phosphatidyl ethanol-amine proceed in similar fashion but there are alternatives. For example, condensation of cytidine diphosphoethanolamine with α,β-diglyceride yields phosphatidyl ethanolamine just as in the synthesis of lecithin. However, an exchange of serine for ethanol-amine does take place, yielding phosphatidyl serine.

biosynthesis of cholesterol :: 12.7

All the carbon atoms of cholesterol can be shown to be derived from acetate. The total synthesis of cholesterol, and other steroids derived from cholesterol, has been demonstrated in pieces of tissues such as liver.

The elucidation of all the steps required recognition of interme-diates between acetate and cholesterol. Two intermediates of great value were recognized: *mevalonic acid* and *squalene*. The latter is an isoprene derivative that cyclizes into a steroid structure.

SYNTHESIS OF MEVALONIC ACID : Mevalonic acid,

$$
\begin{array}{ccc}
\text{HO} & & \text{CH}_3 \\
& \diagdown \ \diagup \\
& \text{C} \\
& \diagup \ \diagdown \\
\text{CH}_2 & & \text{CH}_2 \\
| & & | \\
\text{HOH}_2\text{C} & & \text{CO}_2\text{H}
\end{array}
$$

is synthesized in the cell beginning with acetyl-CoA. The first step is the condensation with malonyl-CoA :

$$
\begin{array}{c}
\quad\quad \overset{O}{\overset{\|}{\text{CH}_3\text{C}-\text{SCoA}}} \\
\\
+ \\
\\
\underset{\text{HO}_2\text{CCH}_2\overset{\|}{\underset{O}{\text{C}}}-\text{SCoA}}{}
\end{array}
\longrightarrow
\begin{array}{c}
\text{CH}_3 \quad\quad O \\
| \quad\quad\quad \| \\
\text{C}-\text{CH}_2-\text{C}-\text{SCoA} + \text{CO}_2 + \text{HSCoA} \\
\| \\
O
\end{array}
$$

acetoacetyl-CoA

The intermediate acetoacetyl-CoA condenses with a second molecule of acetyl-CoA :

$$
\begin{array}{ccc}
O & & \text{CH}_3 \\
\diagdown\!\!\!\searrow & \diagup \\
& \text{C} \\
\diagup & & \diagdown \\
\text{H}_2\text{C} & & \text{CH}_2 \\
| & & | \\
O=\text{C} & & \text{C}=O \\
| & & | \\
\text{S} & & \text{S}-\text{CoA} \\
| \\
\text{CoA}
\end{array}
\xrightarrow{\ +\text{H}^+\ }
\begin{array}{ccc}
\text{HO} & & \text{CH}_3 \\
\diagdown & \diagup \\
& \text{C} \\
\diagup & & \diagdown \\
\text{H}_2\text{C} & & \text{CH}_2 \quad + \text{HSCoA} \\
| & & | \\
O=\text{C} & & \text{CO}_2\text{H} \\
| \\
\text{S} \\
| \\
\text{CoA}
\end{array}
$$

3-hydroxy-3-methyl glutaryl-CoA

3-hydroxy-3-methyl glutaryl-CoA becomes enzyme-bound by the sulfhydryl function of the enzyme while HSCoA is displaced. The enzyme-bound intermediate is then reduced to mevalonic acid by 2 moles of NADPH + H$^+$:

$$
\begin{array}{ccc}
\text{HO} & & \text{CH}_3 \\
\diagdown & \diagup \\
& \text{C} \\
\diagup & & \diagdown \\
\text{H}_2\text{C} & & \text{CH}_2 \\
| & & | \\
O=\text{C} & & \text{CO}_2\text{H} \\
| \\
\text{S} \\
| \\
\text{E}
\end{array}
\xrightarrow{\ 2\text{NADPH} + 2\text{H}^\cdot\ }
\begin{array}{ccc}
\text{HO} & & \text{CH}_3 \\
\diagdown & \diagup \\
& \text{C} \\
\diagup & & \diagdown \\
\text{H}_2\text{C} & & \text{CH}_2 \quad + 2\text{NADP}^+ + \ ^-\text{S}-\text{E} \\
| & & | \\
\text{HOH}_2\text{C} & & \text{CO}_2\text{H}
\end{array}
$$

ISOPENTENYL PYROPHOSPHATE : The need to postulate active intermediates led eventually to the discovery of isopentenyl pyrophosphate, which is the active isoprene unit in the biosynthesis of isoprenoids in general:

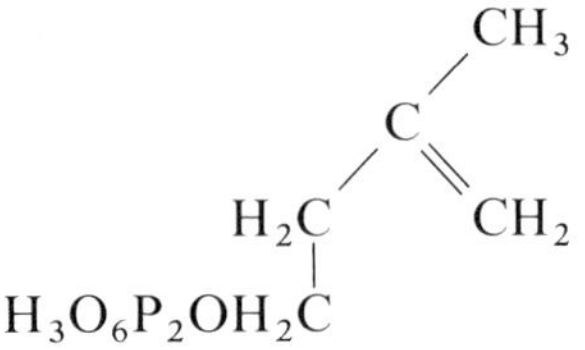

isopentenyl pyrophosphate

It is formed from mevalonic acid by a series of phosphorylations

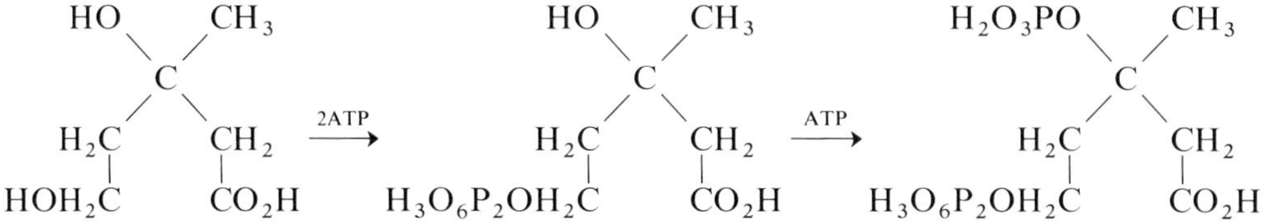

followed by decarboxylation of the phosphorylated intermediate and loss of phosphate:

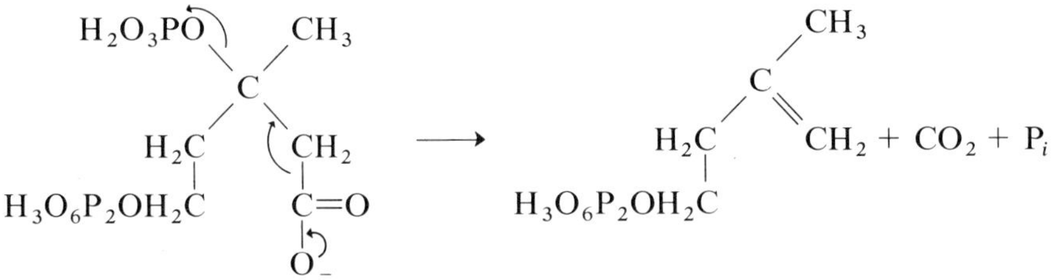

FARNESYL-PYROPHOSPHATE : The reactivity of isopentenyl pyrophosphate is such that it can condense into units of 15 and 30 carbons without the need of additional ATP. First, one molecule of isopentenyl pyrophosphate isomerizes to dimethyl allyl pyrophosphate which condenses with isopentenyl pyrophosphate:

isopentenyl pyrophosphate

dimethylallyl pyrophosphate

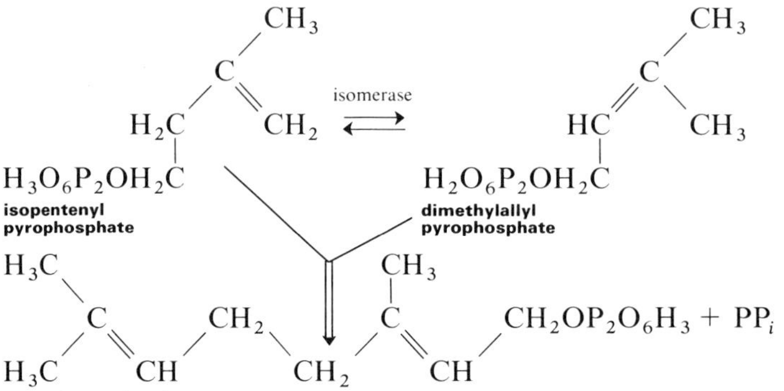

geranyl pyrophosphate

A second molecule of isopentenyl pyrophosphate can be added by a similar condensation mechanism to yield farnesyl pyrophosphate:

H_3C ... CH_3 ... $CH_2OP_2O_6H_3$ + H_3C ... $CH_2OP_2O_6H_3$

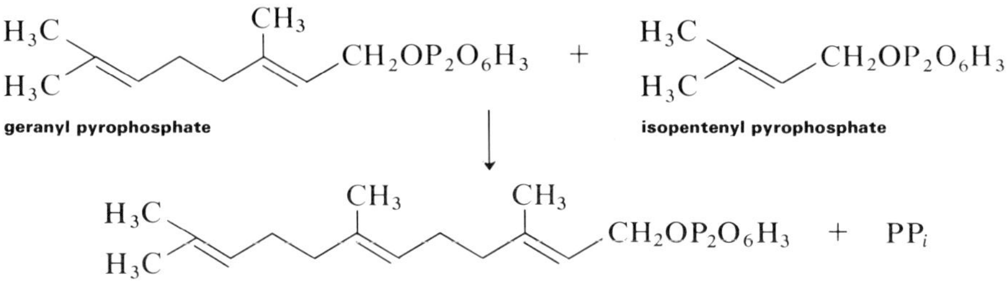

geranyl pyrophosphate   isopentenyl pyrophosphate

H_3C ... CH_3 ... CH_3 ... $CH_2OP_2O_6H_3$ + PP_i

farnesyl pyrophosphate

Free rotation allows this structure to be changed conveniently into one showing its relation to rings A and B of the steroid nucleus:

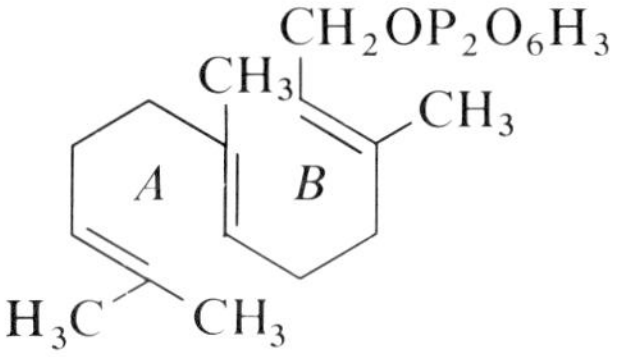

$CH_2OP_2O_6H_3$
CH_3 CH_3
A B
H_3C CH_3

SQUALENE : The phosphorylated intermediates are quite reactive, as we have seen. If the process of successive condensations is carried one step further, it is possible to form a long-chain hydrocarbon by condensing head to head two molecules of farnesyl pyrophosphate.† The product is squalene:

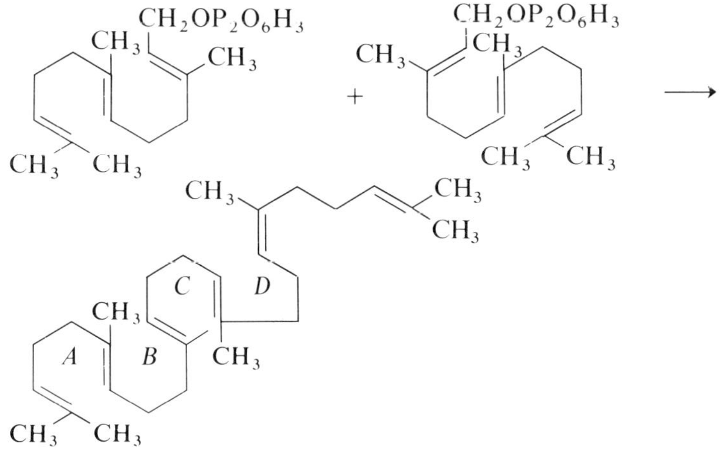

$CH_2OP_2O_6H_3$ ... CH_3 ... CH_3 $CH_2OP_2O_6H_3$ ... CH_3 ... CH_3
CH_3 CH_3 + CH_3 CH_3 →

CH_3 ... CH_3 ... CH_3
C D
CH_3
A B CH_3
CH_3 CH_3

squalene

† It is probable that one molecule of farnesyl pyrophosphate isomerizes to nerolidol pyrophosphate before condensing with the other molecule of farnesyl pyrophosphate.

The relation of squalene to the steroid nucleus is easily seen by depicting the structure of squalene in the configuration shown.†† Cyclization brought on by enzymatic action yields *lanosterol*, the first steroid product in biosynthesis. But cyclization is not the only step; first there is hydroxylation and somehow a migration of a methyl group:

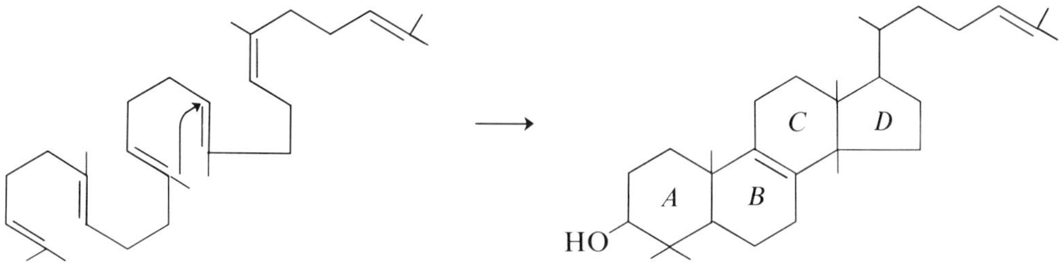

lanosterol

From lanosterol, cholesterol is produced by reactions entailing: (1) oxidative loss of three methyl groups, (2) reduction of the double bond on the side chain, and (3) shift of the double bond in ring **B**:

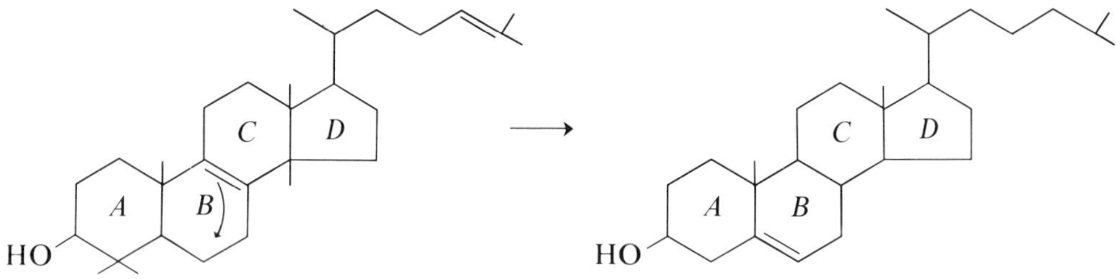

cholesterol

Cholesterol is a precursor of other steroids in the organism. Enzymes are known that hydroxylate the steroid ring or cleave parts of the side chain. The relation of cholesterol to bile acids and to some steroid hormones is shown in Figures 12.1 and 12.2.

† It is customary to write steroid structures in the manner shown here, without, however, the methyl substituents.

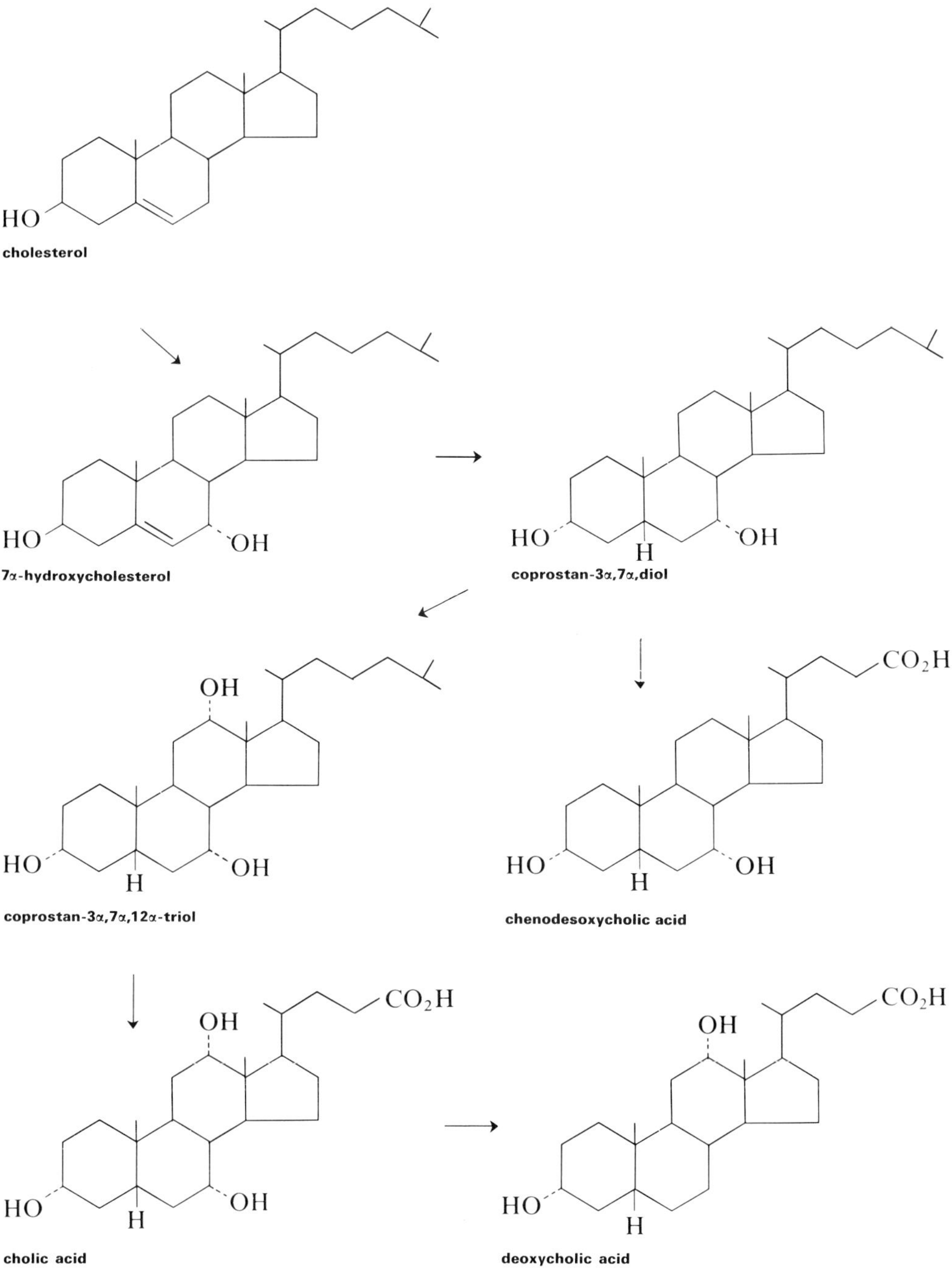
HO
cholesterol
HO
OH
7α-hydroxycholesterol
HO
H
OH
coprostan-3α,7α,diol
OH
HO
H
OH
coprostan-3α,7α,12α-triol
CO_2H
HO
H
OH
chenodesoxycholic acid
CO_2H
OH
HO
H
OH
cholic acid
CO_2H
OH
HO
H
deoxycholic acid

figure 12.1 :: Relation between cholesterol and bile acids. Bile acids exist mainly as the amides of glycine or taurine ($H_2NCH_2CH_2SO_3^-$).

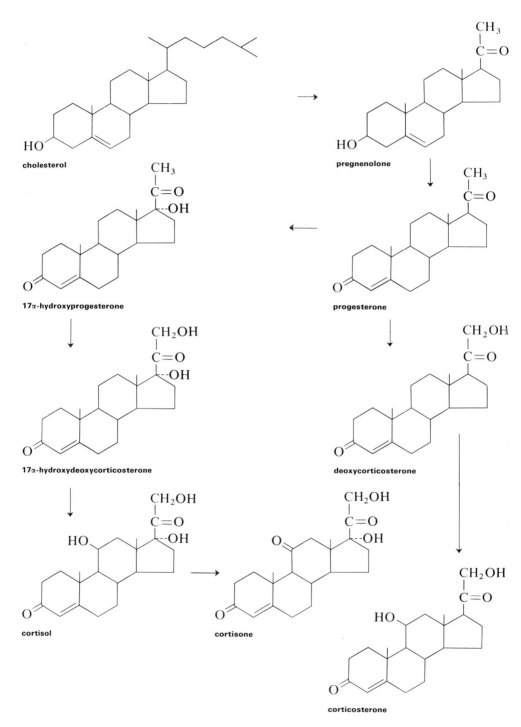

figure 12.2 :: Relation between cholesterol and some steroid hormones.

The porphyrin ring system is the basic structure of heme, chlorophyll, the prosthetic groups of cytochromes, peroxidase, and catalase, just to mention a few.

The precursors in the biosynthesis of the porphyrin ring are glycine and succinyl-CoA. This has been shown by the detection of radioactivity in porphyrin derivatives synthesized from radioactive precursors. The following steps are involved:

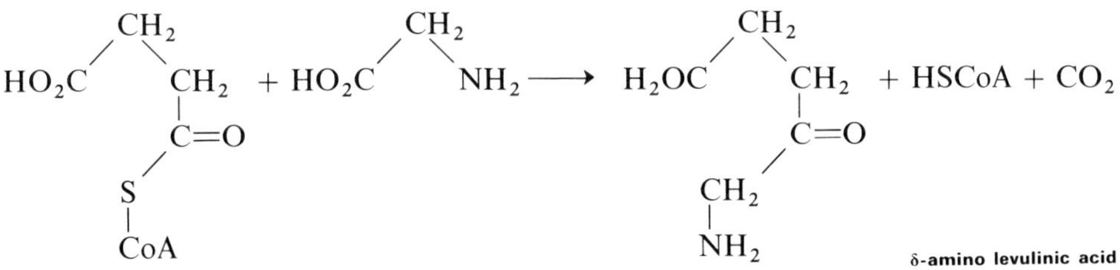

δ-amino levulinic acid

Condensation of two molecules of δ-amino levulinic acid yields porphobilinogen:

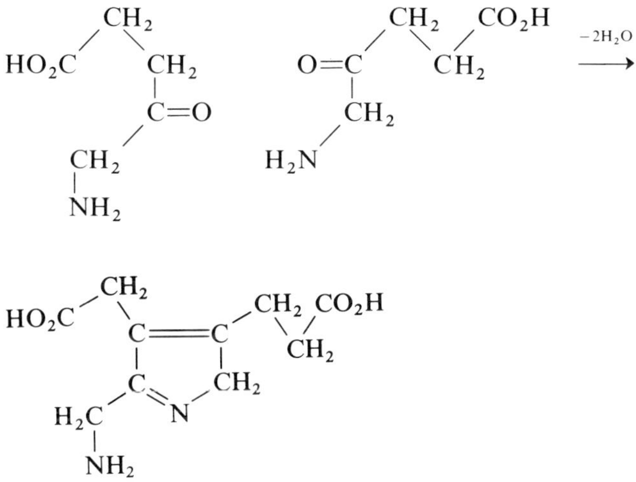

$-2H_2O$

Two structures for porphobilinogen are possible:

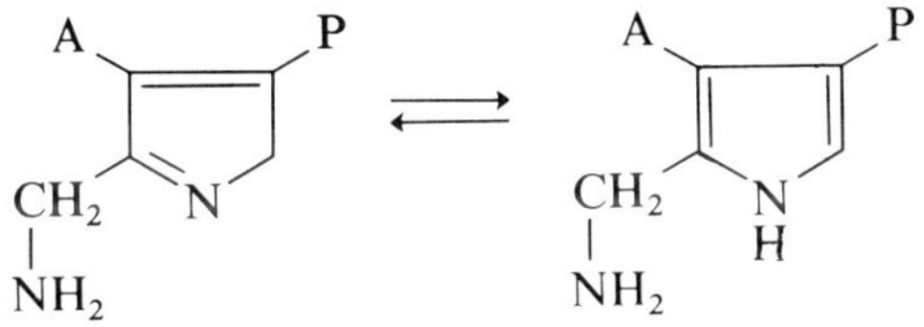

The condensations that follow to yield uroporphyrin III, the precursor of heme, involve deamination and isomerization:

uroporphyrin III

(The side chains are represented by A, acetic acid, and P, propionic acid.) Loss of the $-NH_2$ group leaves the $-CH_2$ group as a reactive group that becomes the methylene bridges in the porphyrin ring systems. Uroporphyrin III is not only a precursor of heme but also of the cytochromes.

references ::

DAVIDSON, J. N., *The Biochemistry of Nucleic Acids*, London: Methuen & Co., Ltd., 1960.

BLOCH, K., "Biological Synthesis of Cholesterol," in *Harvey Lectures*, Vol. 48, pp. 68–88 (1952–1953). New York: Academic Press, Inc., 1954.

GREEN, D., "The Synthesis of Fat," *Scientific American*, February, 1960.

biosynthesis ::: 13
of macromolecules :::

IN THE PRESENT DISCUSSION IT WILL BE CONVENIENT TO DIFFERENTIATE between macromolecules that do not carry sequence information, such as cellulose, starch, and latex, and those which carry sequence information, nucleic acids and proteins.

Those molecules of the first group are synthesized in the cell by reactions similar to those responsible for the synthesis of small but complex molecules such as steroids and porphyrins. That is to say, their synthesis proceeds by the concerted action of several enzymes catalyzing sequential reactions until the final product is built.

In molecules such as cellulose and starch the monomeric units (glucose) are not ordered into information-carrying sequences. These are simple homopolymers of varying chain length and well suited to perform their biological function: cellulose as a supporting material and starch as a form of storage of glucose molecules.

On the other hand, nucleic acids and proteins are biological macromolecules in which the monomeric units are ordered into information carrying sequences. Their synthesis involves more than a series of enzymes catalyzing sequential reactions, because a new dimension has been added—the precise arrangement of nucleotides in nucleic acids and the precise arrangement of amino acids in proteins.

The consequence of a precise, specified arrangement of amino acids or nucleotides into biological macromolecules is best appreciated by considering an enzyme as an example. The catalytic properties of an enzyme, as discussed in Chapter 6, reside within the active center of the enzyme, which is made up of amino acid side chains oriented in a precise and unique way. In the discussion of active centers, it was pointed out that the unique orientation of the amino acid side chains in the center is a consequence of the tertiary structure of the protein. The tertiary structure is itself ultimately dictated by the arrangement of amino acids in the protein. Or, put another way, the biological properties of a nucleic acid or a protein are dictated by information-carrying sequences of the monomeric units.

How then is a cell capable of synthesizing that particular enzyme over and over? How does a cell manage to arrange hundreds of amino acids in a unique order every time the enzyme molecule is synthesized? The same question can be asked about the synthesis of nucleic acids, in which hundreds of nucleotides are aligned in a unique order.

To answer the question, the concept of template surfaces had to be introduced. A template, as the name implies, is a molecule capable of serving as a pattern for the synthesis of another molecule just like the template. In other words, the template concept implies true molecular replication.

Later in the chapter it will be shown that only nucleic acids possess template properties and that proteins are synthesized on nucleic acid templates.

biosynthesis of polysaccharides :: 13.1

In Chapter 10, the breakdown of starch and glycogen was considered as catalyzed by the digestive enzymes (amylases) and also by the intracellular enzymes (phosphorylases). It would seem almost certain that a reversal of the phosphorolytic cleavage of glycogen or starch would lead to its formation. The reaction can be formulated by the chemical equation

$$[C_6H_{10}O_5]_n + H_3PO_4 \rightleftarrows [C_6H_{10}O_5]_{n-1} + \text{glucose-1-phosphate}$$

and the equilibrium equation can be written

$$K_{eq} = \frac{[C_6H_5O_{10}]_{n-1}[\text{glucose-1-phosphate}]}{[C_6H_{10}O_5]_n[H_3PO_4]} = 0.3$$

in which K_{eq} is such that the reversal is, in fact, possible. However, this is in the test tube and not in the cell, where the high concentration of phosphate prevents glycogen synthesis. It is evident that in the cell phosphorylases are catabolic enzymes, while other independent routes of synthesis operate.

Leloir's discovery of uridine diphosphate glucose as a precursor in the biosynthesis of starch was immediately followed by the discovery of other nucleoside diphosphate derivatives of sugars. These precursors, together with specific enzymes, are responsible for the formation of glycans in general.

Nucleoside diphosphate derivatives of sugars are formed in the cell as part of the activation process according to the following general reaction:

nucleoside triphosphate + sugar-1-phosphate $\rightleftharpoons$ nucleoside diphosphate sugar + PP_i

We have already discussed this reaction in connection with galactose epimerization (Chapter 10).

The enzyme responsible for glycogen synthesis is called trivially "glycogen synthetase." The enzyme catalyzes the formation of linear polymers of glucose connected through α-1,4-glycosidic bonds. The reaction starts on a "primer," that is, a trace of ready-made glycogen, which is known to be a branched polymer. The role of the enzyme in this case is to add to the nonreducing end of the branches glucose molecules from UDP-glucose:

However, there is more to glycogen synthesis; as the chains grow to become 10 or more glucose units long, they are attacked in the cell by a second enzyme, a transglycosydase. The role of the second enzyme is to catalyze cleavage of several glucose units and their immediate condensation on the same branch or another branch. Being specific for α-1,6-glycosidic bonds, branches are formed as depicted schematically here:

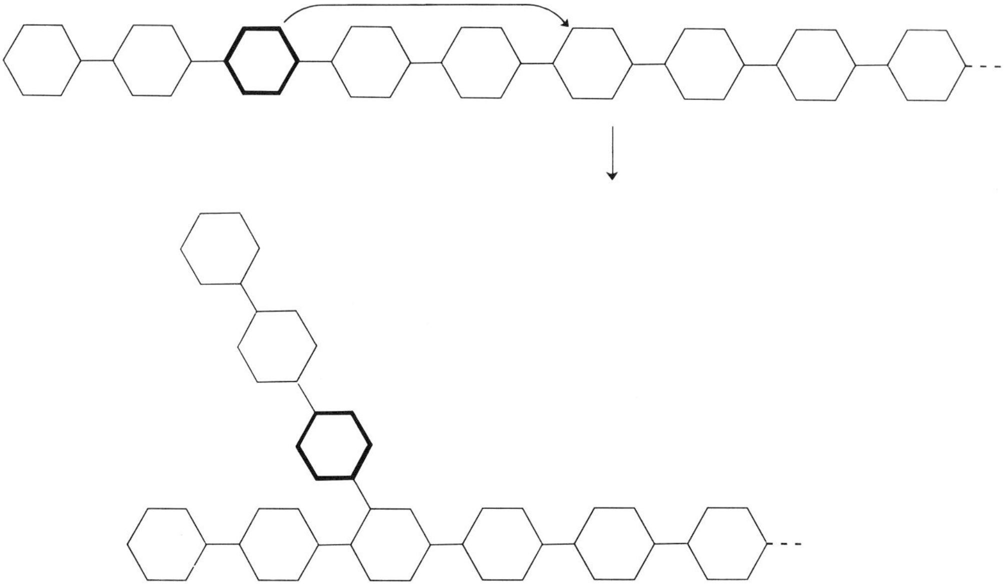

UDP-glucose can also act as a precursor for the biosynthesis of starch, but other nucleoside diphosphate derivatives have also been found to be more effective. It is likely that ADP-glucose is the precursor of starch.

Cellulose is produced from UDP-glucose in some microorganisms and from GDP-glucose in some plants. The same mechanism applies to other homoglycans. A number of nucleoside diphosphate derivatives of sugars have been discovered in both plants and animals. Some of the more common ones are listed in Table 13.1.

biosynthesis of DNA :: 13.2

The concept of template macromolecules arose from the need to explain replication of genetic material (DNA) during cell division. A priori, a template molecule for the replication of DNA had to offer unique properties for which there was no known precedent.

First, it had to be a molecule endowed with a mechanism for the recognition of monomers during the synthesis of DNA. Only then could a template orient each nucleotide in its proper place in the final DNA molecule synthesized. Second, the forces binding the

table 13.1 :: Nucleoside diphosphate derivatives of some common sugars

NUCLEOSIDE DIPHOSPHATE	SUGAR
uridine diphosphate	Glucose, galactose, glucosamine, mannosamine, N-acetylglucosamine, N-acetylgalactosamine, glucuronic acid, arabinose, xylose
adenosine diphosphate	Glucose
guanosine diphosphate	Glucose, galactose, mannose, fucose, rhamnose
deoxythymidine diphosphate	Glucose, galactose, mannose, glucosamine, N-acetylglucosamine, N-acetylgalactosamine, rhamnose

nucleotides to the template had to be sufficiently strong to allow temporary alignment and association to the template but not so strong as to prevent dissociation of the product from the template.

WATSON-CRICK THEORY : In the DNA model of Watson and Crick, provisions were made to include the two basic conditions for a template molecule. Recognition of nucleotides is possible by the restrictions inherent in the way bases are paired in the DNA molecule. That is, adenine pairs only with thymine and guanine pairs only with cytosine. By acting as a template in this fashion, each DNA strand promotes synthesis of its complementary strand.

The second condition for a template is satisfied by the hydrogen bonds formed when two bases form a pair. Hydrogen bonds are relatively weak and therefore easily broken, allowing for the dissociation of the product from the template DNA.

In conformity with these ideas, Watson and Crick proposed a mechanism in broad terms to explain DNA replication. This is depicted in Figure 13.1. In this mode of replication, the original template DNA is used over and over again, and for this reason it is known as the *conservative mode of replication*.

But evidently this is not the most likely mechanism of DNA replication. The prevailing view now, which originated in an ingenious experiment of M. Meselson and F. W. Stahl, is the *semiconservative mode of replication*. According to this view, the original strands of DNA untwist and each serves as a template for new strands. The new strands become partners to the templates, so that in each of the two double-stranded DNA molecules, one strand is the original template. This idea is depicted in Figure 13.2. A difficulty here is that untwisting two long strands in DNA requires a great deal of energy, and to this moment it is not known how the two strands separate. Other alternatives have been suggested and those will be discussed shortly.

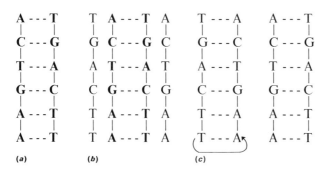

figure 13.1 :: Conservative mode of DNA replication: (*a*) template; (*b*) complementary strands formed; (*c*) new DNA molecule identical with template.

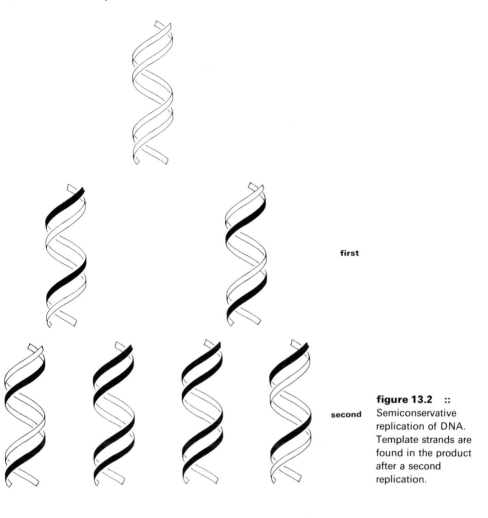

first

second

figure 13.2 ::
Semiconservative
replication of DNA.
Template strands are
found in the product
after a second
replication.

FORMATION OF INTERNUCLEOTIDE BONDS : In the simplified picture
just presented, no account is made for the formation of the internucleotide bonds. This is clearly an endergonic process to which
energy must be furnished.

The extensive study by A. Kornberg and associates of enzymes
that catalyze the polymerization of nucleoside triphosphates
yielded the needed information. They isolated in concentrated form
from *E. coli* an enzyme, DNA polymerase, which catalyzes the net
synthesis of DNA. The enzyme attacks a mixture of the four
nucleoside triphosphates only in the presence of a DNA *primer*.
The product was like the primer in base composition and ratios,
but because much more DNA was found at the end of the experiment than was used for primer, net synthesis had to occur.

Because the properties (base composition and ratios of A-T and G-C) of the synthetic DNA were like those of the primer, it was suggested that the added DNA is both a primer and a template as well. The DNA requirement of DNA polymerase suggested a possible mechanism for DNA synthesis and replication.

DNA polymerase catalyzes the following reaction:

$$\left.\begin{array}{l} n\ \text{dATP} \\ n\ \text{dGTP} \\ n\ \text{dCTP} \\ n\ \text{TTP} \end{array}\right\rangle \xrightarrow{\text{DNA}} \text{DNA} + 4n\text{PP}_i$$

The energy requirements for the reaction are satisfied by the high chemical potential of nucleoside triphosphates to be converted to monophosphates.

The polynucleotide chain is probably formed stepwise along the template by adding one nucleotide after another:

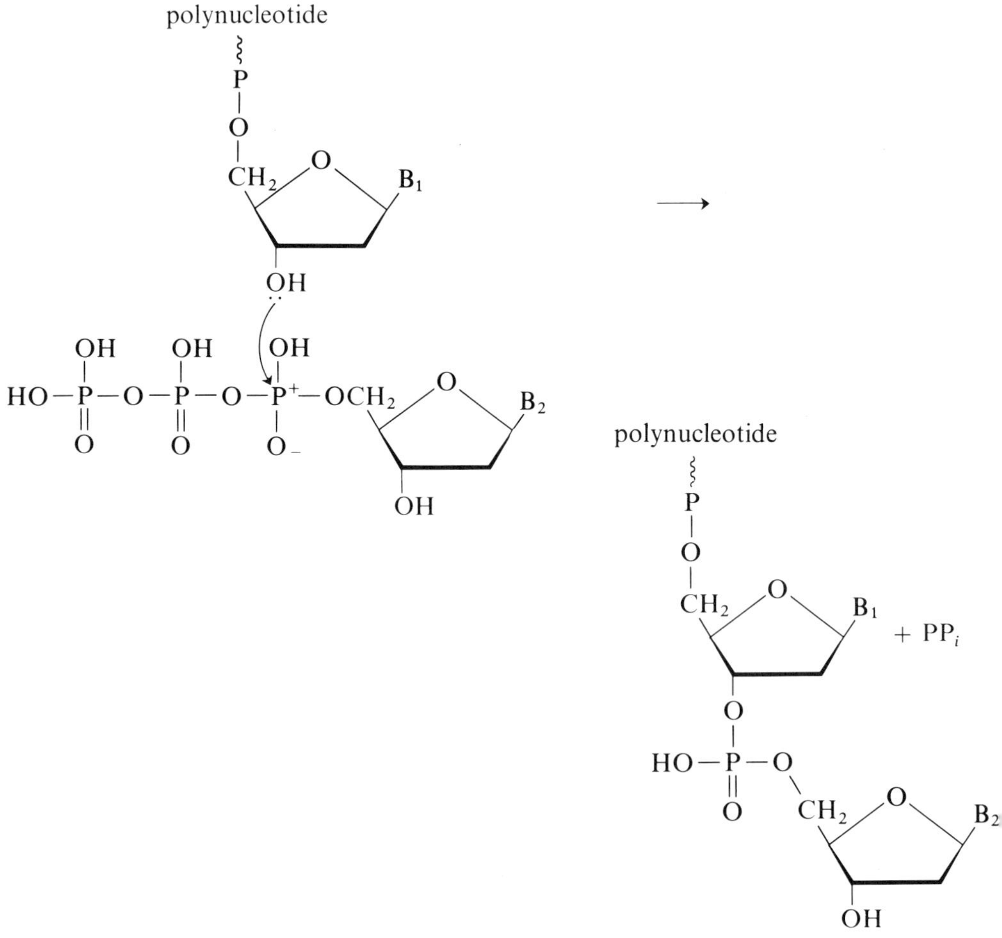

In accordance to this mechanism, the chain grows from the 3′-OH group. But the other possibility is that it grows from the 5′-OH end.

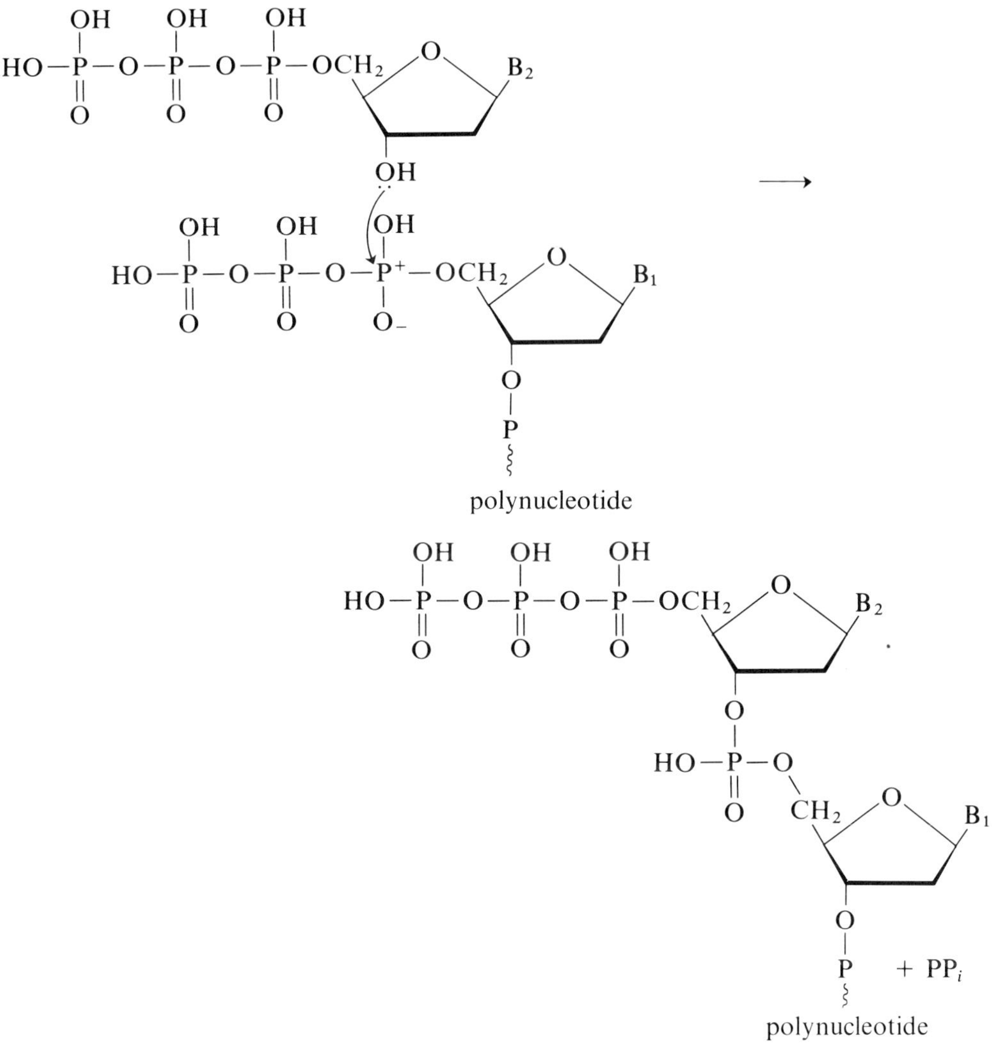

polynucleotide

polynucleotide

In the first mechanism the polynucleotide always ends with deoxyribose with a free 3′-OH; in the second mechanism it must always end with a 5′-triphosphate of the terminal deoxyribose. There is no certainty as to the direction of growth.

SEPARATION OF STRANDS : If one accepts a double-stranded DNA as the natural template, it then becomes necessary to suggest some mechanism for opening the two strands in order to serve as templates as visualized in the original theory.

We do not know how the strands are opened or what forces are involved in their separation. The problem has been skirted by Watson and Crick, who proposed a different mode of replication. They proposed that only a small region of DNA separates and synthesis is initiated on the short regions of single DNA. As synthesis proceeds more separation occurs. This situation is depicted in Figure 13.3 and is commonly referred to as the *Y mechanism*.

If accepted, we must accept the simultaneous operation of the two ways of chain growth just described. The reason is that the two strands in DNA are antiparallel with respect to their 3′-5′ internucleotide bonds. This is another problem in DNA replication that has not been solved completely.

To summarize: The present theories of DNA replication rest upon verifiable experimental facts. Some of the details are still not clearly understood, but the fundamental principles evolved with respect

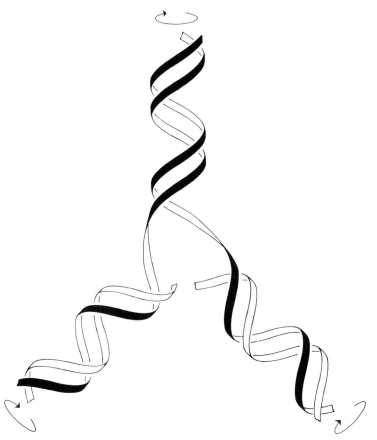

figure 13.3 ::
Y replication of DNA according to Watson and Crick. Parental strand (black) unwinds and is replicated in semiconservative fashion.

to template function are now accepted as one of the most funda-mental laws of biology.

Only nucleic acids, by virtue of their specific base pairs, serve the template function not only for other nucleic acids but also for proteins.

biosynthesis of RNA :: **13.3**

With the basic principles of the template theory laid down, the synthesis of RNA became accessible to further investigation. At first it was difficult to apply the rules of DNA replication to RNA replication, because less is known about the macromolecular structure of RNA.

Before discussing RNA replication it should be recognized that RNA is a collective name for several functionally distinct types of RNA: (1) ribosomal RNA, (2) messenger RNA, (3) soluble or transfer RNA, and (4) viral RNA.

Structurally alike in some respects, the various types of RNA differ considerably in molecular weight and are distributed in different parts of the cell. Viral RNA has served as a model of RNA replication.

It was known for some time that viruses made up of RNA protein replicate themselves. This knowledge was inferred from the obser-vation that in infected cells the RNA virus reproduces and therefore the infected cell must somehow synthesize more virus RNA. An enzyme needed for RNA synthesis was isolated from cells infected by RNA viruses and shown to be a RNA polymerase. Outside the cell the enzyme carries on the same function if added to a mixture of the four ribonucleotides and primer RNA from the virus. Net synthesis of viral RNA was observed, so the inevitable conclusion was that RNA has the same template function as DNA.

The other types of RNA are synthesized in the cell by similar mechanisms. These will be discussed in turn.

BIOSYNTHESIS OF MESSENGER RNA : The existence of a short-lived type of RNA was predicted on theoretical grounds by F. Jacob, J. Monod, and associates. The name *messenger RNA* (mRNA) was used to describe a form of RNA that would be made in the cell nucleus but would be transferred to the cytoplasm, where proteins are synthesized.

The necessity to invoke a mRNA arose from earlier observations on protein synthesis. It was known for sometime that proteins are synthesized in the cytoplasm in regions rich in RNA. The new theories predicted that the amino acid sequence in a given protein was determined by DNA, which is mainly in the nucleus. The information in DNA—in the form of a specified sequence of bases— had to be transferred somehow to the cytoplasm.

The notion of a mRNA demanded that DNA act as template for RNA synthesis. The principle of base pairs still applies here, be- cause uracil in RNA has the same dimensions as thymine in DNA, and one can substitute for the other. In this manner a DNA strand could function as template for RNA synthesis:

A - T - T - G - A - C   DNA
U - A - A - C - U - G   mRNA

The theory has found experimental support, and the evidence for the existence of the predicted mRNA is substantial. mRNA is found attached to ribosomes; several ribosomes combine with a mRNA molecule and form the active polysome, where protein is synthesized.

An enzyme was discovered not long ago that catalyzes the synthe- sis of RNA from four nucleoside triphosphates but only when DNA is added as primer. The last observation was crucial in the solution of the problem of protein synthesis. The enzyme, RNA polymerase, has been isolated from tissues and purified extensively. The RNA produced by the action of RNA polymerase can be shown to have a sequence of pyrimidines and purines complemen- tary to that of the DNA primer.

Before the discovery of RNA polymerase, an enzyme was found by S. Ochoa and associates that catalyzes the polymerization of nucleoside diphosphates to yield products of random composition. The enzyme, polynucleotide phosphorylase, yields products the composition of which is determined by the ratios of the four nucleoside diphosphates in the reaction mixture. The role of the phosphorylase is uncertain, but there is reason to believe that it serves to degrade mRNA by phosphorolytic cleavage. Here again, as shown for glycogen, two independent pathways operate in the cell: one for synthesis and one for degradation.

BIOSYNTHESIS OF TRANSFER RNA : *Transfer RNA* (tRNA; also called *soluble RNA*, sRNA) is of low molecular weight. The struc- ture of one type of tRNA has been shown in Chapter 3. Although the details of its synthesis are not known, it is known that tRNA is synthesized on DNA templates by steps similar to those of the other types of RNA.

Several aspects of tRNA merit some comment. One is that all tRNA types so far isolated contain the same sequence of bases at one end of the molecule, cytosine-cytosine-adenine. Another interesting observation is that in tRNA one invariably finds nucleotides not yet described: pseudouridylic acid and ribothymidylic acid:

pseudouridylic acid   ribothymidylic acid

The presence of the two bases presents a problem. If synthesis of tRNA proceeds by the same mechanism as other types of RNA, the enzymes involved in tRNA synthesis must be assumed to have unique specificity for the two new nucleotides. A more attractive idea is that tRNA is formed from the familiar four ribonucleotides, and by enzymatic modification of selected uridylic acid units in the tRNA, the new nucleotides are formed. Pseudouridylic acid could be the product of an isomerization reaction of tRNA. Ribothymidylic acid is known to be formed by methylation of uridylic acid present in tRNA.

The characteristic terminal —C—C—A sequence is believed to be added enzymatically after tRNA is already made.

RIBOSOMAL RNA : Little is known about the bulk of RNA, which is localized in the ribosomes intimately associated with protein. It is RNA of high molecular weight, apparently consisting of two types differing somewhat in size. Some evidence suggests that this RNA is also synthesized on a DNA template.

biosynthesis of proteins :: 13.4

Three aspects of protein biosynthesis must be considered: (1) formation of peptide bonds and the energy requirements, (2) alignment of amino acids in a precise sequence, and (3) folding of the polypeptide chain into a three-dimensional structure.

The first aspect of protein biosynthesis is readily explained. The living cell has apparently one major device to funnel energy into endergonic reactions: activation of precursors, that is, reaction of ATP with an otherwise unreactive substance to yield a substance with high transfer potential. The existence of activated amino acid derivatives for protein synthesis was predicted long before they were found.

The second aspect, with which most of this section will be concerned, has presented the greatest problems. It was evident that a template was needed on which amino acids would orient themselves and form a polypeptide of specified sequence. The notion that a polypeptide could be a template on which amino acids would orient themselves received no experimental support. Theoretically the idea was also inadequate because there is no known reason why an amino acid, say, leucine, should orient itself near leucine residues of the polypeptide chain.

The observation made long ago that protein synthesis occurs in regions rich in RNA made nucleic acid the most likely molecule to act as template for proteins as we shall see in a moment.

But first let us consider the last aspect, which has not been solved. The tertiary structure of a protein determines the protein's biological properties, as we know. It is unlikely that enzymes are involved in the folding of the polypeptide chain; it is more likely that once a polypeptide chain is synthesized it will attain spontaneously the most stable conformation. There is some evidence that a polypeptide will fold itself in the same way every time, as a result of interactions among side chains and surroundings or mutual side-chain interactions.

In dealing with the second aspect of the problem we recognize these steps in protein synthesis: (1) activation of amino acids, (2) orientation of active amino acids on a template, and (3) formation of the peptide bond. These will now be discussed.

ACTIVATION OF AMINO ACIDS : The formation of active derivatives of amino acids was studied extensively by P. Zamecnik and associates. They were the first to obtain a "cell-free extract" with catalytic properties to synthesize protein. The extract was a mixture of enzymes, ribosomes, a soluble form of RNA (tRNA) cofactors, and ATP. On addition of an amino acid labeled with ^{14}C, it could be shown that the ^{14}C appeared in protein, but under special circumstances it appeared in tRNA. An amino acid derivative of tRNA was postulated as the intermediate in protein synthesis.

Moreover, its formation required an active form of the amino acid, a form not yet isolated. The mechanism finally conceived for aminoacyl-tRNA formation is shown here:

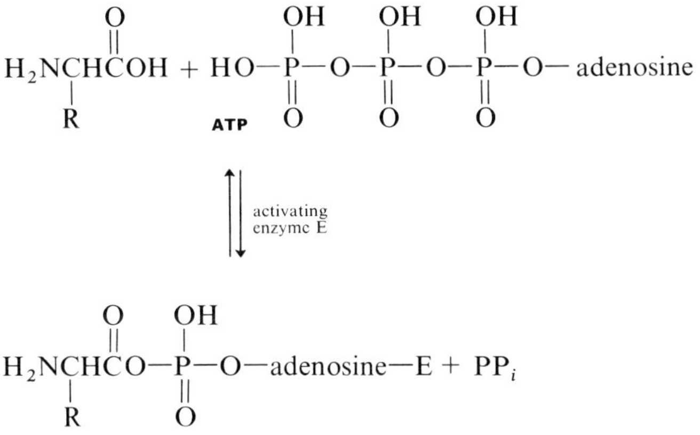

$$H_2NCHCOH + HO-\overset{OH}{\underset{O}{\overset{|}{\underset{||}{P}}}}-O-\overset{OH}{\underset{O}{\overset{|}{\underset{||}{P}}}}-O-\overset{OH}{\underset{O}{\overset{|}{\underset{||}{P}}}}-O-adenosine$$

with O double bonded at top of first carbon and R below the CH, ATP labeling the triphosphate.

activating enzyme E

$$H_2NCHCO-\overset{OH}{\underset{O}{\overset{|}{\underset{||}{P}}}}-O-adenosine-E + PP_i$$

with O double bonded on the acyl carbon and R below the CH.

aminoacyl-AMP-E

The resulting aminoacyl-AMP does not dissociate from the enzyme; instead it reacts with a specific type of tRNA. A similar mechanism is seen in the synthesis of fatty acyl-CoA derivatives mentioned in Chapter 8. The specificity of the activating enzyme for tRNA and amino acid is crucial in the final disposition of the amino acid. There are as many activating enzymes and tRNAs as there are types of amino acids in proteins. The reaction between the aminoacyl-AMP-enzyme complex and tRNA is through the terminal adenine of the —C—C—A end sequence of the tRNA, as formulated at the top of page 266.

It is interesting to note that all tRNA so far known has the same terminal sequence at one end. Specificity of tRNA for a given amino acid and a given enzyme must clearly reside on another structural feature of the tRNA molecule.

Formation of the ester bond is possible because amino acyl-AMP has a sufficiently high transfer potential to esterify the 3' hydroxyl, but we are not certain that it does not esterify the 2' hydroxyl.

Once the amino acid is attached to its specific tRNA, the fate of the amino acid is already determined. A moment ago it was said that a nucleic acid had to be the template for protein synthesis. By having the amino acid riding on tRNA, we need no longer concern ourselves with the amino acid. The tRNA will, in accordance to the rule of base pairs, orient itself on a template surface (mRNA) and ipso facto orient the amino acid, as we shall see next.

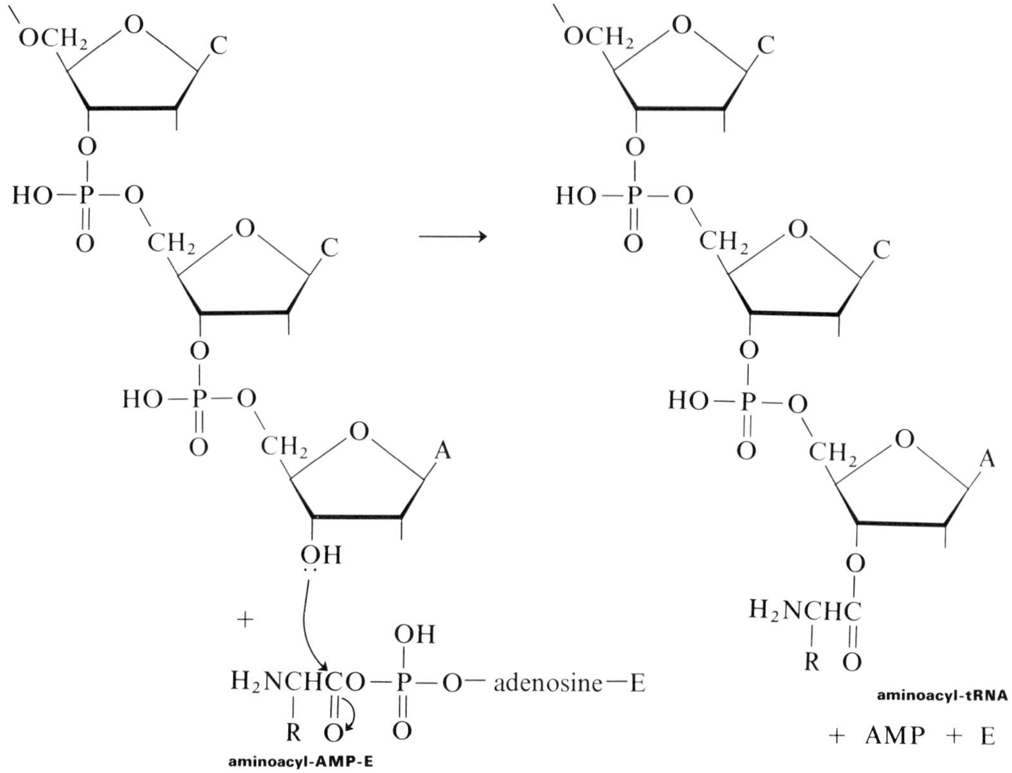

aminoacyl-AMP-E

aminoacyl-tRNA

+ AMP + E

ORIENTATION OF AMINO ACYL-tRNA ON TEMPLATES : mRNA, as explained previously, is synthesized on a DNA template in the nucleus. It is guessed that mRNA moves into the cytoplasm, where it interacts with ribosomes. The interaction is complex in nature but in essence several ribosomes stick to mRNA, forming a complex, the polysome. Here protein synthesis takes place as depicted in Figure 13.4.

The events on the polysome are visualized as follows. Amino acyl-tRNA interacts with the polysome but its correct orientation is determined by a sequence of three bases somewhere in the tRNA molecule. In Figure 13.5 is depicted a section of mRNA on the polysome containing the base sequence -A-A-U-G-C-U-; an aminoacyl-tRNA with the reactive three-base sequence U-U-A will combine, forming H bonds with its complement on mRNA : A-A-U. A second amino acyl-tRNA interacts the same way with the next three bases. The H bonds involved in three base pairs are known to be too weak to hold the two types of tRNA molecules in close proximity on mRNA long enough to react. This would be a

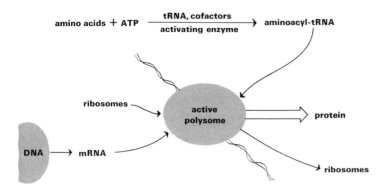

figure 13.4 ::
Scheme of protein synthesis. Interaction between mRNA and ribosomes produces the active polysome. Aminoacyl-tRNA units bind specifically on the polysome and are oriented according to a code on mRNA. As the ribosome moves along mRNA, the polypeptide chain grows by addition of aminoacyl-tRNA units. Synthesis begins from the amino end of the polypeptide. Completion of synthesis is attended by release of the polypeptide from the polysome.

serious drawback, but we must remember that there is support from the ribosome, where the actual operation of peptide synthesis occurs. The two amino acids are close enough to react as shown forming a peptide bond. The dipeptide remains attached through the second tRNA on the ribosome while the first tRNA dissociates.

It is evidently of no consequence what hangs at the end of tRNA; its position on the polysome is irrevocably determined. The high degree of specificity of the activating enzyme is in fact as important as the template in determining the position of the amino acid in a protein.

FORMATION OF PEPTIDE BONDS : The picture just presented is quite incomplete. It is still necessary to explain the order in which amino acyl-tRNA units interact with mRNA. The experimental evidence is suggestive of a stepwise addition of amino acids, so that beginning with the $-NH_2$ group the polypeptide grows in linear fashion. The other possibility is that a polypeptide could be formed at random all along the mRNA until all parts are connected into a single polypeptide. This is not a very attractive idea, as it creates too many problems.

According to present theory, the ribosomes are not fixed on mRNA but "move" on the mRNA; it is also possible that mRNA moves with respect to the ribosomes. The net effect is the same either way. In the stepwise growth theory, several ribosomes are moving along mRNA so that one single mRNA molecule serves as template for the simultaneous synthesis of several protein molecules. As shown in Figure 13.6, as the ribosome moves with respect to mRNA, it picks up a new amino acyl-tRNA and adds one more amino acid to the growing polypeptide. Finally, at the end of the line the ribosome dissociates from mRNA and the newly made protein dissociates from the ribosome.

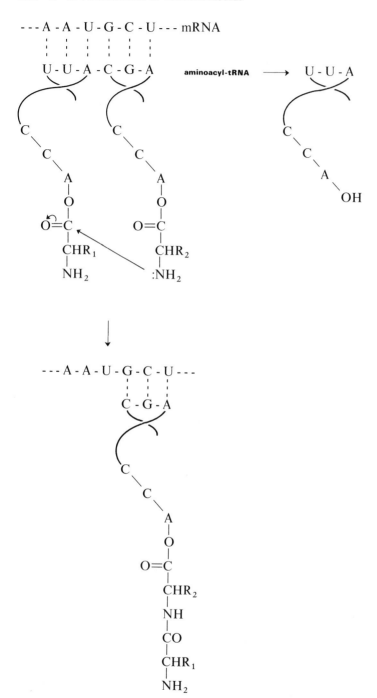

figure 13.5 :: Alignment of aminoacyl-tRNA on mRNA and peptide bond formation. Note that the tRNA of the first amino acid is released while the dipeptide remains attached to the polysome through the last incoming tRNA.

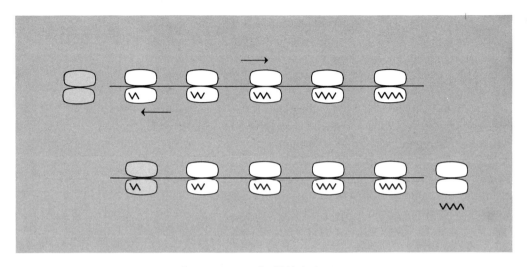

figure 13.6 :: Scheme representing movement of mRNA (←) or movement of ribosomes (→). As ribosomes (or mRNA) move, the polypeptide chain grows by addition of aminoacyl-tRNA. After synthesis is completed, the polypeptide is released from the ribosome; a new ribosome begins the journey along mRNA. A single mRNA can accommodate several ribosomes.

The picture of a moving part in a biochemical reaction is somewhat disturbing. But it should be remembered that this is only a working hypothesis; as more experimental observations are made the picture will be probably modified.

genetic code :: **13.5**

A sequence of three bases somewhere on the tRNA molecule determines its position on mRNA according to the rule of base pairs. Also for each amino acid there is at least one specific tRNA. Consequently, the three reactive bases in the tRNA molecule represent a code symbol for the amino acid.

The idea of a code was suggested sometime ago. It had to be postulated to explain alignment of amino acids on nucleic acid templates even before the mechanism of protein synthesis was known in detail.

The modern concept of transmission of hereditary characteristics from one cell to another rests on the theory of DNA replication. A gene, the "unit of function," is a region of DNA molecule having a specific sequence of bases, perhaps a thousand. The sequence represents in the case on hand coded information that is translated into amino acid sequences in a protein molecule. The information thus transmitted from cell to cell is the blueprint for a specific protein. We do not know how morphologic characteristics are transmitted because they are not susceptible to the same type of analysis as proteins are.

The code in DNA is copied in the form of mRNA. But since little was known about the base sequences in DNA the genetic code seemed a remote goal never to be attained. But in few years the genetic code became known as a result of ingenious experimentation mainly in the laboratories of M. W. Nirenberg, S. Ochoa, and H. G. Khorana. It would be difficult to go into the subtleties of their experimental approach in a book such as this.

In principle, the elucidation of the genetic code rested on the feasibility of protein synthesis in a test tube. All the components needed for protein synthesis are brought together under controlled conditions: 20 amino acids, one of which is labeled with ^{14}C, tRNA, activating enzymes, other soluble enzymes, cofactors, ATP,

table 13.2 ::
Assignment of code symbols in mRNA†

1	2				3
	U	C	A	G	
U	Phe	Ser	Tyr	Cys	U
	Phe	Ser	Tyr	Cys	C
		Ser			A
	Leu	Ser		Try	G
C		Pro	His	Arg	U
	Leu	Pro	His	Arg	C
		Pro	Gln	Arg	A
	Leu	Pro	Gln	Arg	G
A	Ileu	Thr	Asn	Ser	U
	Ileu	Thr	Asn	Ser	C
		Thr	Lys	Arg	A
	Met	Thr	Lys		G
G	Val	Ala	Asp	Gly	U
	Val	Ala	Asp	Gly	C
	Val	Ala	Glu	Gly	A
	Val	Ala	Glu	Gly	G

† Data from M. Nirenberg *et al.*, *Proc. Nat. Acad. Sci.*, **53**: 1161 (1965), and from D. Soll *et al.*, *Proc. Nat. Acad. Sci.*, **54**: 1378 (1965).

and ribosomes that contain mRNA. After a period of time all the protein is precipitated; it can be shown that the labeled amino acid is in protein. Nirenberg made the crucial observation that if ribosomes were freed of any mRNA, synthesis did not take place. But more important was the observation that a synthetic polynucleotide could act as mRNA. He added polyuridylic acid to the mixture above. Each of the 20 amino acids was tested for its ability to enter into protein structure. This, of course, is possible by using a radioactive amino acid; radioactivity is readily measured in the formed protein even when the level of protein formation is very low. Of the 20 amino acids tested, only phenylalanine went into protein synthesis significantly. If polyuridylic acid was omitted, no protein with radioactive phenylalanine was formed.

Nirenberg concluded that the code symbol for phenylalanine must be U-U-U, that is, assuming a triplet code. A triplet was considered likely, because it gives 64 possible combinations of the four bases ($4^3 = 64$). Combinations of two bases would only give 16 combinations ($4^2 = 16$), and combinations of more than three did not seem necessary. The polyuridylic acid acting as mRNA has no other bases present, and the only triplet combination had to be U-U-U. This means that there must exist in the cell a tRNA with a sequence of three bases, -A-A-A-, which interacts with the artificial mRNA and is specific for phenylalanine.

By use of the same experimental approach and the same reasoning, code symbols have been assigned to all 20 amino acids. The code originally proposed has undergone modifications from time to time. The present code is given in Table 13.2. Recently Khorana has obtained a great deal of additional information on the order of bases in the code symbols by repeating Nirenberg's experiments with synthetic polynucleotides of known sequences.

One more comment pertaining the genetic code: It is, from all appearances, a universal code. For example, it has been shown that aminoacyl-tRNA made in bacteria can form protein if transferred to the active polysomes of mammalian cells. The position of the amino acid in the mammalian protein has been shown to be determined solely by the tRNA, despite its bacterial origin.

references ::

CRICK, F. H. C., "The Genetic Code: III," *Scientific American*, October, 1966.
INGRAM, V. M., *The Biosynthesis of Macromolecules.* New York: W. A. Benjamin, Inc., 1965.
WATSON, J. D., *Molecular Biology of the Gene.* New York: W. A. Benjamin, Inc., 1965.

THE PRODUCTION OF CARBOHYDRATES FROM ATMOSPHERIC CO_2 AND H_2O under the influence of light is known as photosynthesis. Photosynthesis is the first event in the carbon cycle, in which carbon flows from atmospheric CO_2 to organic substances and back to atmospheric CO_2. Plants and some types of microorganisms serve as the producers of organic matter upon which animals feed.

Organisms, as discussed in previous chapters, obtain energy by oxidizing organic compounds to CO_2 and H_2O and thus return carbon to atmospheric CO_2. The oxidation is accompanied by a large decrease in free energy, a substantial portion of which is *trapped* as ATP.

It is obvious, then, that the prime source of energy in the living world is light, which is converted to chemical potential energy according to the equation

$$6CO_2 + 6H_2O \xrightarrow{\text{light}} C_6H_{12}O_6 + 6O_2$$

The process is the reverse of the oxidation of carbohydrate, glucose in this case; since 686 kcal is released by the oxidation of

1 mole of glucose, its synthesis from $CO_2 + H_2O$ must be driven by 686 kcal/mole. This energy is furnished as light.

Photosynthesis is an attribute of plants, including the algae, and also an attribute of the photosynthetic microorganisms. Among the latter are found protozoa (*Euglena*) and bacteria (purple and green sulfur bacteria).

They all have highly specialized organelles within their cells which contain pigments: chlorophyll, carotenoids, and xanthophyll. These pigments are primarily responsible for the conversion of electromagnetic energy (as light) into chemical potential energy.

This chapter will deal with two aspects of photosynthesis: the photochemical reaction and the path that carbon from CO_2 follows on its way to carbohydrate and other organic substances.

chloroplast :: **14.1**

The photosynthetic equipment of plant cells is found in the chloroplast. Like the mitochondrion, the chloroplast is thought of as a self-contained unit capable of transforming one form of energy into another. For this reason it has been called a "biochemical machine."

The chloroplast is a ellipsoidal body about 3 to 5 μ in length. The electron microscope reveals that its internal structure consists of small disklike bodies that contain pigments; these bodies are called *grana* and are depicted in Figure 14.1.

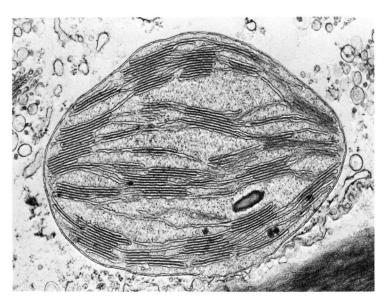

figure 14.1 :: A chloroplast from *Nitella*. Magnification about 23,000. (*Courtesy of Dr. Myron C. Ledbetter.*)

The pigments, chlorophyll, carotenoids, and xanthophyll, are present in varying proportions depending on the organism. Chlorophyll is believed to be embedded in layers of lipid and protein in an organized fashion rather than distributed at random. A probable arrangement is shown in Figure 14.2.

In addition to the structural components just described, the chloroplast also contains DNA and RNA in small but significant amounts. The chloroplast probably has the capacity to "reproduce" and in this way keep pace with the growth of the cell.

Of the pigments mentioned, chlorophyll is the one responsible for the green color of plants. It is a collective name for several types of magnesium-porphyrin structures that participate in photosynthesis. One, known as chlorophyll a, has the structure shown below:

$$R = CH_3\overset{\underset{\displaystyle |}{CH_3}}{C}HCH_2(CH_2CH_2\overset{\underset{\displaystyle |}{CH_3}}{C}HCH_2)_2CH_2CH_2\overset{\underset{\displaystyle |}{CH_3}}{C}=CHCH_2- \qquad ROH = \text{phytol}$$

Note that the chlorophyll structure has a conjugated system of double bonds. This allows for many resonance structures that impart stability to the molecule; it also furnishes mobile π

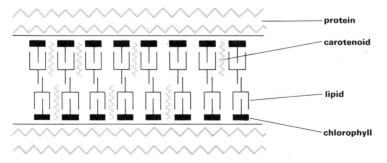

protein

carotenoid

lipid

chlorophyll

figure 14.2 ::
Schematic representation of a lamella. Chlorophyll is embedded in layers of lipid and protein.

electrons, which are easily raised to higher energy states when chlorophyll absorbs light of specified frequencies. As we shall see in a moment, this is crucial in the interpretation of the role of chlorophyll in photosynthesis.

photochemical reaction :: **14.2**

The production of carbohydrate from CO_2 and H_2O is a process entailing the reduction of CO_2 and the consumption of energy to drive the process. Biological reductions are commonly brought on by NADH and NADPH, and in this case also the reduced co-enzymes are the agents by which reduction takes place. The energy needed to drive the reactions in the formation of carbohydrates is provided by ATP. Both the reduced coenzymes and ATP are formed by photochemical reactions that can be written, with no consideration of the mechanisms involved, as

$$2NADP^+ + 2H_2O \xrightarrow[\text{chloroplast}]{\text{light}} 2NADPH + 2H^+ + O_2$$

$$ADP + H_3PO_4 \xrightarrow[\text{chloroplast}]{\text{light}} ATP + H_2O$$

The two reactions above summarize the photochemical reactions that must occur to produce carbohydrate from CO_2. The precise mechanism of the two reactions is a subject that is undergoing considerable change, and for this reason the discussion will be limited to a few fundamental principles.

CYCLIC PHOTOPHOSPHORYLATION : The formation of ATP in the chloroplast is in a way analogous to mitochondrial oxidative phosphorylation. That is, ADP is phosphorylated by a process coupled with the transfer of electrons from one carrier to another.
  The chlorophyll molecule absorbs light; this event is attended by a change in the electronic configuration from a *ground state* to an *activated* or *excited state*. From the excited state, chlorophyll could return to the ground state, but, if it does, energy is released as heat or light emission. In the latter instance what is observed is the phenomenon of fluorescence.
  Photoactivated chlorophyll evidently loses an electron during photosynthesis, leaving an ionized chlorophyll behind:

chlorophyll $\longrightarrow$ chlorophyll$^+$ + e^-

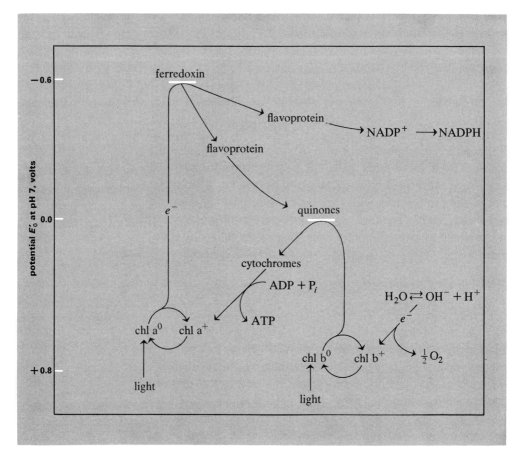

figure 14.3   ::   Electron transport during photosynthesis. Both cyclic and noncyclic photophosphorylations are shown.

the reactions responsible for the synthesis of carbohydrate, for example, are not dependent on light. This is, in fact, true, because given the enzymes involved, plus ATP and NADPH, synthesis of carbohydrate proceeds in the dark.

A subtle difference between photosynthetic and nonphotosynthetic reactions should be recognized. As we know, both ATP and NADPH are produced by reactions in which substrates are degraded. In photosynthesis, however, the cofactors are produced photochemically. The question is how to recognize the origin of the cofactors. This is difficult, but Melvin Calvin has proposed that in photosynthesis the reactions generally involve condensations and that even the synthesis of amino acids, fats, and other products can be immediately dependent upon the photochemical production of cofactors. This idea is in opposition to the belief that only carbohydrate is produced photosynthetically and that other products in the plant are formed from carbohydrates by ordinary biochemical reactions.

CO_2 FIXATION : The path of CO_2 in the photosynthesis of organic compounds was discovered mainly by Calvin, J. A. Bassham, and their associates. One of the great difficulties was to find the first product of CO_2 fixation. They resolved this problem by using very short periods of photosynthesis with radioactive CO_2. The flow of radioactive carbon (^{14}C) into organic compounds was easily detected by paper chromatography.

One of the first products found containing ^{14}C was 3-phospho-glycerate, in which only the carboxyl group was found containing ^{14}C:

$^{14}CO_2H$
|
$HCOH$
|
$CH_2OPO_3H_2$

3-phosphoglycerate

The formation of this product from CO_2 is not immediately apparent. It is not actually the first product in photosynthesis. With additional work it became apparent that 3-phosphoglycerate is produced by a mechanism involving a pentose. In the first step, CO_2 is fixed to form an unstable intermediate that cleaves readily. The reaction is between CO_2 and ribulose diphosphate:

$CH_2OPO_3H_2$		$CH_2OPO_3H_2$		$CH_2OPO_3H_2$
$C=O$		COH		$HO_2{}^{14}CCOH$
$HCOH$	$\rightleftarrows$	$\overset{\|\|}{C}OH$	$\xrightarrow{CO_2}$	$C=O$
$HCOH$		$HCOH$		$HCOH$
$CH_2OPO_3H_2$		$CH_2OPO_3H_2$		$CH_2OPO_3H_2$

ribulose-1,5-diphosphate   **2-carboxy-3-keto-1,5-diphosphoribitol**

The first stable intermediate observed is 3-phosphoglycerate, which is produced in accordance with the reaction

$$
\begin{array}{ccc}
& \underset{|}{CH_2OPO_3H_2} & \underset{|}{CH_2OPO_3H_2} \\
& & HO\overset{|}{C}H \\
HO_2{}^{14}C\overset{|}{C}OH & & {}^{14}CO_2H \\
\overset{|}{C}=O & \xrightarrow{\;H_2O\;} & \\
H\overset{|}{C}OH & & CO_2H \\
\underset{|}{CH_2OPO_3H_2} & & H\overset{|}{C}OH \\
& & CH_2OPO_3H_2
\end{array}
$$

Note that only one carbon and thus only one of the two molecules of 3-phosphoglycerate is radioactive. The evidence obtained by Calvin is that the carboxylation reaction results in the formation of only one free molecule of 3-phosphoglycerate per molecule of CO_2 entering the cycle.

The carboxylation of ribulose-1,5-diphosphate is catalyzed by an enzyme present in the chloroplast. The phosphorylation of ribulose-5-phosphate also occurs in the chloroplast and ATP is required.

carbon-reduction cycle :: 14.4

The production of 3-glycerophosphate from ribulose-1,5-di-phosphate would come to a halt if ribulose-1,5-diphosphate could not be regenerated. To account for the continuous production of 3-glycerophosphate it is necessary to arrange the reactions in a cyclic manner as shown in Figure 14.4. The cycle, known as the *carbon-reduction cycle*, starts with three molecules of ribulose-5-phosphate that are phosphorylated by ATP originally produced during the light reaction. As the cycle continues, three molecules of CO_2 react to produce one triose molecule (glyceraldehyde-3-phosphate), and the cycle ends by producing three molecules of ribulose-5-phosphate.

The overall reaction for the formation of triose from CO_2 and H_2O can be written

$$3CO_2 + 5H_2O + 9ATP + 6NADPH + 6H^+ = \text{glyceraldehyde-3-phosphate} +$$
$$9ADP + 8P_i + 6NADP^+$$

The intermediates of the cycle shown in Figure 14.4 are familiar substances, and the sequence of reactions by which they are produced resembles in many ways the reactions of the pentose phosphate pathway of glucose degradation. In similarity with the pentose pathway, the flow of carbons can be depicted as shown in

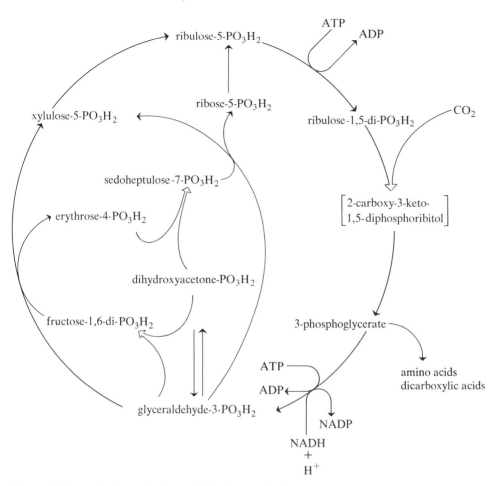

figure 14.4 :: Carbon-reduction cycle in photosynthesis.

Figure 14.5, in which the stoichiometry of the process is indicated. It remains now to discuss briefly the reactions involved in the process.

1. PRODUCTION OF 3-PHOSPHOGLYCERATE : The reaction has been discussed already as CO_2 fixation. The product, 3-phosphoglycerate, undergoes reduction to glyceraldehyde-3-phosphate:

$$
\begin{array}{l}
\underset{\text{3-phosphoglycerate}}{
\begin{array}{l}
\overset{\text{O}}{\overset{\|}{\text{C}}}\text{OH} \\
\text{H}\overset{|}{\text{C}}\text{OH} \\
\overset{|}{\text{C}}\text{H}_2\text{OPO}_3\text{H}_2
\end{array}}
\quad + \text{ATP} \longrightarrow
\underset{\text{1,3-diphosphoglycerate}}{
\begin{array}{l}
\overset{\text{O}}{\overset{\|}{\text{C}}}\text{O} \sim \text{PO}_3\text{H}_2 \\
\text{H}\overset{|}{\text{C}}\text{OH} \\
\overset{|}{\text{C}}\text{H}_2\text{OPO}_3\text{H}_2
\end{array}}
\quad + \text{ADP}
\end{array}
$$

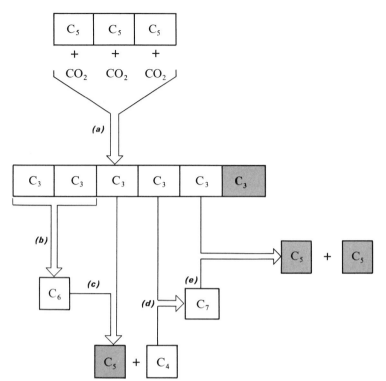

figure 14.5 ::
Stoichiometry of the
carbon-reduction cycle.
Each reaction shown is
discussed in the text.

$$
\begin{array}{c}
\underset{\substack{\displaystyle\text{O}\\ \displaystyle\|}}{\text{C}}\text{O} \sim \text{PO}_3\text{H}_2 \\
\text{HCOH} \\
\text{CH}_2\text{OPO}_3\text{H}_2
\end{array}
+ \text{NADPH} + \text{H}^+ \longrightarrow
\begin{array}{c}
\text{CHO} \\
\text{HCOH} \\
\text{CH}_2\text{OPO}_3\text{H}_2
\end{array}
+ \text{NADP}^+ + \text{P}_i
$$

glyceraldehyde-3-phosphate

The reduction of 3-phosphoglycerate shown above is exactly the reverse of the oxidation step in the glycolytic pathway; the enzyme, phosphotriose dehydrogenase, that catalyzes the reaction is probably quite similar to the dehydrogenase of glycolysis.

At this stage in the cycle, three molecules of ribulose-5-phosphate and three molecules of CO_2 have reacted to produce six molecules of triose (as glyceraldehyde-3-phosphate). The process consumes nine molecules of ATP: three to phosphorylate the three molecules of ribulose-5-phosphate and six to phosphorylate the six molecules of 3-glycerophosphate prior to reduction by six molecules of $NADPH + H^+$.

2. PRODUCTION OF FRUCTOSE-6-PHOSPHATE : Glyceraldehyde-3-phosphate is readily converted to its isomer, dihydroxyacetone phosphate. The two condense to form fructose-1,6-diphosphate in a reaction catalyzed by aldolase. The process is identical to the reverse of the breakdown of fructose-1,6-diphosphate discussed in Chapter 9 :

$$
\begin{array}{ccc}
\text{CHO} & & \text{CH}_2\text{OH} \\
|\ & \rightleftharpoons & |\ \\
\text{HCOH} & & \text{CO} \\
|\ & & |\ \\
\text{CH}_2\text{OPO}_3\text{H}_2 & & \text{CH}_2\text{OPO}_3\text{H}_2
\end{array}
$$

glyceraldehyde-3-
phosphate   dihydroxyacetone phosphate

$$
\begin{array}{c}
\text{CH}_2\text{OPO}_3\text{H}_2 \\
|\ \\
\text{CO} \\
|\ \\
\text{HOCH} \\
|\ \\
\text{HCOH} \\
|\ \\
\text{HCOH} \\
|\ \\
\text{CHOPO}_3\text{H}_2
\end{array}
$$

fructose-1,6-diphosphate

Fructose-1,6-diphosphate is dephosphorylated to yield fructose-6-phosphate before undergoing additional change.

3. PRODUCTION OF XYLULOSE-5-PHOSPHATE : Regeneration of pentoses is made possible by the intervention of two enzymes: transketolase and transaldolase. Fructose-6-phosphate reacts with glyceraldehyde-3-phosphate to yield the first pentose of the cycle, xylulose-5-phosphate, and also a tetrose, erythrose-4-phosphate. The reaction is catalyzed by *transketolase* :

$$
\begin{array}{cccccc}
\text{CH}_2\text{OH} & & \text{CHO} & & \text{CH}_2\text{OH} & \text{CHO} \\
|\ & & |\ & & |\ & |\ \\
\text{CO} & & \text{HCOH} & & \text{CO} & \text{HCOH} \\
|\ & + & |\ & + & |\ & |\ \\
\text{HOCH} & & \text{CH}_2\text{OPO}_3\text{H}_2 & & \text{HOCH} & \text{HCOH} \\
|\ & & & \rightleftharpoons & |\ & |\ \\
\text{HCOH} & & & & \text{HCOH} & \text{CH}_2\text{OPO}_3\text{H}_2 \\
|\ & & & & |\ & \\
\text{HCOH} & & & & \text{CH}_2\text{OPO}_3\text{H}_2 & \\
|\ & & & & & \\
\text{CH}_2\text{OPO}_3\text{H}_2 & & & & &
\end{array}
$$

fructose-6-phosphate   glyceraldehyde-3-phosphate   xylulose-5-phosphate   erythrose-4-phosphate

As shown in Figure 14.4, xylulose-5-phosphate is readily isomerized to ribulose-5-phosphate, which is its epimer.

4. FORMATION OF SEDOHEPTULOSE-1,7-PHOSPHATE : Regeneration of two more pentoses is made possible by first forming sedoheptulose-1,7-phosphate by the reaction of erythrose-4-phosphate and another molecule of dihydroxyacetone phosphate. The reaction is catalyzed by *transaldolase*:

$$
\begin{array}{l}
\text{CH}_2\text{OH} \\
|\\
\text{CO} \\
|\\
\text{CH}_2\text{OPO}_3\text{H}_2 \\
\textbf{dihydroxyacetone phosphate} \\
\\
+ \\
\\
\text{CHO} \\
|\\
\text{HCOH} \\
|\\
\text{HCOH} \\
|\\
\text{CH}_2\text{OPO}_3\text{H}_2 \\
\textbf{erythrose-4-phosphate}
\end{array}
\qquad\longrightarrow\qquad
\begin{array}{l}
\text{CH}_2\text{OPO}_3\text{H}_2 \\
|\\
\text{CO} \\
|\\
\text{HOCH} \\
|\\
\text{HCOH} \\
|\\
\text{HCOH} \\
|\\
\text{HCOH} \\
|\\
\text{CH}_2\text{OPO}_3\text{H}_2 \\
\textbf{sedoheptulose-1,7-diphosphate}
\end{array}
$$

5. FORMATION OF RIBOSE-5-PHOSPHATE : The sedoheptulose-1,7-diphosphate produced in reaction 4 dephosphorylates to sedoheptulose-7-phosphate and reacts with another molecule of glyceraldehyde-3-phosphate; the reaction is catalyzed by transketolase:

$$
\begin{array}{l}
\text{CH}_2\text{OH} \\
|\\
\text{CO} \\
|\\
\text{HOCOH} \\
|\\
\text{HCOH} \\
|\\
\text{HCOH} \\
|\\
\text{HCOH} \\
|\\
\text{CH}_2\text{OPO}_3\text{H}_2
\end{array}
\;+\;
\begin{array}{l}
\text{CHO} \\
|\\
\text{HCOH} \\
|\\
\text{CH}_2\text{OPO}_3\text{H}_2
\end{array}
\;\rightleftharpoons\;
\begin{array}{l}
\text{CHO} \\
|\\
\text{HCOH} \\
|\\
\text{HCOH} \\
|\\
\text{HCOH} \\
|\\
\text{CH}_2\text{OPO}_3\text{H}_2 \\
\textbf{ribose-5-phosphate}
\end{array}
\;+\;
\begin{array}{l}
\text{CH}_2\text{OH} \\
|\\
\text{CO} \\
|\\
\text{HOCH} \\
|\\
\text{HCOH} \\
|\\
\text{CH}_2\text{OPO}_3\text{H}_2 \\
\textbf{xylulose-5-phosphate}
\end{array}
$$

Both products, ribose-phosphate and xylulose-5-phosphate, isomerize readily to ribulose-5-phosphate. Of the six glyceraldehyde-3-phosphate molecules produced at the beginning of the cycle, five have been utilized in the reactions discussed. The remaining one is the net gain in the process.

Not all the 3-phosphoglycerate produced during the carbon reduction cycle reacts as shown before; part enters into reactions that yield products outside the cycle, for example, serine. The three carbons of serine can be shown to be derived from 3-phosphoglycerate, which probably undergoes the following reactions:

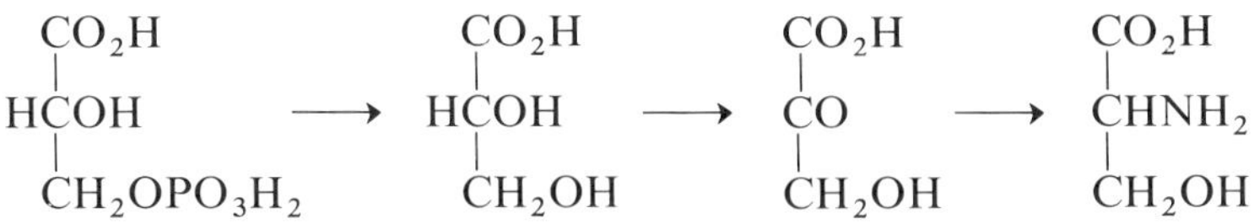

$$
\begin{array}{ccccccc}
CO_2H & & CO_2H & & CO_2H & & CO_2H \\
| & & | & & | & & | \\
HCOH & \longrightarrow & HCOH & \longrightarrow & CO & \longrightarrow & CHNH_2 \\
| & & | & & | & & | \\
CH_2OPO_3H_2 & & CH_2OH & & CH_2OH & & CH_2OH \\
\text{3-phosphoglycerate} & & \text{glycerate} & & \text{hydroxypyruvate} & & \text{serine}
\end{array}
$$

The resulting serine gives rise to alanine and less directly to pyruvate. Pyruvate in turn is carboxylated to four-carbon dicarboxylic acids, which are precursors of aspartate.

Calvin and Bassham have concluded from experiments with ^{14}C that amino acids and fats are formed during very short periods of photosynthesis. The formation of these substances is attributed to reactions truly photosynthetic.

It is important to recognize that photosynthetic reactions occur within the chloroplasts while the light is on and that reactions outside the chloroplasts are driven by energy derived from substrates photosynthesized in the chloroplasts but diffused to other parts of the cell.

references ::

CALVIN, M., AND J. A. BASSHAM, *The Photosynthesis of Carbon Compounds*. New York: W. A. Benjamin, Inc., 1962.

GOODWIN, T., ed., *Biochemistry of Chloroplasts*. New York: Academic Press, Inc., 1966.

EXPERIMENTAL TECHNIQUES HAVE CONTRIBUTED SUBSTANTIALLY TO the growth of modern biochemistry. Few of the techniques developed in the recent past have influenced the course of biochemical research as much as chromatography.

Chromatographic methods are used as analytical and preparative procedures for proteins, nucleic acids, polysaccharides, amino acids, sugars, carboxylic acids, fatty acids, and a long list of other substances.

Chromatography is one of several separation methods based on differential migration. Originally conceived as a method to separate plant pigments (hence the name chromatography, *writing in color*), the method has undergone numerous modifications, each adapted to a particular problem. In Figure A.1, for example, is shown how the pigments extracted from leaves are separated into six discrete bands, each corresponding to a different pigment extracted from the leaf. The extract has been percolated through a glass tube containing finely powdered calcium carbonate and then washed with light petroleum.

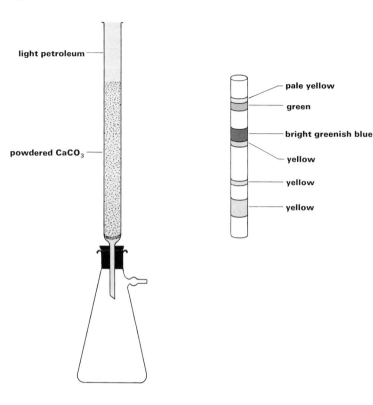

light petroleum

powdered CaCO₃

pale yellow

green

bright greenish blue

yellow

yellow

yellow

figure A.1 ::
Chromatography of a
leaf extract. After
development six
pigments separate into
bands. (*Redrawn from
L. Zechmeister, in
Principles and Practice
of Chromatography.
New York: John Wiley
& Sons, Inc., 1943.*)

The separation of the pigments in the above example is due to differences in affinity of the pigments for the calcium carbonate, which is acting as an adsorbant. Pigments most strongly adsorbed migrate more slowly than do those adsorbed weakly; differences in adsorption in this case result in differences in migration rates so that it is possible to collect each pigment separately if the column is continued to be washed with solvent.

Two forces are recognizable in the process: a *driving force* and a *resistive force*. Whereas the driving force—gravity in this case—is of the same magnitude for all the components of the mixture, the resistive force varies. Adsorption is the resistive force in the example above. The force of adsorption prevents all the components in the mixture from migrating at the same rate as the solvent and, by affecting each component to a different degree, separation becomes possible.

Two phases can be distinguished in the chromatographic procedure: a *stationary phase*, represented above by the calcium carbonate, and a *mobile phase*, represented by the solvent traveling down the column. In all other forms of chromatography the same basic conditions apply. All chromatographic techniques deal with the same forces (driving and resistive) and the same phases (stationary and mobile).

partition chromatography :: **A.1**

The stationary phase in *partition chromatography* is water held by any type of material with a great capacity for hydration but with relatively little power of adsorption. Finely powdered cellulose, starch, and silica gel are examples of suitable materials. Resolution in a partition column results from differences in the distribution coefficient of the individual components of a mixture between the stationary phase (water) and the mobile phase (an organic solvent saturated with water).

Partition chromatography was conceived and developed in 1941 by the British scientists A. J. P. Martin and R. L. M. Synge as a method to separate amino acid mixtures into individual amino acids. Its popularity declined somewhat with the introduction of partition paper chromatography, developed by the same scientists.

paper chromatography :: **A.2**

In *paper chromatography* the stationary phase is the water retained by the cellulose fibers of the filter paper used for this purpose. The mobile phase is generally, but not always, a solvent poorly miscible with water but saturated with water before use.

Paper chromatography is one of the simplest laboratory procedures known. It is adaptable to many uses and best used as a micromethod. As shown in Figure A.2, the assembly for paper

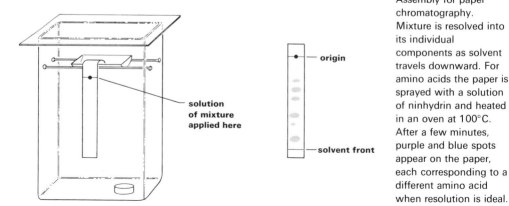

solution
of mixture
applied here

origin

solvent front

figure A.2 ::
Assembly for paper chromatography. Mixture is resolved into its individual components as solvent travels downward. For amino acids the paper is sprayed with a solution of ninhydrin and heated in an oven at 100°C. After a few minutes, purple and blue spots appear on the paper, each corresponding to a different amino acid when resolution is ideal.

chromatography consists of a glass jar with a tightly fitting cover, a glass trough, and filter paper. A small sample of the solution to be analyzed (0.001 ml is adequate) is applied to the paper on a line near the edge of the paper strip. The spot dries quickly if hot air is blown on the paper. The edge near the point of application is dipped in the solvent contained by the glass trough while the paper strip hangs from the trough. The glass jar is sealed and the solvent allowed to travel by capillarity. To maintain a saturated atmosphere a dish containing water-saturated solvent is placed at the bottom of the jar.

As the solvent travels down the paper it carries with it the components of the mixture. They travel at rates dictated by their solubility in water versus solvent. The run is ended when the solvent front reaches the end of the paper. The paper is then removed from the jar and dried.

The substances that have been separated are detected by spraying the paper with a reagent that forms colored derivatives. Sometimes they are detected by observing the paper under ultraviolet light; radioactive substances are detected by specially adapted counters.

Amino acids, for example, react with ninhydrin to yield purple derivatives visible even when the concentration of amino acid on the paper is a few micrograms. The relative position of each amino acid in this case is easily detected as purple spots on the paper strip.

The relative position of each component in the mixture resolved by paper chromatography is recorded as the R_f value, defined by

$$R_f = \frac{\text{distance traveled by substance}}{\text{distance traveled by solvent}}$$

Distances are measured from the point of application of the sample to the solvent front and to the center of each spot appearing on the strip.

Paper chromatography lends itself to an almost unlimited number of variations, each adapted to a given situation. It is not usual, for example, to find a solvent that separates all 20 amino acids in a protein hydrolysate. If all 20 amino acids are to be resolved, two solvents can be used consecutively in the procedure known as *two-dimensional chromatography*. Instead of a paper strip, a sheet of paper is used. The solution is applied near a corner of the square paper and then treated in the same way as the paper strip. At the end of one run in the first solvent the sheet is removed, dried, and placed in a second jar containing a different solvent.

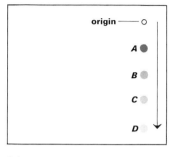

(a)

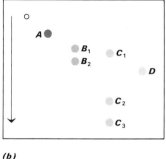

(b)

figure A.3 :: Two-dimensional chromatography of a mixture with seven components. The mixture separates in solvent 1 (*a*) into four components. Components *B* and *C* are resolved in solvent 2 (*b*) into individual components B_1 and B_2 and C_1, C_2, and C_3, respectively.

This time the paper is positioned in the trough at 90 degrees in relation to the direction of the first run. In this way, substances not separated by the first solvent are separated by the second solvent in a different direction, as shown in Figure A.3.

thin-layer chromatography :: A.3

Thin-layer chromatography is a more recent development than paper chromatography. Its greatest single advantage is versatility in the use of stationary phases. In this method, a glass plate is coated, by means of a special device, with the material that will constitute the stationary phase mixed with calcium sulfate and made into a slurry or thin paste. The paste sets as a hard surface after drying. As shown in Figure A.4, the assembly is as in paper chromatography, a glass jar, but in this case the plate is immersed in the solvent. The solvent travels upward by capillarity, and in a matter of 1 to 2 hours it covers the plate. The plate is removed, dried, and otherwise treated just like paper.

In addition to affording a wide choice of stationary phases, thin-layer chromatography is fast (1 to 2 hours as against 18 to 24 hours for paper) and has a greater capacity than paper, because the layer can be made thicker.

ion-exchange chromatography :: A.4

The phenomenon of ion exchange has been known for a long time for many natural substances. Synthetic substances with ion-exchange properties have only recently been introduced and are now used widely. Among these substances the most commonly used are the *ion-exchange resins*. They are made by polymerizing substances such as styrene and divinyl benzene and then introducing a polar group into the polymer matrix. Cation-exchange resins bear a strongly acid group such as sulfonate or a weakly acidic group such as a phenolic or carboxylic group. Anion-exchange resins bear an amine or a quaternary ammonium derivative.

Ion exchange can be illustrated with a sulfonic acid-bearing resin. The sulfonic acid dissociates, releasing its proton, but because the sulfonate is fixed on the polymer matrix, the proton remains fixed near the negatively charged sulfonate. If another cation approaches the proton, the proton can migrate and exchange with the entering cation. The process is depicted with NaCl:

$$\text{Resin}-SO_3^-H^+ + NaCl = \text{Resin}-SO_3^-Na^+ + H^+Cl^-$$

Ion-exchange resins have been used as the stationary phase in columnar chromatography; they have been used with great success in the analysis of amino acids, particularly amino acid mixtures resulting from the hydrolysis of proteins.

In the chromatography of amino acids long columns of cation-exchange resin are employed; the amino acid mixture is in a buffer solution of relatively low pH, so all the amino acids will be positively charged. The reaction taking place in the resin can be represented by

$$X^-AA^+ + Res^-H^+ \rightleftharpoons Res^-AA^+ + X^-H^+$$

At low pH the amino acids are in the form of salts in which X^- is an anion (Cl^-, for example). Buffers of increasing pH are forced through the column; as the pH of the buffer changes, the dissociation of the amino acids also changes, in accordance with their pKs. The rate at which amino acids travel down the column with the buffer is dictated mainly by the pK of the amino acid and the pH of the buffer. A set of conditions has been combined that permits

figure A.4 :: Thin-layer-chromatography assembly. The glass plate is held in an upright position by a glass frame. The edge of the glass plate is immersed in solvent, which travels upward by capillarity.

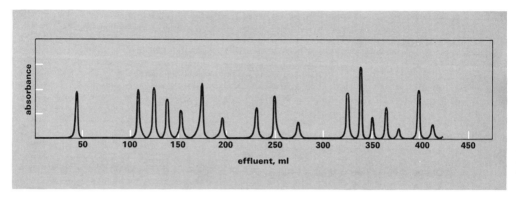

figure A.5 :: Automatically recorded chromatographic analysis of a mixture of 17 amino acids. The absorbance of the color produced by the effluent as it reacts continuously with ninhydrin is recorded on the ordinate. The position of each peak is characteristic for each amino acid, and the area of each peak is proportional to the concentration.

the quantitative separation of the 20 amino acids found in proteins. The method has been made fully automatic and, as shown in Figure A.5, each amino acid emerging from the column is analyzed as the colored derivative formed with ninhydrin and recorded as a series of peaks. Each peak represents a different amino acid and the area under each peak is proportional to the concentration of the amino acid.

Other types of ion-exchange substance are used for the separation of proteins. The most widely used are cellulose derivatives made by the chemical treatment of cellulose powder so that it bears polar groups. Two types are widely used: carboxymethylcellulose (CMC) as a cation exchanger and diethylaminoethylcellulose (DEAE) as an anion exchanger.

The advantage of cellulose derivatives over ion-exchange resins is that cellulose derivatives have a greater capacity and are therefore useful in preparative chromatography. Proteins are separated by the cellulose derivatives in a manner similar to that described for the chromatography of amino acids by ion-exchange resins. Protein are polyionic molecules and, like amino acids, most proteins bear a positive charge at acid pH or a negative charge at basic pH. They exchange with one or the other type of cellulose derivative, depending on the pH of the solution. They are selectively eluted from the column by buffers of increasing or decreasing pH. For example, if a mixture of proteins is placed on a CMC column at pH 4, the proteins are eluted from the column by increasing the pH of the buffer. Selective elution can also be accomplished by using solutions of salts of increasing ionic strength.

Some types of gels have the ability to distinguish among molecular species differing in size. Based on this principle, J. Porath and P. Flodin introduced in 1959 particulate dextran gels as a means of separating inorganic salts from proteins in solution. More recently the method known as *gel filtration* has gained wide acceptance as a method of separation of substances differing in molecular weight.

Dextran is a high-molecular-weight glucan. Its properties are modified by cross-linkages introduced under controlled conditions to yield spherical particles that imbibe water and swell considerably as they hydrate. (Dextran of this type is commercially known as Sephadex.) The resulting gel is used as the stationary phase in columns just as in other types of chromatography. Here the stationary phase is the water imbibed by the dextran particles; the mobile phase is the water moving in the void space between the particles.

Separation of two substances differing in molecular weight is due to differences in the distribution coefficient (K_D) of the substances between the water imbibed by the dextran particle and water outside the particle. Generally small molecules and inorganic ions diffuse freely in and out of the particles but large molecules are excluded. The distribution coefficient in the first instance approaches 1 ($K_D \rightarrow 1$), whereas in the case of large molecules it approaches zero ($K_D \rightarrow 0$). By applying the expression

$$V = V_0 + K_D V_i$$

it is possible to calculate the volume V of effluent from a column that will contain a solute from a mixture. Here V_0 is the void volume of the column and V_i is the volume of water imbibed by the particles of the gel.

The separation of NaCl ($K_D = 0.9$) from a protein ($K_D = 0$) is illustrated in Figure A.6. The solution of protein and salt is introduced in the column of gel and water added continuously. The protein appears in the column effluent after a volume of water equal to the void volume has been collected ($V = V_0$). NaCl appears in the column effluent at volume $V = V_0 + K_D V_i$.

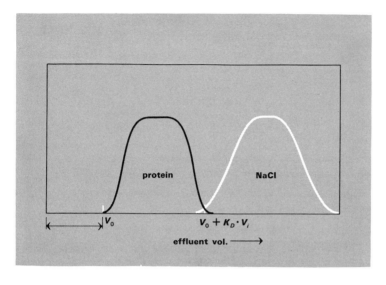

figure A.6 ::
Separation of a protein
($K_D = 0$) and sodium
chloride ($K_D = 0.9$) by
gel filtration of a
Sephadex column.

Gel filtration in the example just given replaces dialysis as a method to separate small from large molecules. Mixtures of large molecules are also resolved into their components by the same procedure.

gas chromatography :: **A.6**

In *gas chromatography* the stationary phase is a solid adsorbant, in which case the procedure is known as gas-solid chromatography, or a liquid absorbent, in which case the procedure is known as gas-liquid chromatography. The mixture of substances to be analyzed are volatilized into the vapor phase and carried through long capillary tubes or just tubes of small bore containing the stationary phase. The mixture of vapors is swept through the column by a carrier gas. As the substances traverse the capillary tube or column, they adsorb or dissolve in the stationary phase at rates dictated by their individual properties. As they flow through the column they dissolve and evaporate numerous times until they emerge at the other end of the tube.

Gas chromatography is an extremely sensitive method capable of detecting traces of substances that cannot be detected by any other means. The reason for its sensitivity lies mainly in the detection system at the outlet of the column. There are several types of detectors that measure some property related to the mass of the substance that emerges from the column.

The *retention time*, the time it takes for a given component to emerge, is characteristic of a given substance and serves for its identification. As each substance emerges, the detector records the information automatically; the record is one of a series of peaks, each corresponding, under ideal conditions, to a single component of the mixture. The area under each peak is proportional to the mass of substance present.

Gas chromatography has become one of the most widely used chromatographic methods. It is fully automated and extremely versatile, but its uses in biochemistry are somewhat limited by the instability of many biological molecules to the high temperatures employed in gas chromatography. It is successfully applied when the mixtures consist of volatile substances such as fatty acids.